Workshop Technolog

by the same author
Introduction to Jig and Tool Design
Materials for Engineers

other titles of interest
Technician Science Book I   M. G. Page
Technician Workshop Processes and Materials   R. T. Pritchard

A complete list of titles for
Technician Education Council Courses
is obtainable from the publishers.

Workshop Technology for Technicians

M. H. A. Kempster

C. Eng., M.I.Mech.E., A.F.R.Ae.S., M.I.Prod.E.

Senior Lecturer in Production Technology
Rolls-Royce Technical College, Bristol

HODDER AND STOUGHTON
LONDON SYDNEY AUCKLAND TORONTO

British Library Cataloguing in Publication Data

Kempster, Maurice Henry Albert
  Workshop technology for technicians. – 4th ed.
  1. Machine-shop practice
  I. Title II. Introduction to workshop technology
  621.7′5   TJ1160

ISBN 0 340 23018 5 boards edition
ISBN 0 340 23019 3 paperback edition

First published 1950 as *National Certificate Workshop Technology*
by the late T. Nuttall
Second edition 1955
Reprinted 1956, 1958, 1960, 1963, 1964
Third edition 1972 published as *Introduction to Workshop Technology*
by M. H. A. Kempster
Reprinted 1976
Fourth edition 1978

Copyright © 1978 M. H. A. Kempster

Printed in Great Britain for Hodder and Stoughton Educational,
a division of Hodder and Stoughton Ltd.,
Mill Road, Dunton Green, Sevenoaks, Kent, by
Richard Clay (The Chaucer Press), Ltd., Bungay, Suffolk

Preface to Fourth Edition

This book is based on the writer's *Introduction to Workshop Technology* which, in turn was based on *National Certificate Workshop Technology* by the late T. Nuttall.

The chapter on casting has been completely revised, and new chapters on powder metallurgy, metrology, and the study of surface texture have been written, and the book now contains the topics in the Materials and Processes, and the Manufacturing Technology units leading to the TEC certificate in Mechanical and Production Engineering.

As before, the writer considers that lengthy and often tedious descriptive text is now unnecessary in many cases because of the current system of practical training, in accordance with the requirements laid down by the Engineering Industry Board, and because of the extensive laboratory backing to classroom work; this allows a more fundamental approach to the subject.

A short summary is included at the end of each chapter, followed by a selection of questions. As in the original work, the questions are divided into two sets, Set A for general use, and Set B as a stimulant for further study or for use as the basis for project work.

The writer wishes to acknowledge the assistance given by the manufacturers mentioned in the text, and to his wife, who once again checked the original manuscript and generally assisted in the production of the book.

It is hoped that this book continues to meet the high standard set by the original author.

M. H. A. Kempster

Contents

light waves; production of interference using optical flats; the study
of slip gauges using an optical flat—flatness, parallelism, length.
Collimation; principles; the autocollimator; the angle dekkor; angle
slips. Summary.

Chapter 1
Introduction to Engineering Materials, Manipulation, and Measurement

1.1 Introduction
Manufacturing technology is basically the science of the manipulation of material and the measurement of the product. When a product is designed, its shape and the material from which it is made must be considered with due regard to its manufacture in addition to its performance when in service. When the manufacturing method is planned, it must be done with due regard to the material to be manipulated, the shape to be produced, and the required degree of accuracy. The economics of manufacture and the organisation of the manpower must also be taken into account to ensure that the enterprise is successful.

1.2 Choice of material
The choice of material to be used in a component is governed by three principal considerations.

(a) The material must be suited to the working conditions to which the component will be subjected in service.

(b) The material must be amenable to the processes required to make the component.

(c) The cost of the material must not be excessive in relation to the selling price of the article.

1.2.1 Classification of engineering materials.
Engineering materials can be classified into (a) metallic materials, and (b) non-metallic materials. The non-metallic materials include asbestos, concrete, rubber, wood, oil, ceramics, diamond, and plastics. Plastics materials are being used in ever-increasing quantities, and are replacing metals in domestic equipment, photographic equipment, and similar products.

Metallic materials are classified as:

(a) ferrous metals, which consist of iron, and alloys of iron with up to about 30% of other materials;

(b) non-ferrous metals and non-ferrous alloys. Non-ferrous metals are metals other than iron; non-ferrous alloys are alloys that contain little or no iron.

Iron is the commonest and cheapest metal used in engineering, other common metals being copper, aluminium, zinc, magnesium, tin, lead, nickel, chromium, manganese, and tungsten. Abundance does not necessarily mean that a metal is inexpensive; aluminium, for example, is the most abundant metal in the earth's crust, but is more expensive than iron, since it must be refined by electrical means.

Pure metals are not used extensively in engineering. Some common metals (e.g. iron) are difficult to produce in anything like the pure condition; furthermore, pure metals tend to have extreme properties, such as excellent electrical conductivity and poor strength, so *alloys* are used to obtain compromise properties.

Generally, an alloy has a *base*—a single metal which forms more than 50% of the total mass—and one or more *alloying elements*, which may be present in large or extremely small amounts, depending upon the properties required. Obviously the cost of the base metal will have a great effect upon the cost of the alloy; so cheap metals are used whenever possible. Steel is an example of this: iron is the base of steel, and is quite cheap, but expensive alloying elements, such as molybdenum, vanadium, chromium, or nickel, may be present in relatively small amounts to produce special properties.

1.2.2 Properties of metals and alloys. Certain properties of metals are of great importance to engineers, and various methods are employed to investigate these properties.

Tenacity. This can be defined as the resistance to rupture when subjected to tensile forces. The measure of tenacity is *tensile strength* (see section 2.2.1). Two similar properties are *compressive strength* and *shear strength*, related to compressive forces and shear forces respectively. These strengths are usually reduced when the metal is heated.

Elasticity. This can be defined as the ability of the material to return to its original shape when the deforming force is removed. When a material is subjected to a tensile force, it will be elongated; but if the force does not exceed an amount called the *elastic limit*, the material will return to its original dimensions, and is said to be *elastic*. If the elastic limit is exceeded, the material will not return completely to its original dimensions, and will be deformed: the material is said to be partly *elastic* and partly *plastic*. Figure 1.1 illustrates a typical force-extension diagram for mild steel (an alloy of iron and about 0·2% carbon): point E is the elastic limit for this material. The elastic limit is lowered by heating. Metals and alloys are usually chosen to be elastic when in service.

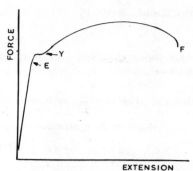

Fig 1.1 Force-extension diagram for mild steel

The modulus of elasticity. When a metal is subjected to a tensile force, the extention is initially proportional to the force; or more specifically, the *strain* is proportional to the *stress* in the material.

$$\text{strain} = \frac{\text{extension}}{\text{original length}}. \qquad \text{stress} = \frac{\text{force}}{\text{area}}.$$

When the force exceeds an amount called the *limit of proportionality*, the strain will no longer be proportional to the stress, although the material will still be elastic until that limit is exceeded.

It can be stated that *within the limit of proportionality, the stress is proportional to the strain.* This is a somewhat more modern version of Hooke's Law.

Table 1.1. Some typical values of Young's modulus of elasticity

Material	E (N/mm^2)
aluminium	69×10^3
copper	124×10^3
iron and steels	206×10^3
lead	16×10^3
magnesium	44×10^3
nickel	200×10^3
tin	41×10^3
zinc	90×10^3

Thus stress is proportional to strain

or   stress = strain × a constant.

The constant in the above equation applies to a specific material, and is known as *Young's modulus of elasticity* for that material. It is given the symbol E.

The above equation can therefore be written as

$$\text{stress} = E \times \text{strain}.$$

Design calculations are based upon the assumption that the stresses are kept well below the limit of proportionality.

Taking a simple example—if a steel bolt 250 mm long is stressed to 60 N/mm², what will be the increase in its length?

From table 1.1, $E = 206 \times 10^3$ N/mm².

Stress = E × strain

$$60 \text{ N/mm}^2 = 206 \times 10^3 \text{ N/mm}^2 \times \frac{\text{increase in length in mm}}{250 \text{ mm}}$$

$$\text{Therefore, increase in length} = \frac{60 \times 250}{206 \times 10^3}$$

$$= 0.073 \text{ mm}$$

It is of interest to note that, for practical purposes, it can be taken that E is the same for all steels; but that the strength, limit of proportionality, and elastic limit are not the same for all steels. This implies that all steels will stretch the same amount when subjected to the same stress, but that the limit to which this can be taken varies from steel to steel.

Ductility. A ductile material is one which can be drawn out permanently by a tensile force. This property is particularly important to the production engineer when he makes wire, or when he forms steel sheet to produce a motor-car body. Reference to fig. 1.1. will show that mild steel will, when the *yield point* (Y on fig. 1.1) is reached, suddenly stretch for only a small increase in force or stress, and then continue to stretch very considerably when the force is increased. During this ductile extension, the material becomes thinner, until a stage is reached when, if the material has not already broken, the thinning becomes localised, and the material eventually breaks. The local thinning is called *waisting* or *necking*.

A well-defined yield point is typical of soft steels, but most metals do not display a yield point when so tested (see fig. 1.2). Figure 1.3 illustrates the force-extension diagram for a material with low ductility, and the reader should compare this with fig. 1.1. It must be emphasised

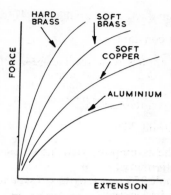

Fig 1.2 Force-extension diagram
(non-ferrous)

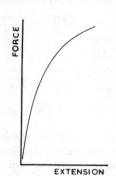

Fig 1.3 Force-extension diagram
showing low ductility

that the absence of a definite yield point does not in itself imply that the material has a low ductility.

The ductility of many materials increases with an increase in temperature.

Malleability. Malleability is the ability of a material to be hammered or rolled out without cracking. Very few materials have a good malleability when cold, but most are malleable when heated to a suitable temperature.

Plasticity. This is the property that allows a material to flow when under pressure in the solid state, to change its shape, and to retain that shape when the pressure is removed. An appreciable time may elapse before plastic flow is completed. Increase in pressure and temperature improves plastic flow.

Toughness. A tough material resists fracture by blows, because considerable energy is required to crack or break it. Tough materials have a high tenacity, combined with good or fair ductility. Toughness decreases with an increase in temperature.

Hardness. Hardness can be defined as resistance to indentation or scratching, and is usually stated relative to other materials. Scales of hardness usually give high numbers to hard materials, and low numbers to soft materials. Hardness is reduced by heating.

Brittleness. This property is the opposite to toughness. Brittle materials may resist a steady force, but fail easily when subjected to a sharp blow. Brittle materials are neither ductile nor malleable. Hard materials are usually brittle.

The foregoing properties are evaluated by mechanical tests which damage the material, and they are therefore termed *mechanical properties*. Those properties that are evaluated by other means are termed *physical properties*; the following are typical physical properties:

Density. This property is defined as the mass per unit volume. Products such as cameras, vacuum cleaners and aircraft must be of low mass, and are therefore made of low density materials, but balance weights and ballast must usually be small but of high mass and are therefore made of high density materials. Materials data often includes the 'strength/weight' (strength/mass) ratio because increasing the thickness of a part to compensate for low strength may cause it to be of too high a mass.

Melting point. This property is important not only in connection with casting, but also in service because the strength of a metal is lowered as its temperature approaches its melting point; high melting point metals are often stronger at room temperature than low melting point metals, and are more suitable for high-temperature applications.

Coefficient of thermal expansion. This is defined as the increase in length per unit length per degree rise in temperature, and is an important property when a part is subjected to temperature variation. Length-measuring devices that are used in conditions where temperature cannot be controlled are made from a metal that has a coefficient of thermal expansion of little more than zero; bolts for use in gas turbine engines and metal parts used with glass (as in cathode ray tubes) must be made from metal with a coefficient of thermal expansion that matches that of the parts in the vicinity to avoid the ill effects of differing expansion of the parts; and thermostats are made from metal that expands a suitable amount with temperature variation to produce the required cut-off.

Thermal conductivity and specific heat. When heat must not be lost or where the transfer of heat can make the product awkward to use, the thermal conductivity must be low, but when a part must conduct heat away from another part to cool it, or, in the case of a cooking utensil, conduct heat from a heat source, it must be made from a material of high thermal conductivity. Specific heat is an indication of the amount of heat required to raise the temperature of a material; the 'heat sink' of a rocket is made from a high conductivity, high specific heat material that will absorb the heat at re-entry to the earth's atmosphere, yet not itself become so hot that the crew and instruments are in danger.

Magnetic properties and electrical properties. Material that is non-magnetic, or is suitable for use as an electrical insulator may have to be used, but if it is to respond to a magnetic force or an electrical force, then the precise characteristics must be known so that the system can be correctly designed.

1.2.3 The protection of metals against corrosion. Corrosion presents one of the greatest problems associated with the use of metals. Many pure metals have high corrosion-resistance, but they are usually weak and are often expensive; and when metals are alloyed to obtain greater strength or to reduce costs, an inferior corrosion-resistance is usually the result (this is not always so—for example, steel can be made to have a high degree of corrosion-resistance by alloying).

Reasonably good protection can be obtained by covering the surface with grease or oil to exclude air and moisture, and when components are regularly greased or oiled as part of the maintenance routine, or when they operate in an oil bath, this method is satisfactory. When this form of protection is unsuitable, the metal is given a surface treatment.

Protection using paint is one of the most common methods. This is effective if the surface is free from corrosion and clean when the paint is applied, and continues as long as it excludes air and moisture.

Metal is a more durable protection medium; the protection that it gives can be *direct* or *sacrificial*. Direct protection is obtained by coating with a metal that has a high resistance to corrosion, but it is effective only as long as the coating is intact. Sacrificial protection is obtained by using a coating metal that has a lower corrosion-resistance than that to be protected, so that in the event of the coating being incomplete, it will corrode instead of the metal to be protected (for example; when steel is coated with tin, the protection will be direct; when it is coated with zinc, the protection will be direct if the coating is complete, and sacrificial if the coating is broken). The coating metal can be applied using one of the following methods: electroplating (for example, chrominium plating), hot-dipping (for example, tin plating), electro-galvanising (zinc coating), cladding (for example, cladding aluminium alloy sheet with a thin layer of pure aluminium on each side by hot-rolling), cementation (for example, 'Sherardising', in which a zinc case is produced by heating the metal to be protected when it is surrounded by zinc in powder form) and spraying using a heated pistol to project tiny particles of molten metal on to the surface.

A chemical protection can be obtained by phosphating or chromating, to produce a base for painting.

The corrosion-resistance of aluminium and its alloys can be improved by an electrical process called *anodising*, which thickens up the oxide film that forms naturally when their surfaces are exposed to air.

1.3 Choice of manipulation method

The choice of manipulation method is governed by five principal factors.

(*a*) The material to be manipulated.
(*b*) The properties to be developed.
(*c*) The shape to be produced.
(*d*) The required accuracy.
(*e*) The quantity required and the allowable costs.

1.3.1. When material is to be manipulated into shape it is usually heated and poured into a mould where it is solidified. The shape so produced may be a simple and convenient form that is made into the finished shape either by manipulating it into shape in the solid state, by removing metal to obtain the finished shape, or by combining manipulation and metal removal; manipulation in the solid state is called *working*. The shape that is produced by melting and solidification may be so accurate that little or no metal removal is necessary to produce the required shape and accuracy; such a form is called a *casting*.

1.3.2. By starting with solid material in powder form and subjecting it to heat and pressure, the shape may be produced without melting the material; such a process is called *powder metallurgy* when applied to metals, and *moulding* when applied to plastics. The forms produced by these processes are usually so accurate that no further manipulation is necessary.

1.3.3. It is convenient to classify the primary manipulation methods as:

(*a*) casting, (*b*) working and (*c*) powder metallurgy (or moulding).

1.3.4. The product of a primary manipulation process may be subjected to a secondary manipulation process. One of these, metal-removal, has already been mentioned; the material may otherwise be subjected to an operation whereby the material is bent, drawn, and so on—processes of this type are termed *forming* processes.

1.3.5. It is convenient to classify the metal-removal operations according to the way in which the metal is removed. The usual classification being:

(*a*) mechanical, (*b*) thermal and (*c*) chemical.

The mechanical methods involve the removal of metal in the form of chips, and includes, for example, turning, drilling milling, and grinding; mechanical processes are the subject of the chapters on metal-removal in this book. The other methods are newer ones—thermal methods remove metal by local melting (spark erosion, electron beam, plasma arc and laser beam are thermal metal-removal techniques), and chemical methods remove metal by chemical attack (electro-chemical machining and chemical machining are in this group).

1.4 Choice of inspection method

It is necessary to employ some form of inspection to control the form and the dimensions of the product; inspection is often done at strategic stages during the manufacture of a product and upon the finished product. The choice of inspection method is governed by four principal factors:

(*a*) The accuracy to be maintained.
(*b*) The degree of reliability that is required of the product.
(*c*) The production rate.
(*d*) The inspection skill to be used.

When the rate of production is small, or if the degree of reliability demanded of the product is high, a full dimensional inspection which requires a highly skilled inspection staff, will be done. A high rate of production requires a more rapid inspection system, and a system of gauging will be used which indicates if each dimension being inspected is acceptable because it is neither too small nor too large (the actual dimension is not obtained using this system).

If only partial inspection is required so that the manufacturing system can be corrected before parts become faulty, or when allowances are to be made to purchasers to account for a controlled quantity of faulty products, a statistical quality control will be used. In this method, a calculated quantity of products is measured, and from this inspection, the quality of a batch is calculated. This system is applicable when the products are each examined by the stockist before he sells them; the inspection of electric lamp bulbs being a typical example.

Summary

1 The choice of material for a component is governed by (*a*) the working conditions expected, (*b*) the manufacturing processes used to produce the component, and (*c*) the acceptable cost of the completed component.

2 Engineering materials are classified into (*a*) metallic materials, and (*b*) non-metallic materials. Metallic materials are further classified into (i) ferrous alloys, and (ii) non-ferrous materials and alloys.

3   Alloys are extensively used to obtain compromise properties.
4   Tenacity, elasticity, toughness, and hardness are typical properties associated with working conditions.
5   Ductility, malleability, and plasticity are typical properties associated with manufacturing processes.
6   Metals can be protected against atmospheric attack by excluding air. The protection material may be metal with a better corrosion-resistance than that to be protected (giving protection as long as the coating is intact) or be metal with a poorer corrosion-resistance than that to be protected (giving sacrificial protection if the coating becomes damaged).
7   The choice of manipulation method is governed by (*a*) the material, (*b*) the properties to be developed, (*c*) the shape to be produced, (*d*) the accuracy to be obtained and (*e*) the economics.
8   Primary manipulation methods can be classified as (*a*) casting, (*b*) working, and (*c*) powder metallurgy (or moulding).
9   Secondary manipulation methods can be classified as (*a*) metal-removal and (*b*) forming.
10 Metal-removal methods can be classified as (*a*) mechanical, (*b*) thermal, and (*c*) chemical.
11 The choice of inspection method is governed by (*a*) the accuracy required, (*b*) the reliability required, (*c*) the production rate, and (*d*) the inspection skill.
12 Inspection may be by (*a*) measurement, (*b*) gauging, (*c*) statistical methods.

Questions

Set A
1   (*a*) Define the meaning of the term 'base metal' applied to engineering materials.
    (*b*) Give an instance of an expensive alloy, and explain why it is expensive, and why the expense is justifiable.
2   Explain why ferrous materials are used to make the majority of engineering components. Name two parts which are almost always made from ferrous materials, and two parts which are rarely made from ferrous materials. Give reasons for your choices.
3   Define the terms 'elasticity' and 'tenacity'. What is the difference between them, and how is a metal tested for these properties?
4   Two materials have the same tensile strength, but material A has a modulus of elasticity of 206×10^3 N/mm^2 while material B has a modulus of elasticity of 100×10^3 N/mm^2. Explain what this means, and what difference you would expect to find when using 15-mm-diameter bolts of each material.
5   Two material specifications are handed to you, reading as follows:

	A	B
yield point, N/mm^2	240	550
tensile strength, N/mm^2	500	900
elongation, % on 50 mm	30	14

Draw the approximate force-extension diagrams of the two materials on the same graph. Assume that both have the same modulus of elasticity.

6   Explain the difference between *elastic extension* and *ductile extension*. Draw, approximately, the force-extension curve for mild steel, and indicate the two extensions on it. If the curve drawn was that of material for cold riveting, which would you consider the important points?

7   Explain how casting, working, and powder metallurgy differ.

8   Explain why it may be necessary to follow a casting process by metal-removal.

Set B (questions requiring further study)

9   Study the properties of several engineering materials to obtain the connection between strength, hardness, toughness, and ductility.

10   Examine a number of components, and discuss how the material from which they were made was selected for service, manufacture, and economy.

11   Explain why the advent of the gas turbine has caused the development of new materials and processes.

12   Study several engineering components with a view to recording how they were produced and why that particular method was used.

13   Further to question 12, discuss the possible inspection system that was used for each component.

Chapter 2
The Commercial Testing of Materials

2.1 Research tests and routine tests

The research testing of materials is carried out to determine their suitability for a given duty and for the processes which are to be used to manipulate them into the required shape. When an engineer specifies a material, he also specifies certain tests, and the performance figures required under those tests. The tests that are carried out to verify the quality of material are shorter than the research tests, and are often called routine tests. Much useful work has been done by the British Standards Institution in setting up certain test standards for all the common engineering materials. These standards can form the basis of contracts between the manufacturer and the purchaser of materials.

Many materials are sold under trade names which may also conform to a British Standard. Manufacturers usually supply literature giving suitable applications of their products, in addition to the heat-treatment procedures, and the manipulation, machining, joining, and finishing techniques that apply. It is not usual to find this information in British Standards, as the latter are instruments of quality control, rather than design aids.

2.2 The tensile test

In this test the material is placed in a machine and pulled until it breaks. To ensure uniformity, test-piece dimensions are specified in the British Standard for tensile testing (BS 18). Figure 2.1 Shows a typical testpiece, and it will be seen that a section is of reduced diameter, so that the extension and the breakage will occur along that part of the test-piece. The extension of a length called the *gauge length* is studied during the test. The points that indicate the ends of the gauge length are called the *gauge points*. In a routine test, these points are marked by centre punch, but, if a more detailed test is to be carried out, the extension is measured by an instrument called an *extensometer*, which produces the gauge points when it is attached to the test-piece. There is a fixed relationship between the gauge length and the cross-sectional area of the test-piece at the reduced diameter. If the material is ductile,

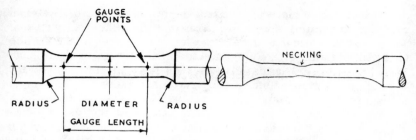

Fig 2.1 Standard test-piece   Fig 2.2 Test-piece before breakage

it will develop a 'neck' or 'waist', as shown in fig. 2.2; but if it is brittle, it will break before local extension occurs. Chapter 1 contains some diagrams illustrating the curves obtained when the force is plotted against the extension, but it is more usual to plot the stress against the strain. In order to save continually having to measure the diameter of the test-piece during the test, the stress is taken to be the force divided by the original cross-sectional area, and the strain is taken to be the extension divided by the gauge length. Figure 2.3 illustrates a typical curve showing the result of plotting the stress against the strain.

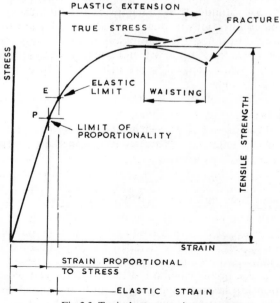

Fig 2.3 Typical stress–strain curve

When a ductile material is tested, the reduction in cross-sectional area due to waisting causes an increased stress without an increased force, and it is usual to reduce the force, to ensure that extension proceeds uniformly. When this reduced force is divided by the original area, the stress so determined is less than the true stress, and so the term 'nominal stress' is often used. Figure 2.3 includes a broken line to show how the true stress differs from the nominal stress. In practice, this variation does not cause difficulties, because, in the case of a ductile material, the stress to cause waisting is taken as the tensile strength of the material. During a research test, sufficient information is recorded to plot the curve, in addition to the dimensions of the test-piece before and after the test; but during a routine test, only the maximum force and the test-piece dimensions are recorded.

The following information is obtained from a commercial tensile test.

2.2.1 The tensile strength (R_m). This is defined as the maximum force taken by the test-piece, divided by the original area. This value is used to compare the strength of materials, but a *safety factor* is applied when making design calculations, to bring the working stress well below the limit of proportionality (this is also discussed in section 1.2.2).

2.2.2 The yield point (see section 1.2.2). When the material does not display a yield point, a quantity known as the *proof stress* is used when making design calculations. The proof stress is defined as that stress which will produce a certain specified non-proportional extension in the test-piece (usually 0·1% or 0·2% of the gauge length). In order to ensure that the structure is stable, the working stresses are kept well below the yield point or the proof stress.

2.2.3 The percentage elongation after fracture. This is used as an indication of the ductility of the material. To determine this value, the two pieces of the broken test-piece are placed together, and the extension of the gauge length is measured. The percentage elongation after fracture is calculated as follows:

percentage elongation after fracture

$$= \frac{\text{elongation of the gauge length after fracture}}{\text{gauge length}} \times 100\%$$

When the percentage elongation is specified, it is necessary to specify the gauge length also, as, for a given material, the local extension will be the same whatever the gauge length.

2.2.4 The percentage reduction of area. This value also indicates the ductility of the material, but, because it is assumed that the material remains circular in section, this value is less reliable than the percentage elongation after fracture. To determine the reduction of area, the two pieces of the broken test-piece are placed together, and the diameter of the waist is measured using a micrometer (special end caps are fitted to the spindle and anvil of the micrometer, so that the reduced diameter can be measured accurately). The percentage reduction of area is evaluated as follows:

$$\text{percentage reduction of area} = \frac{\text{maximum reduction of area}}{\text{original area}} \times 100\%$$

22.5. The shape of the stress–strain diagram is of importance both to the designer and to the production engineer. The designer is interested in the shape below the elastic limit, the limit of proportionality, and the yield point (or proof stress), because he is mainly concerned in designing stable structures; and he bases his calculations on the assumption that the material obeys Hooke's Law (see section 1.2.2). The production engineer is interested in that part of the curve below the elastic limit when making small parts by bending, because the material will tend to spring back, and must be bent further than finally required, to allow for this. He is also interested in that part of the curve above the elastic limit, because, if the material is to be severed during the manufacturing process, the stress must be high enough; but, if it is to be shaped, without fracture, by rolling, forging, etc., the stresses must be greater than the elastic limit, but lower than the tensile strength. If the material is heated, the elastic limit and the tensile strength are reduced, and so the stresses required to work the material will be less than when the material is worked at room temperatures.

2.3 Bend tests

A bend test is a simple test for ductility that does not require special equipment, or a specially shaped test-piece. A piece of round- or square-section bar must be bent through a specified angle without it cracking to be accepted by this test. Figure 2.4 shows a flat piece of metal that has been bent through an angle of 180°. Sheet metal may be

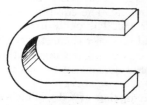

Fig 2.4 Bend-test specimen

given a single bend test, or alternatively may be given a reverse bend test, in which it must bend backwards and forwards through a specified angle (usully 90° or 180°) without it cracking.

2.4 Hardness tests

The most common hardness tests are those in which an indentor is forced into the surface of the material under test. Some methods use the surface area of the indentation as an index of hardness, and others use the depth of the indentation as the index of hardness.

2.4.1. The Brinell test is typical of the first group. In this test, a hardened steel ball is forced into the surface of the material under a standard load, which is maintained for 15 seconds to ensure that plastic flow is completed. The specimen is removed, and the diameter of the impression is measured with a low-power microscope fitted with a graticule or measuring scale. The diameter is then compared with a table, from which the hardness is read off: the smaller the impression, the higher the number. This test is suitable for materials with a low or medium hardness.

2.4.2. The Vickers diamond pyramid test is similar to the Brinell test, but it employs a small diamond of pyramid shape, instead of a steel ball. It produces more reliable results for high hardness materials, but identical values for softer materials.

2.4.3. The Rockwell machine forces a specially shaped indentor, termed a 'brale', into the material, and automatically records the depth of the impression. The hardness number is then read on a dial on the machine. The Rockwell test is very quick, and is suitable for mass inspection of parts.

2.4.4. It should be noted that these tests indicate only the surface hardness of the material.

2.5 Impact tests

Impact tests provide a measure of the shock resistance or toughness of a material, and also indicate how sensitive the material is to weakening caused by sharp corners, etc. The equipment consists of a heavy pendulum mounted in a frame. The pendulum is allowed to swing freely from a fixed height, and to strike the test-piece, which is mounted in a vice at the bottom of its swing. The shape of the test-piece is such that it is broken by the pendulum, which swings on after breaking it. The tougher the material, the more energy will be lost by the pendulum in breaking the test-piece; and so it will swing further past the bottom dead centre after breaking a brittle material than after breaking a tough material. The equipment includes a scale from which the impact value can be read directly. A tough material will have a high impact number, and a brittle material will have a low impact value. Figure 2.5 shows the principle of the Izod test; the test-piece is of square section, and a notch is machined in it. The test-piece is gripped by the vice

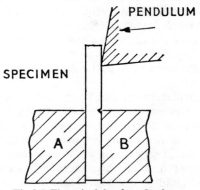

Fig 2.5 The principle of the Izod test

jaws, A and B, and the notch is set level with the top of the vice. The Charpy test is similar to the Izod test, the main difference being that here the test-piece is held horizontally, and supported at both ends, the pendulum striking it half-way between these points.

2.6 Special tests
If more unusual conditions are expected when the material is in service, special tests are conducted. Typical of these are tests to determine resistance to fatigue and to creep.

2.6.1 Fatigue. Fatigue failure is caused by repeated stress cycles, such as reversal or alternating stresses (reversal of direction of bending or torsion, or alternating compressive and tensile stresses), fluctuating stresses (variation of intensity of stresses), and repeated stresses (application and removal of stresses). This form of failure is encountered very frequently in engineering, and, although much publicity has been given to the fatigue of aircraft structures, this form of failure is very common in more ordinary circumstances; motor-car half shafts, crown wheel and pinion assemblies, and pedal-cycle crank spindles are susceptible to fatigue failure.

When the fatigue resistance of a material is to be determined, a number of test-pieces is prepared and tested in turn under conditions that produce fatigue failure, and the number of stress cycles that produce failure is recorded. The first test is carried out with a high maximum stress, and each subsequent test employs a lower maximum stress. The object of the series of tests is to determine the highest maximum stress that will permit a given 'life' in terms of stress cycles; alternatively, the fatigue limit may be required. (The fatigue limit is the highest maximum stress that will permit the material to undergo an 'infinite' number of stress cycles before failure.) If fatigue conditions are present, the material will fail at a stress that is much lower than that associated with a static force. The fatigue strength of a material is between 0·35 and 0·65 of the tensile strength, depending upon composition; but the fatigue strength of a component is reduced by poor finish, sharp corners, and corrosion.

2.6.2 Creep. Creep is defined as a continuous gradual extension under a steady force or stress over a long period of time, and causes the material to fail at a stress that is well below that associated with short-time loading. Creep is important when a material is to be used at elevated temperatures: high melting-point materials resist creep better than lower melting-point materials. Creep is very important in gas turbines, because the high temperatures and high stresses produced by the high rotational speeds produce rapid creep, and the clearances between the tips of the blades and the turbine casing cannot be made great, to allow for the extension of the blades, as this would reduce the engine efficiency.

When a material is to be creep tested, a rig is used that incorporates the means of slowly applying the required load, heating the test-piece to the testing temperature, and of recording the gradual extension that takes place during the test. Design data is obtained as a result of tests of up to about 10 000 hours duration, and graphs are produced to relate extension (or strain) to the duration of the test. The designer can then relate the rate at which creep proceeds, the temperature, and the force to his design problem. Routine tests must, of necessity, be short-time tests of about 48 hours duration, but they are related to the performance of the material when subjected to long-time tests.

Summary

1 Research tests are done to investigate the properties of materials: routine tests are done to verify the quality of materials.
2 The tests are standardised by standardising the test-pieces and/or the testing technique.
3 The tensile test is carried out to determine or verify the tensile strength and also the ductility of materials.
4 The bend test is a test for ductility.

5 The hardness test is a test of resistance to abrasion, but also gives an indication of strength.
6 The impact test gives an indication of toughness.
7 Special tests include fatigue tests and creep tests.

Questions

Set A
1 You are given a piece of brass sheet, 50 mm long, 12 mm wide, and 1·5 mm thick. Suggest a method of testing the ductility of the material.
2 Look up the values and complete the following table:

Material	Tensile strength	Percentage elongation	Brinell no.
grey cast iron			
mild steel			
wrought iron			

3 Three samples of steel have the properties set out below.

Sample	tens. str. N/mm^2	Percentage elongation	Izod impact	Brinell no.
A	350	34	30	105
B	1200	4	10	650
C	750	16	42	280

What are the relative merits of the three steels with respect to the following properties: shock resistance, cutting ability as a knife, ductility, wear resistance, tenacity?

Set B (questions requiring further study)
4 Explain why the extensometer used in the tensile test requires to register very accurately. An extensometer is mounted on gauge points 25 mm apart on a mild-steel specimen. A tensile stress of $60 \times N/mm^2$ is induced. Calculate the extension recorded. $E = 206 \times 10^3 \ N/mm^2$.
5 (a) Make a sketch of a well-known type of extensometer.
(b) Explain why the length between gauge points and the diameter of a tensile test specimen must always be measured accurately.
6 Describe the Brinell hardness test, and discuss its limitations.
7 Briefly outline the various tests which indicate the ductility of a material.

8   Make a sketch of the Charpy impact-testing machine, and the specimen used. If you were given the results of tensile tests of a number of materials, could you form some idea of their probable impact strengths? Give reasons for your answer.

9   Outline the essential features of testing equipment for (*a*) fatigue testing, and (*b*) creep testing.

Chapter 3
Pig Iron, Wrought Iron, and Cast Irons

3.1 Pig iron and its production

Iron ore, coke, and limestone are charged into a blast furnace to produce *pig iron*. Pig iron can be regarded as an impure form of cast iron, and is the first step in the production of *wrought iron, cast irons,* and *steels*.

A blast furnace is a vertical steel shell that is roughly cylindrical in shape, and is lined with a refractory material. Hot air is introduced at the bottom of the furnace, to burn with the coke, producing intense heat and a reducing agent, carbon monoxide. The ore is reduced at the top of the furnace, and absorbs some of the carbon from the carbon monoxide, forming an alloy that melts at about 1200°C, and which can easily be tapped from the furnace (pure iron melts at 1535°C). Limestone is introduced to act as a flux to remove some of the impurities in the form of a slag. The waste gases are collected in a large downpipe, and their heat is extracted to preheat the incoming air, and so improve the efficiency of the furnace. The slag and the pig iron are tapped from the furnace from time to time: the pig iron may be run into sand moulds or metal moulds to produce castings called 'pigs', and later used to produce wrought iron or cast irons. In a large steelworks, the pig iron is usually conveyed, in the molten state (usually known as 'blast furnace metal'), to the melting shops, to be made into steels.

Pig iron contains between 3% and 4% carbon, and various amounts of silicon, phosphorus, sulphur, and manganese, which must be removed to produce a useful alloy. Pure iron is difficult to produce, but certain grades of commercially pure iron, chiefly of Swedish and American origin, are used in electrical work for rotor stampings and transformer cores: a well known grade is 'Armco' iron. Pure iron is very soft, very weak, and very ductile.

3.2 Elements present with iron in iron-base alloys

3.2.1 Carbon. This is the most important element in iron-base alloys. It may be present with the iron to form a solid solution called *ferrite*,* which can contain no more than 0·006% of carbon by weight, and which is similar to pure iron. If the carbon content of an alloy exceeds 0·006%, the excess carbon will, with some of the iron, form iron carbide (Fe_3C), or *cementite*. Cementite contains 6·67% carbon, and is very hard and brittle. Ferrite and cementite tend to form a laminated structure called *pearlite*, which combines the hardness and brittleness of cementite with the softness and ductility of ferrite, thus producing 'all-round' properties. Figure 4.1 illustrates the connection between the carbon content, the microstructure, and the mechanical properties of a range of steels. (The term 'microstructure' implies the structure as seen with the aid of a microscope.) When silicon is present in an iron–carbon alloy, some of the carbon may be present in the free condition, or as *graphite*.

3.2.2 Silicon. Silicon is used as a softener in cast iron. Increasing the silicon content of the alloy tends to increase the quantity of graphite, and decrease the quantity of cementite.

3.2.3 Manganese. This important element is present in almost all ferrous alloys, either as an impurity or as an alloying element. It has a strong affinity for sulphur, and readily forms the compound manganese sulphide (MnS), so improving the quality of the alloy, since this compound is not harmful, as is the iron sulphide (FeS) which would be produced if the manganese were not present. Sufficient manganese should be present to take up the sulphur content, but the manganese content must be controlled, because any manganese over and above that necessary to offset the ill-effects of sulphur improves the quality of the alloy, and it will be appreciated that even a useful element must be controlled if an alloy is to have uniform properties from one batch to the next. When present in cast iron, manganese tends to increase the hardness, because it promotes combined carbon; and so the balance between silicon and manganese contents is important.

3.2.4 Phosphorus. This element, like sulphur, is inherent in cast iron. It embrittles cast iron by forming iron phosphide (Fe_3P), but is less dangerous than sulphur. Its amount present is kept as low as possible, except in certain light intricate castings, where it is encouraged because it improves the fluidity of the molten cast iron.

---

* A solid solution is said to be formed when the atoms of one metal or constituent in an alloy either take the place of, or are present between those of the parent metal when the alloy is in the solid state. A solid metal resembles a pure metal, even when seen under a powerful microscope, and has properties that are similar to those of the parent metal.

3.2.5 Sulphur. It has already been mentioned that sulphur is a dangerous element. Unfortunately, it is invariably present in cast iron, as it is picked up from the coke used in the production of pig iron, and in the melting during the production of cast iron when a coke-fired furnace is used. The percentage of sulphur is kept as low as possible, because it forms iron sulphide, which has a low melting-point, and so forms between the grains that make up the alloy. Iron sulphide is very brittle, and so the alloy will be brittle, as it cannot be tough if the grain boundaries are brittle.

Sulphur is particularly troublesome in the case of steels, since steels are iron-carbon alloys that are intended for working. ('Working' implies manipulation when the alloy is in the solid state—forging is a typical working process.) Sulphur causes steel to be so brittle that it cannot be cold-worked without it cracking, and the steel is then said to be *cold-short*. Similarly, the low melting-point of iron sulphide causes local melting to take place when the steel is heated up for hot-working. The steel flies to pieces during forging, and is said to be *hot-short*. These ill-effects are offset by the addition of manganese, since manganese sulphide has a higher melting-point, and solidifies early during the solidification of iron-base alloys, so that it is present in the form of small harmless pellets.

3.3 Wrought iron and its production

Wrought iron is produced from pig iron in a puddling furnace, in which the impurities, including most of the carbon, are removed in the form of slag. At the final stage of the process, some of the slag is stirred back into the melt, before the product is removed from the furnace. The product is then forged, so that the remaining slag, mainly iron silicate, is elongated into fibres, as shown in fig. 3.1 The alloy contains about 0·02% carbon, and the slag fibres, and these give it its characteristic properties.

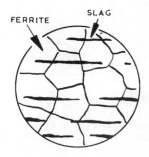

Fig 3.1 Microstructure of wrought iron

3.3.1. The fibres tend to let the alloy crack slightly, rather than fracture outright if overloaded, and so give a warning of danger. The slag also acts as a flux when wrought iron is forge-welded. Wrought iron resists atmospheric corrosion; but is unsuitable as a casting alloy, since it has a high melting-point, owing to its low carbon content.

3.3.2. Wrought iron is used for special chains and crane hooks, and for bolts subjected to shock loading; but it is now used only in small quantities, as it is so expensive to manufacture.

3.4 Cast iron

Cast iron is produced by melting pig iron with scrap steel or scrap iron, to control the percentage of carbon and impurities. The cupola furnace (fig. 3.2) is economical to operate, and is used during the production of about 90% of iron castings. This furnace may be oil-, gas-, or coke-fired. When, for example, the coke-fired cupola is used, a coke fire is first of all lit, and then the furnace is charged with alternate layers of pig iron mixed, with iron and steel scrap, and coke. Some limestone may be added to flux the coke ash, but the process is one of composition control, rather than of refining. More sophisticated furnaces, such as the rotary furnace, and the electric arc furnace, are used when a closer control of composition is necessary, and when it is necessary to prevent the fuel from coming into contact with the charge, in order to keep down the carbon content of the product.

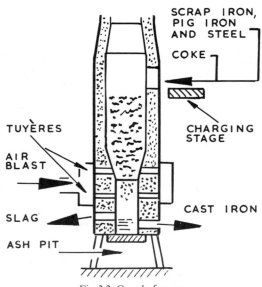

Fig 3.2 Cupola furnace

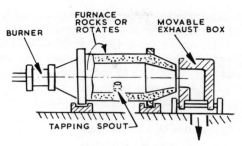

Fig 3.3 Rotary furnace

The rotary furnace (fig. 3.3) is fired using pulverised fuel, oil, or gas. During the melting, the furnace is continuously rotated or rocked by chain or friction drive, so that the lining is continuously heated up by the gases, and then gives up that heat to the charge, to effect its melting. The electric arc furnace (see fig. 4.5) is the cleanest to operate, as only heat energy is introduced into it to melt the charge.

3.4.1 White iron and grey iron. Carbon can be present in cast iron as part of the ferrite, part of the cementite, or free (known as graphite). When the carbon is present only as ferrite and cementite, the cast iron is hard and brittle, and has a 'steel-white' appearance when fractured. It is therefore called *white iron*. Figure 3.4 illustrates the appearance of white iron when seen with the aid of a microscope (called the 'microstructure' of white iron).

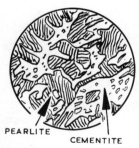

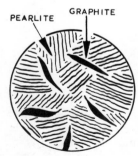

Fig 3.4 Microstructure of white iron

Fig 3.5 Microstructure of grey iron

When cast iron also contains graphite, it is greyish when fractured, and is called *grey iron*. The microstructure of grey iron is illustrated by fig. 3.5. Grey iron is softer than white iron, and tends to be weak in tension, owing to the weakening effect of the graphite flakes, although the graphite produces the good vibration-damping properties and the self-lubricating characteristics of grey cast iron. Intermediate grades of cast iron are called *mottled irons.*

Cast iron has a lower melting-point than steels—between about 1135°C and 1250°C, compared with about 1500°C for steels. A typical cast iron contains 3·25% C, 2·25% Si, 0·65% Mn, 0·10% S, and 0·15% P. The quantity of phosphorus may be increased if an ornamental casting is required, and where strength is of less importance (see also section 3.2.4).

The mechanical properties of grey cast iron depend upon its composition, but the tensile strength is between 150 and 400 N/mm², the hardness between 155 HB and 320 HB, and the compressive strength between about three and four times the tensile strength.

3.4.2 Control of structure during cooling. The presence of silicon tends to cause the cementite to break down during cooling, to form ferrite and graphite, and so the silicon content influences the degree of 'graphitisation' that takes place. Graphitisation requires sufficient time, and so the effect of silicon can be offset by speeding up the cooling by using a cold mould, or by burying iron plates (called 'chills') in the mould, to conduct away the heat. Thick sections of a casting cool more slowly than thin sections, and so chills can be used to produce uniformity of structure even if the thickness of the casting being produced varies (fig. 3.6). Chills are also used to produce local surface hardness by causing local surface areas to be white, so that local wear resistance is produced.

Fig 3.6 Application of a chill

The structure is therefore controlled by the composition of the pig iron, by the design of the casting to be produced, and by foundry technique.

3.4.3 Control of structure by heat-treatment of the casting. As already stated (section 3.4.1), grey cast iron is weak in tension. This is because the edges of the graphite flakes act as stress raisers, and because the distance between the edge of one flake and that of the next is comparatively short. One method of improving the strength of cast iron is to change the shape and the size of the graphite by subjecting it to a lengthy heat-treatment known as *malleabilising*. The cast iron must be white, because in that condition the carbon is more evenly distributed throughout the structure, as part of the cementite, enabling the desired effect to be more easily obtained. Malleable cast iron is available in three forms: *whiteheart*, *blackheart*, and *pearlitic*—the names describing the microstructure produced by the treatment.

In the whiteheart process, the castings are packed into boxes with haematite ore, slowly heated to about 900°C, held at that temperature for several days, and finally cooled to room temperature. Thin sections are completely decarburised, but the core of thick sections will contain ferrite and pearlite, or pearlite and particles of graphite (fig. 3.7). The tensile strength of whiteheart cast iron is about 350 N/mm², the elongation about 5%, and the hardness about 120 HB at the surface, increasing to about 220 HB at the core. Whiteheart cast iron is used for motorcycle frame sockets, agricultural machines, etc.

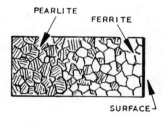

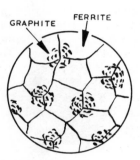

Fig 3.7 Microstructure of thick section of whiteheart

Fig 3.8 Microstructure of black heart cast iron

In the blackheart process, the iron castings are heated in a similar way as in the whiteheart process, except that air is excluded, by surrounding the castings in the containers with an inert substance, to prevent decarburisation. The result is illustrated in fig. 3.8: the process causes the cementite to break down to form rosettes of graphite in a matrix of ferrite. This process demands that the carbon content be no more than 2·4%, and so special melting methods are necessary to ensure that no carbon pick-up occurs. The melting-point of iron-carbon alloys is lowered with increased carbon content, and so these irons are more difficult to cast, as they have a slightly higher melting-point than other cast irons (with a carbon content of about 3·5%). The tensile strength of blackheart malleable iron is about 300 N/mm², and the elongation is about 10% (the properties are uniform across the section). Blackheart malleable iron is used for axle-boxes, rear axle housings, wheel hubs, etc.

Pearlitic cast iron is produced in a similar way to blackheart malleable iron: the pearlitic structure is produced by increasing the manganese content to about 1%, or by heating a quenched and tempered blackheart malleable iron. The object of the process is to obtain a structure that is more like that of steel. The tensile strength is about 450 N/mm^2, and the elongation about 5%. This is the newest type of cast iron, and is being used for axle and differential housings, gears, and camshafts.

3.4.4 High-duty cast iron. The properties of ordinary grey cast iron can be improved by using refined pig iron, or by introducing a large quantity of steel scrap into the cupola. As already described, the shape of the graphite can be altered by a lengthy heat-treatment, or, as an alternative, the cast iron can be inoculated. Inoculation implies the addition of a graphitiser to the molten iron as it leaves the furnace, while it is in the ladle, or while the iron is poured from the ladle into the mould.

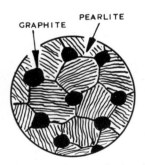 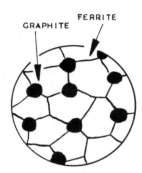

Fig 3.9 Microstructure of spheroidal   Fig 3.10 Heat-treated SG cast iron
graphite cast iron   (showing graphite set in ferrite)

Spheroidal graphite cast iron (known as 'SG iron') This iron is inoculated with magnesium or cerium to control the size and the shape of the graphite. As cast, the structure consists of spheroids of graphite set in pearlite (fig. 3.9); but, if heated to 900°C, soaked for a few hours, and then cooled, the cementite will break down to produce graphite set in ferrite (fig. 3.10). The properties of SG iron are intermediate between those of grey cast iron and steel. A typical SG iron has a tensile strength of 500 N/mm^2, and an elongation of 7%. SG iron is used for automobile crankshafts, brake drums, etc.

Pearlitic cast iron is produced by inoculation with, for example, calcium silicide: its microstructure consists of small flakes of graphite set in pearlite. The tensile strength of pearlitic cast iron is about 470 N/mm^2.

3.4.5 Alloy cast irons. Larger amounts of alloying additions are added to cast iron when special properties are required. In general, the effect of these elements is the same as when added to steel (see section 6.2), but these effects are modified because of the larger amount of carbon that is present, and because the size and shape of a casting affect the cooling rate. Alloying elements are added to improve the strength, hardness, corrosion resistance, and response to heat-treatment; and also to produce special physical properties.

Nickel is added to promote graphitisation, and so offset the effect of thin sections by producing uniformity over thick and thin sections. It also lowers the hardening temperature, and so enables cast iron to be quench-hardened (like steel—see Chapter 5) without cracking. Chromium stabilises cementite, and so produces hardness without the extreme brittleness associated with white cast iron. Small amounts of molybdenum cause cast iron to become tough, and small amounts of copper produce an improvement in the resistance to atmospheric corrosion.

Summary

1 Pig iron is the starting material for the production of wrought iron, cast irons, and steels. It is produced in the blast furnace from iron ore.

2 Carbon is the most important element in iron-base alloys. At room temperatures, carbon may be present with iron to form the solid solution, ferrite, and, if the carbon content exceeds 0.006%, as part of cementite (iron carbide). Ferrite and cementite form a laminated structure called pearlite.

3 Silicon, manganese, phosphorus, and sulphur are also present in various amounts. Although impurities, these elements can be used to produce variation of properties.

4 Wrought iron has a small carbon content, but includes slag, in the form of fibres. It is an ideal forging material, and is specially suitable for crane hooks, etc., as it does not fail suddenly. It is very expensive.

5 Cast iron is an iron-carbon alloy with a high carbon content (about 3.5%) that makes it an ideal casting alloy. The properties of cast iron can be controlled by variation of impurities, rate of cooling during casting, and the thickness of the casting being produced.

6 The properties can be modified by heat-treatment of the casting by the whiteheart, blackheart, or pearlitic systems.

7 High-duty cast irons are produced by an inoculation process.

8 Alloy cast irons are produced by adding special elements to produce better strength, hardness, corrosion resistance, and response to heat-treatment, and to obtain special physical properties.

Questions

Set A

1 Write brief notes on the following substances in relation to cast iron: (*a*) iron sulphide, (*b*) iron carbide, (*c*) silicon.

2 (*a*) Look up a trade paper and give the current price of pig iron, and the current price of mild-steel plates. Why is the pig iron cheaper than the plate?
(*b*) Why is it customary to keep several grades of pig iron in a foundry?

3 In the foundry, the hardness of pig iron is usually judged by breaking a pig, and examining the fractured surface. Why is this a suitable method? What elements determine the hardness of cast iron?

4 In casting small iron wheels for trucks and barrows, an iron bar is used as the centre core. The wheel-bore is then left unmachined. Suggest reasons for this practice.

5 (*a*) Grey cast iron machines readily, and no cutting solution is used. Suggest reasons for this.
(*b*) What is 'mottled' cast iron?

6 Suggest reasons why lathe beds are made of cast iron.

Set B (questions requiring further study)

7 Make a simple diagram of a blast furnace, and explain how the furnace works.

8 Compare the manufacture of an iron casting with that of a wrought iron part, and relate these to microstructure, mechanical properties, and costs.

9 Compare malleabilised iron castings with those produced by inoculation with respect to (*a*) structure, (*b*) mechanical properties, (*c*) effect of thickness, and (*d*) relative costs.

10 Explain why components that were previously forged are now being produced by casting in iron.

Chapter 4
Plain Carbon Steels

4.1 Ferrite, cementite, and pearlite

Plain carbon steel is an alloy of iron and carbon, the theoretical carbon content being between 0·1% and 1·7%, depending upon the properties required (in practice 1·5% carbon is very rarely exceeded). Plain carbon steel also contains, in controlled quantities, the impurities silicon, manganese, sulphur, and phosphorus (the effect of these impurities is discussed in section 3.2). The essential difference between steel and cast iron is that steel never contains free carbon (graphite). As stated in section 3.2, a small amount of carbon forms part of the solid solution *ferrite*, and the remainder forms *cementite* (iron carbide) with the iron. Cementite contains 6·67% carbon. It is usual to state the amount of carbon present in a steel, and from this information the amount of cementite present can be calculated by multiplying by 100/6·67 = 15. A 0·3% carbon steel, therefore, contains 4·5% cementite.

4.1.1. It has already been stated (in section 3.2.1) that ferrite is soft, weak, and ductile; and that cementite is hard and strong, but very brittle. Ferrite and cementite tend to form a laminated structure called *pearlite*, which combines the softness and weakness of ferrite with the hardness and brittleness of cementite, to produce 'all-round' properties. As shown in fig. 4.1, low carbon steel contains grains of ferrite and grains of pearlite, the amount of pearlite increasing with increased carbon content. When the carbon content is 0·83%, all the grains will be pearlitic: when this amount is exceeded, the excess carbon will form free cementite at the grain boundaries, causing a reduction of the tensile strength, due to the localised brittleness.

Figure 4.1 shows the connection between the microstructure, mechanical properties, and applications of plain carbon steels. The structure and properties are for steels in the normalised condition. (Steels may be heat-treated to make them soft and weak, or strong and brittle, or to have intermediate properties, as required. Normalising produces the 'normal' microstructure, and hence the normal properties of steels.)

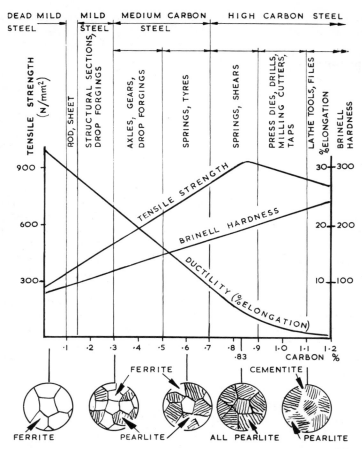

Fig 4.1 Microstructure, properties and applications of steels

4.1.2. The melting-point of iron-carbon alloys depends upon the carbon content: a low carbon steel has a melting-point of about 1500°C, and a high carbon steel has a melting-point of about 1400°C.

4.2 Steel-manufacturing processes

Steel, like cast iron, is produced from pig iron; but the carbon, sulphur, silicon, phosphorus, and manganese contents of steel must be more closely controlled. The terms *acid* and *basic* are frequently used when steel is discussed. These terms are associated with the nature of the furnace lining, and of the slag produced.

The type of process used depends upon the phosphorus content of the pig iron. Phosphorus is a highly undesirable impurity because it makes steel brittle, and its amount must be reduced to about 0·05%. It may be present in some iron ores in only small quantities, but other iron ores may contain as much as 2·5% phosphorus. Pig iron produced from low phosphorus ores does not require special refining techniques, and in this case the furnace lining is of an acid nature, so that it does not react with the slag, which is also of an acid nature, due to the high silicon content of the pig iron. When pig iron is produced from high phosphorus ores, it will contain a high percentage of phosphorus that can be removed only by introducing a large quantity of limestone into the converter or furnace. This produces a slag that is of a basic nature, and so the lining must also be of a basic nature, so as not to react with the slag.

Most British ores are of a high phosphorus content, and so about 85% of all steels produced in Britain are of the basic type. At one time it was believed that acid steels were superior, but with modern techniques there is little difference between the quality of basic steels and of acid steels.

Modern steelmaking processes can be classified as converter processes, open-hearth processes, and electrical processes.

4.2.1 Converter processes. The Bessemer process is the oldest method of producing steel in large quantities, and its invention cheapened steel far below the price of wrought iron. Bessemer steel superseded wrought iron for most industrial purposes, but was always less popular in Britain than in the United States, as the problems associated with the removal of phosphorus were, quite incorrectly, associated with this process.

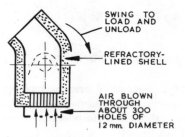

Fig 4.2 Bessemer converter

The Bessemer converter is a steel shell that is open-mouthed, refractory-lined, and mounted upon a trunnion, so that it can be swung into a horizontal position for charging and pouring, and into a vertical position for 'blowing'. The converter is charged with molten pig iron; and, when about half filled, it is turned up, and air is blown through the holes in the bottom of the refractory, to oxidise the impurities and the carbon. The heat so produced keeps the charge molten. The carbon content is finally adjusted by adding manganese-rich pig iron, the steel is poured into a ladle, and then teemed into ingot moulds. The converter capacity is between 25 000 and 60 000 kg, and the process takes about 25 minutes. It is necessary that the process be stopped at this point, as the iron itself would start to combine with the oxygen, to form iron oxide, and the charge would start to become solid when all the impurities were removed. Figure 4.2 illustrates a Bessemer converter.

During recent years, a variation of the Bessemer process, using oxygen instead of air, has become popular. This variation produces high temperatures, and permits up to 15% steel scrap to be employed, instead of only about 5% as in the original process. It also produces a better-quality steel, as nitrogen is not introduced into the converter in large quantities.

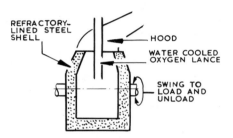

Fig. 4.3 Lintz-Donawitz (LD) converter

Variations of the Bessemer process have been developed using oxygen blown on to the surface of the molten pig iron. One method, the Lintz-Donawitz (LD) process, was developed in Austria, and has become popular in Britain. In this process (fig. 4.3), oxygen is blown on to the top of the molten pig iron in a vertical converter.

Converters may operate using either the acid or the basic method, using a suitable lining material. When the basic process is used, limestone must be introduced into the converter before the molten pig iron. Recent trends indicate that, in Britain, converter processes are becoming more popular than the open-hearth process.

4.2.2 The open-hearth process. The open-hearth furnace is used to produce low and medium carbon content steels by an acid or basic method, according to the nature of the furnace lining. This furnace, illustrated by fig. 4.4, consists of a box-like brickwork shell, lined with a refractory material, and strengthened with steelwork. The furnace hearth is shaped like a large saucer, and the capacity is between about 150 000 and 300 000 kg. The furnace is fired with producer gas

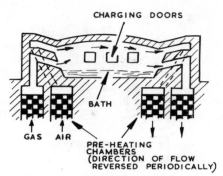

Fig 4.4 Open hearth furnace

and coke-oven gas, or by fuel oil. It uses the regenerative principle: the waste gases being used to heat the stoves, so that they attain a temperature of between 900°C and 1200°C. These stoves enable the necessarily high temperature to be attained, and, at the same time, save fuel.

In this process, the furnace is charged with pig iron and steel scrap—the pig iron need not be molten, but, in a large integrated steelworks, it is sound economics to keep it molten. When the basic process is used, limestone is introduced with the pig iron. The flames play upon the surface of the charge, causing some of the impurities to form a slag on the surface of the melt. Iron ore or millscale is then added, mainly to remove carbon by oxidation. Upon completion of the refining, the tapping notch is broken open, and the steel is tapped into a ladle. The open-hearth is tapped about once every twelve hours: during the later stages of the refining, a number of samples are taken, and analysed to ensure that the composition will be correct. The basic slag is used as a fertiliser.

A recently developed variation of this process incorporates an oxygen lance, to blow oxygen on to the surface of the melt.

4.2.3 Electrical processes. If the quality of the steel is to be high, it is necessary that the temperature be controlled, and that the impurities entering the furnace during the refining are minimised: these requirements can be met only if electric furnaces are used. In Britain, the initial steel refining is done using the open-hearth furnace or a converter, and the further refining is done using an electric-arc furnace. The electric-arc furnace is shown in fig. 4.5, and is of between 25 000 and 100 000 kg capacity. It is fitted with three carbon electrodes in the roof, and these are adjusted automatically to strike an arc directly with the metal. This furnace can be lined to suit either the basic or the acid

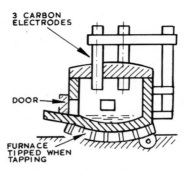

Fig 4.5 Electric-arc furnace

method, and the material charged into it can include scrap of known composition.

The high-frequency induction furnace (fig. 4.6) is used for the melting and alloying of special steels, and is not a refining furnace. It consists of a coil of wire wound around a crucible, so that, when energised with an electric current, it will produce circulating currents

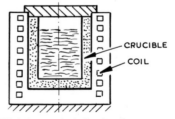

Fig 4.6 High-frequency induction furnace

within the metal in the crucible, and so cause melting. When the charge is molten, these currents produce a stirring action. The capacity of this furnace is up to about 6000 kg.

4.2.4 Spray steelmaking. This process is being developed in Britain to enable molten pig iron to be refined rapidly, to produce a wide range of plain carbon and low alloy steels. It has already been found that processes in which oxygen is introduced speed up the rate of carbon oxidation, and this process aims at increasing this still further, by producing a large surface area of metal in an atmosphere of oxygen, by using a spray.

The molten pig iron is introduced into a tundish, from which it flows at a continuous rate. High-pressure jets of oxygen are directed at it, to break it up into droplets of between 1- and 2-mm diameter, and to remove the carbon and other impurities. Lime and other fluxes are introduced in the form of an annular curtain surrounding the metal. The refined metal is collected in the receiving ladle, where the slag settles at the top, and overflows. The composition can be controlled by the flow rate from the blast furnace, and by the flow rate of the oxygen, and it is considered that this process will be particularly suitable for operation by computer.

Summary

1   Plain carbon steel is an alloy of iron and between 0·1% and 1·7% carbon, with small quantities of the impurities sulphur, phosphorus, silicon, and manganese.
2   Unlike cast iron, steel never contains graphite.
3   Plain carbon steel contains ferrite and cementite. Ferrite is a solid solution of carbon in iron, and is soft, weak, and ductile: cementite is iron carbide, and is hard and strong, but brittle. Ferrite and cementite tend to form the laminated structure called pearlite. The balance of ferrite and cementite depends upon the carbon content, and controls the properties of the steel.
4   Steel is produced from pig iron. This can be done by converter, open-hearth furnace, electric furnace, or by the spray technique.

Questions

Set A
1   What would you expect the carbon content to be of the steel used for each of the follwing articles: motor-car body, water piping, vice body, spanner, file, roller of a roller bearing? Give brief reasons for your answers.
2   High carbon steel bar is a common engineering material, but high carbon steel tube is most uncommon. Suggest reasons for this.
3   Explain the meaning of the terms ferrite, cementite, and pearlite.
4   Explain why the carbon content controls the mechanical properties of steels.

Set B (questions requiring further study)
5   Make a diagram of an open-hearth furnace, and write brief notes on the open-hearth process of steel-making.
6   What are the special advantages associated with the production of steel by converter?
7   Why are alloy steels produced by electrical methods?

Chapter 5
The Heat-treatment of Steels

5.1. Heat-treatment can be defined as a process in which solid metal is subjected to one or more temperature cycles to confer certain desired properties. Steel is an important engineering material because, although cheap, it can be given a wide range of mechanical properties as a result of heat-treatment.

Heat-treatment can alter the mechanical properties of steel by changing the size and shape of the grains (crystals) of which it is composed, or by changing its microconstituents. (Microconstituents are constituents that can only be seen with the aid of a microscope.)

In order to understand the theory of heat-treatment of steel, we must study the changes that occur when steel is heated and then slowly cooled.

5.2 The heating and slow cooling of steel

5.2.1 Heating (fig. 5.1). If a piece of plain carbon steel (i.e. steel that does not contain alloying elements) is put into a cool furnace, which is then heated at a uniform rate, its temperature will rise at a uniform rate until a temperature is reached at which this rise is halted for a short time (the temperature may even fall at this point), although the temperature of the *furnace* continues to rise at a uniform rate. At this point, the heat is being used to cause a rearrangement of the iron atoms, which in turn causes the formation of a solid solution called *austenite*. Austenite is a solid solution of carbon in iron, but, unlike *ferrite*, which is also a solid solution of carbon in iron, it can contain up to 1·7% carbon. (Ferrite can only contain up to 0·006% carbon when at room temperature.) Figure 4.1 contains a diagram illustrating the microstructure of ferrite, and fig. 5.2 contains a diagram illustrating austenite; it will be seen that austenite and ferrite are similar in appearance, because they are both solid solutions.

The temperature at which austenite is formed is called the *lower critical point* (*heating*), and is 725°C: at this temperature the pearlite is transformed into austenite.

If the steel contains less than 0·83% carbon, there will be some ferrite present after this change has taken place, and if it contains more than 0·83% carbon, there will be some cementite present. Further heating will cause this ferrite or cementite to be transformed into austenite. This takes place gradually, and requires less heat than does the transformation of pearlite into austenite, so the rate at which the temperature of the steel rises will gradually increase until the structure completely consists of austenite, when its temperature will again rise at a uniform rate. The temperature at which the formation of austenite is completed is called the *upper critical point* (*heating*), and this temperature depends upon the carbon content of the steel.

5.2.2 Cooling (fig. 5.1). If the steel is left in the furnace while the latter cools at a uniform rate, its temperature will fall at a uniform rate until a temperature is reached at which it starts to cool less rapidly. This temperature is called the *upper critical point* (*cooling*), and is 30°C lower than the upper critical point (heating). At the upper critical point (cooling), the austenite starts to break down to produce either ferrite or cementite, according to the carbon content of the steel.

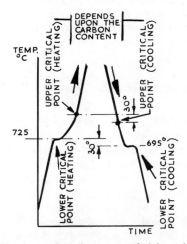

Fig 5.1 Heating and cooling curves of plain carbon steel

This change continues until the *lower critical point* (*cooling*) is reached. This occurs at 695°C, when any remaining austenite is transformed into pearlite, and the fall in temperature is halted for a short time (or the temperature of the steel may even rise slightly). The breakdown of austenite during cooling is caused by the rearrangement of the iron atons, which produces heat which then causes the changes in the rate at which the steel cools. The changes observed during this heating and slow cooling of steel are important in the study of its heat-treatment.

5.2.3 The simplified equilibrium diagram for steels. As a result of extensive research, the structural changes and the temperature at which they occur have been recorded in the form of a diagram called an *equilibrium diagram*. It is conventional for an equilibrium diagram to indicate the changes that take place as a result of slow cooling. The changes that take place during the slow cooling of steel occur in reverse when it is heated, but the temperatures at which they occur are all 30°C higher than those associated with cooling. Figure 5.2 shows a simplified form of the part of the iron–carbon equilibrium diagram, which is of importance in the study of the heat-treatment of steels.

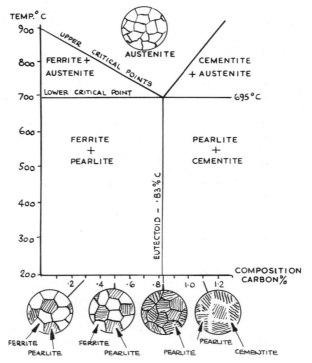

Fig 5.2 Simplified equilibrium diagram for steels

The interpretation of the iron–carbon equilibrium diagram will be illustrated by considering the slow cooling of a 0·4% carbon steel. The changes can be studied by drawing a vertical line passing through 0·4% carbon on the carbon axis. This line indicates that the structure of this steel is austenitic until a temperature of about 800°C is reached, when the austenite starts to decompose to form ferrite, with some austenite still remaining. This process continues, producing more ferrite, until a temperature of 695°C is reached, at which the remaining austenite changes into laminations of ferrite and cementite (the structure known as pearlite), which will be present with the ferrite already produced during the cooling between 800°C and 695°C.

5.2.4 The effect of rapid cooling. If steel is heated to a suitable temperature, and then slowly cooled, the changes indicated by the iron–carbon equilibrium diagram will take place, and the steel will be soft, weak, and ductile. If it is heated to the same temperature, and then rapidly cooled (or 'quenched'), the changes in the arrangement of the iron atoms will still take place, but there will not be sufficient time for the excess carbon to leave the iron and allow ferrite to form. This results in the iron crystals containing more carbon than they should, causing them to be distorted. The steel will be harder, stronger, and very brittle as a result of this treatment.

5.3 The classification of heat-treatment processes
From the foregoing, it can be seen that heat-treatment processes can be classified as:
  (a) heat-treatments which produce equilibrium conditions as a result of heating followed by slow cooling; these are (i) *annealing*, and (ii) *normalising*; and
  (b) heat-treatments which produce non-equilibrium conditions as a result of heating followed by rapid cooling (quenching): the combined processes of *hardening* and *tempering* produce a controlled degree of non-equilibrium.

5.4 Heat-treatment processes producing equilibrium conditions

5.4.1 Annealing. This process is applied to steel to remove stresses, produce uniformity, and induce softness, so that it can be cold-worked (cold-working implies bending, rolling, etc., at room temperature). In full annealing, the steel is heated to a suitable temperature (dependent on its carbon content, as shown in fig. 5.3), held at that temperature (or 'soaked') for about 2 hours, and then very slowly cooled to room temperature. The cooling may be carried out in the same furnace as the heating and soaking; alternatively, the steel may be transferred to another furnace at about 650°C, and held there until the austenite has transformed into pearlite (final cooling can be done in still air), or it may be buried in hot ashes, and left until cool. The latter two methods are economical in furnace heat energy, furnace utilisation, and time. The prolonged heating of steel in air causes carbon to leave it, and

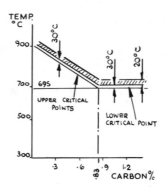

Fig 5.3 Annealing temperatures

cause scaling: this can be prevented by packing it into refractory-lined and sealed boxes, to exclude air during the annealing, or by heating it in a controlled-atmosphere furnace.

If the steel is already uniform in structure, or if it is necessary only to restore ductility lost during previous cold-working, so that further cold-working can be carried out, a variation called *sub-critical annealing* (annealing below the critical temperatures) can be employed. This consists of heating the steel to about 650°C, and soaking, followed by free cooling in still air. The free cooling is permissible since the heating and soaking produce no changes in the microconstituents. A similar process is often carried out upon higher carbon steels, such as tool steels, containing a large amount of free cementite, which makes them brittle. This treatment involves a similar heating and cooling to that done to restore ductility lost by cold-working, but it causes the cementite to be re-formed into small globules set in ferrite. The ferrite 'carries' the globules of cementite, so that the steel as a whole becomes ductile; this process is often called *spheroidising*.

5.4.2 Normalising. Steel is normalised to produce a fine grain, uniformity of structure, and improved mechanical properties. Normalising is usually performed after forging or casting, to put steel in the best condition for machining or hardening. The process is similar to annealing, but, as indicated in fig. 5.4, the heating and soaking are carried out at a temperature high enough to ensure that a fully austenitic structure is produced before the free cooling in still air that follows. It is necessary that a full austenitic structure is produced, to ensure that the final structure is as indicated by the iron–carbon equilibrium diagram, because normalising is the first step towards obtaining the final properties. (Note that it is less important to produce a fully austenitic structure when annealing, as that process is used to obtain temporary ductility.)

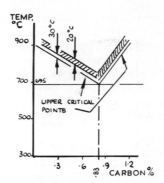

Fig 5.4 Normalising temperatures

5.5 Heat-treatment processes producing non-equilibrium conditions

It has already been stated that hardening and tempering are the two processes that produce a controlled degree of non-equilibrium. The steel is first hardened, so that it is further from equilibrium than required; and it is then reheated to a suitable temperature, below the lower critical temperature, to produce a partial return to equilibrium conditions.

The mechanical properties produced by hardening and tempering depend upon the carbon content of the steel, the rate at which it is cooled during the hardening process, and the tempering temperature.

5.5.1 Hardening. In this process, the steel is heated to a suitable temperature (depending upon the carbon content, as shown in fig. 5.5) to produce all, or sufficient, austenite; held at that temperature, so that its temperature is uniform across its section; and then quenched. If the quenching produces cooling at a certain minimum rate, called the *critical cooling rate* for that steel, all the austenite will be transformed into

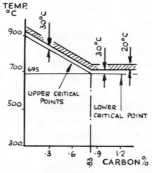

Fig 5.5 Hardening temperatures

a fine, needle-like structure called *martensite*. The appearance of martensite when seen with the aid of a microscope is shown in fig. 5.6. Steel with a martensitic structure is very hard and very strong, but it is also very brittle. Figure 5.7 shows the connection between the maximum hardness produced by hardening, and the carbon content of steel. If it contains less than about 0·15% carbon, steel will not respond to direct hardening.

Fig 5.6 Microstructure of martensite

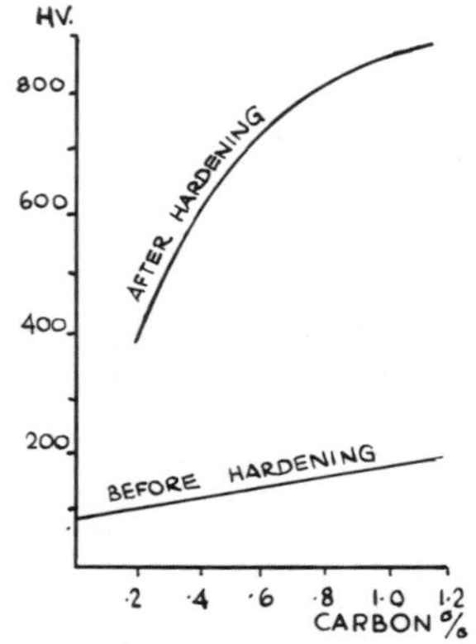

Fig 5.7 Hardness of steels before and after hardening

If the cooling rate is slightly lower than the critical cooling rate, the austenite will be transformed into a fine form of pearlite, called *troostitic pearlite*; and if it is cooled at a slightly lower rate again, but higher than that which would allow pearlite to form, it will be transformed into another fine form of pearlite, called *sorbitic pearlite*. A sorbitic or troostitic steel is hard, strong, and brittle, but it is not as hard and brittle as a martensitic steel.

The rate of cooling is controlled by the quenching medium: a solution of salt or caustic soda in water produces a very rapid quench, and a blast of air produces a slow quench. Water and oil produce intermediate quenches, and are the most common quenching media: air is suitable only for certain special alloy steels, and salt and caustic soda solutions are unsuitable because they are too violent.

The quenching technique must be controlled to prevent the formation of cracks. Cracks are produced by the expansion of steel that takes place when the iron atoms become rearranged during cooling; this causes no trouble when steel is slowly cooled, but it causes cracking when cooling is rapid. This cracking can be accounted for by considering the steel to be made up of layers, the surface of the steel being the outside layer. Each layer is quenched in turn, because the effect of quenching takes time to pass through the section. As each layer is quenched, it expands; and then becomes hard and brittle, because of the formation of martensite. The layers below the surface thus expand against the hardened layers nearer the surface, causing the formation of a crack that spreads across the section. The problem can be overcome to a large extent by using a quenching medium just severe enough to produce the desired hardness and strength. Figure 5.7 implies that a high carbon steel may be quenched in oil to produce the same hardness as is produced when a low carbon steel is quenched in water; and from the foregoing it will be realised that the steel that is oil-quenched will not suffer cracking, as would the water-quenched steel.

The condition of the quenching water calls for little comment, except that it should be clean and particularly free from grease or soap. Quenching oil must have a high flash-point, and ordinary lubricating oil is quite unsuitable. Even the best oil is subject to change, and certain lighter portions are evaporated by the hot metal, thus increasing the viscosity, and lowering the cooling properties. Furthermore, a sludge, consisting of carbonised oil, and scale from the quenched steel, is gradually formed. When cooling by air is used, it must be ensured that the compressor system delivers dry air.

The method of immersing a component in the quenching bath requires forethought. The hot steel will vaporise some of the liquid, and bubbles of vapour may cling to the surface of the steel, or be trapped in blind holes, so that correct quenching does not take place at these points. If long components are dipped at an angle, or horizontally, distortion is more probable than if they are dipped vertically. In many cases, the article is immersed and moved about in the bath; but, in modern installations, jets of oil are directed on to the component at suitable points, the component being placed over the bath. In other cases, the liquid in the bath is arranged to have a steady flow, by means of pumps or rotating paddles. There are also arrangements whereby the oil is constantly withdrawn from the bath, and passed through a cooler before being reintroduced, to maintain an even temperature.

When a thick piece of steel is heated and quenched only the outside will be martensitic; the core being troostitic or sorbitic. This variation of structure is called *mass effect*; mass effect produces a variation of hardness and strength across the section which causes concern if uniformity of properties is required. The resistance of steel to mass effect is called *hardenability* (this property must not be confused with hardness); it can be determined using the *Jominy end-quench test*, in which a standard test piece is quenched from its hardening temperature, so that only the end is quenched, causing the test piece to be cooled at various rates along its length; the hardness of the quenched steel is measured at intervals along its length and a graph of hardness–distance is drawn. The greatest thickness of a piece of steel that has uniform properties when quenched in a specified way is termed its *ruling section*. Hardenability can be improved by including suitable alloying elements.

5.5.2 Tempering. After hardening, steels are usually reheated to a suitable sub-critical temperature, to improve their toughness and ductility (at the expense of hardness and strength) to make them more suitable for service requirements. This reheating is called tempering, and it causes a martensitic type of structure to be transformed into *troostite* or *sorbite*, according to the tempering temperature. These structures consist of ferrite and finely divided cementite, and are different from those produced by mild quenching, which are of a laminated form. The tempering temperature depends upon the particular combination of properties required, but is between about 180°C and 650°C (fig. 5.8). The duration of the heating depends upon the thickness of the material, and cooling is usually in air, to avoid distortion of the part. As

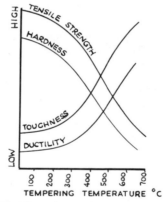

Fig 5.8 Effect of tempering a hardened steel

already stated, the overall effect of hardening and tempering depends upon the carbon content of the steel, the rate of quenching during the hardening process, and the tempering temperature.

5.5.3 Influence of design on heat-treatment. The designer can cause unnecessary problems for the heat-treatment department. Sharp corners and asymmetrical or abruptly changing shapes should be avoided. Consider the two flat gauges shown in figs 5.9 and 5.10. In fig. 5.9, cracks might be set up at B during quenching, and the thin sections at corners A would readily overheat in the furnace. Figure 5.10 shows the same gauge modified to overcome these difficulties, and is the usual form of the ordinary workshop 'snap' gauge.

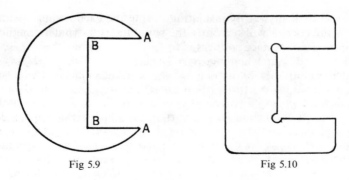

Fig 5.9   Fig 5.10

Certain difficulties have already been mentioned. Blind holes should be avoided if possible, and long, thin parts are a nuisance, since a deep bath is required if they are to be quenched vertically. Hardened parts sometimes appear to have unnecessary holes in them, but on examination it becomes obvious that these holes have been introduced to thin down certain bulky sections, and so give the component a more even thickness throughout.

5.6 The surface-hardening of steel

The hardening and tempering so far described are done mainly to produce a controlled strength. It may be necessary to produce a high surface hardness for wear-resistance, supported by a tough, shock-resisting core. This combination of very different properties in one component can be obtained by surface-hardening.

One method of classifying surface-hardening methods is according to the type of heating employed.

(*a*) Methods in which the whole component is heated during the heat-treatment are (i) *case-hardening*, and (ii) *nitriding*.

(*b*) Methods in which only the surface of the component is heated during the heat-treatment include *flame-hardening* and *induction-hardening*, which differ only in the method used to heat the surface of the steel.

5.7 Case-hardening

Parts to be hardened by this process are made from a steel with a carbon content of about 0·15%, which will not respond to direct hardening. The steel is first subjected to a *carburising* treatment, in which the carbon content of the surface layers is increased to about 0·9%. When the carburised steel is later heated and quenched, only the surface layers will respond, and the core will remain soft and tough, as required, since its carbon content will still be only about 0·15%. (It was explained in section 5.5.1 that steel must have more than 0·15% carbon in order to respond to hardening and quenching.) Selected surface areas can be kept soft by insulating during the carburising operation, so that the carbon will not enter the surface. An alternative method of obtaining local surface softness is to leave surplus metal on these surface areas, so that when the part is machined at these places, after carburising but before hardening, the high carbon case will be removed, to expose the low carbon areas.

Case-hardening is a two-part process:

(*a*) carburising, in which the carbon content of the surface is increased; and

(*b*) heat-treatment, in which the core is refined, and the case is hardened.

5.7.1 Carburising. In this operation the steel is heated to a suitable temperature (fig. 5.11) in a carbonaceous atmosphere, and kept at that temperature until the carbon has penetrated to the depth required. The carbon can be supplied as a solid, a liquid, or a gas.

When the carburising medium is solid, the parts are packed into a suitable metal box, in which they are surrounded by the carburising medium. A lid is fitted to the box, and sealed with fire-clay, so that no carbon gas can escape, and no air can enter the box to cause decarburisation (loss of carbon from the surface of the steel). The carburising medium can be wood, bone, or leather charcoal; but an energiser, such as barium carbonate, is added to speed up the process. Initially the rate of carburising is about 0·3 mm/hour, but this slows down, so it takes about 7 hours to produce a depth of about 1·3 mm of high carbon steel at the surface. The surface can be insulated against carburising by coating it with a suitable paste, or by plating it with about 0·1 mm of copper. The carbon content of the case can be adjusted by mixing old and new carburising material.

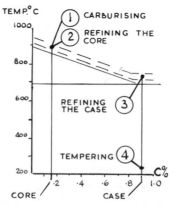

Fig. 5.11 Stages in case-hardening

Carburising can be carried out in a heated salt-bath (sodium carbonate and sodium cyanide are typical carburising salts); this is suitable for thin cases, about 0·3 mm deep. Salt-bath carburising is very rapid, and is not always suitable, since it produces an abrupt change in carbon content from surface to core; this produces a tendency for the case to flake. Gas-carburising is used to carburise to a depth of about 1·0 mm in 4 hours, the carbon content being controlled by the composition of the gas that is allowed to flow through the heated furnace.

5.7.2 Heat-treatment. After the carburising has been completed, the case will contain about 0·9% carbon, and the core will still contain about 0·15% carbon; there will be a gradual transition of carbon content between the case and the core (fig. 5.12). Owing to the prolonged heating, the core will be coarse; and, in order to produce a reasonable toughness, it must be refined.

To refine the core, the carburised steel is reheated to about 870°C, held at that temperature long enough to produce uniformity of structure, and then cooled rapidly, to prevent grain growth during cooling. The temperature of this heating is much higher than that suitable for the case (fig. 5.11), and therefore an extremely brittle martensite will be produced: the case and the outer layers of the core must now be refined.

This refining is done by reheating the steel to about 760°C, to suit the case, and then quenched. Finally, the case is tempered at about 200°C, to relieve the quenching stresses. Figure 5.13 illustrates the appearance of the structure across the section produced by case-hardening.

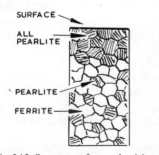
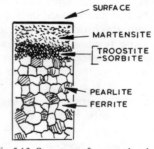

Fig 5.12 Structure after carburising   Fig 5.13 Structure after case-hardening

If the part is not required to resist shock, it is unnecessary to carry out the core-refining operation; in these conditions, a coarse martensite at the surface may not cause trouble, and so the part may be quenched directly after carburising. The so-called *cyaniding* hardening operation, so often carried out upon small jig location pieces, is an example of this treatment, in which parts are quenched directly after being carburised, in a bath containing sodium cyanide and other salts.

Parts made from an alloy steel containing about 3% nickel do not usually require refining, since nickel retards grain growth.

5.8 Nitriding

In this process, a special alloy steel is heated for a considerable time in an atmosphere of gaseous nitrogen. During this heating, hard nitrides are produced at the surface, but it is necessary that the steel contains a small amount of chromium, or small amounts of both chromium and aluminium (according to the surface hardness required), for this hardening to take place. The carbon content of nitriding steel is between 0·2% and 0·5%, according to the core strength required. It will be realised that a nitriding steel will respond to direct hardening, and this technique is used to develop the required core properties before nitriding is carried out.

Parts to be nitrided are given heat-treatment during the early stages of their machining, to develop the required core properties. This treatment consists of hardening by oil-quenching, followed by tempering at between 550° and 750°C, depending upon the composition of the steel, and the properties required. Before final machining, the parts are heated at about 550°C for up to seven hours, and slowly cooled, to remove stresses, and to minimise distortion during the nitriding. These parts can be finish-machined before nitriding, because *no quenching is done after nitriding*, and they will not, therefore, suffer from quenching distortion.

The nitriding process consists of heating the parts at 500°C in a constant circulation of ammonia gas, for up to 100 hours. During the early stages, a case depth of about 0·12 mm is produced in 10 hours, but the rate of penetration decreases as the process is continued, and it takes about 100 hours to obtain a case depth of about 0·7 mm. During the nitriding process, the parts are in an externally heated gas-tight box, fitted with inlet and outlet ports for the ammonia (which supplies the nitrogen). At the completion of the 'soaking', the ammonia is still circulated, until the temperature of the steel has fallen to about 150°C, when the box is opened, and the cooling completed in air. Nitriding causes a film to be produced on the surface, but this can be removed by a light buffing.

Local surface areas can be kept 'soft' by insulating (*a*) by tinning, or (*b*) by plating with copper or nickel to produce a 0·1 mm deposit. Nitriding causes a growth of between about 0·025 and 0·050 mm on diameter (or about 0·015 mm on the sides of rectangular sections); this can be allowed for during operation planning, or, if special accuracy is required, an allowance is made for finish-machining.

The surface hardness depends upon the composition of the steel used; steels with 3% chromium develop about 850 Vickers Pyramid Number (HV), and steels with 1·5% chromium and 1·5% aluminium develop about 1100 HV. As already stated, the core strength developed depends mainly upon the carbon content of the steel.

5.9 Flame-hardening and induction-hardening
In these processes, the part is made from a steel that will respond to direct hardening, but which instead is hardened by very rapidly heating it to its hardening temperature, and then quenching it before the core reaches that temperature.

5.9.1 Flame-hardening. Steels with a suitable carbon content (between about 0·4% and 0·7%, according to the hardness required) can be heated to the hardening temperature by means of an oxy-acetylene flame, and then rapidly quenched, to produce a local hardness. The method is suitable for cases of up to 0·10 mm depth. The flame temperature must be above the melting temperature of steel, in order to produce the rapid heating necessary in this process, and there is a danger of local melting if greater case depths are attempted.

Flame-hardening may be carried out by:
(*a*) heating the surface locally, and then quenching the component in a separate quenching tank;
(*b*) progressive heating and quenching, in which the flame and quenching spray are acting continuously whilst they are passed across the surface to be hardened. The rate at which the unit passes across the surface controls the hardness produced. Progressive heating and quenching can also be carried out in a booth containing a fixed flame and spray unit, through which the parts are fed on a conveyor moving at about 3 mm/s (fig. 5.14);
(*c*) spinning the part past stationary flames that surround it, and then spraying it or immersing it in water to quench it. Long parts can be rotated while the flame units are reciprocated parallel to the axis of rotation.

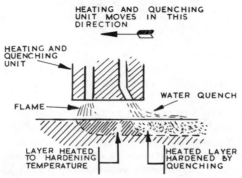

Fig. 5.14 Flame-hardening by progressive heating and quenching

After flame-hardening, steel is usually tempered; this can be done by flame heating, if required.

5.9.2 Induction-hardening. This is a production method of surface-hardening, in which the part to be surface-hardened is placed within an inductor coil through which a high frequency current is passed. The furnace is similar to that used in the production of alloy steels (figs 4.6 and 8.10), but a perforated water jacket is incorporated within the coil, as a quenching unit. The surface of the component is very quickly brought to the hardening temperature, and then quenched while the part is still within the coil. It takes about 5 seconds for a case depth of 3·0 mm to be heated to its hardening temperature. The temperature can be controlled by coil design, and by the distance between the coil and the surface to be hardened. Steels with about 0·45% carbon are most suitable for hardening by this method.

Summary

1   Heat-treatment is a cycle of heating and cooling, during which the metal is in the solid state.
2   When steel is heated, certain changes occur. The steel will retain its original structure if it is cooled slowly; but, if cooled rapidly, it will become hard and strong, but brittle.
3   Annealing and normalising both involve heating and slow cooling. Annealing makes steel particularly weak and ductile, as it involves very slow cooling.
4   Hardening involves heating and very rapid cooling; it is usually followed by tempering (reheating to a suitable temperature) to remove some of the brittleness.
5   Wear resistance can be obtained by surface-hardening. This may involve a local change of composition (case-hardening and nitriding), or local heating followed by rapid cooling (flame-hardening and induction-hardening).

Questions

Set A
1   Write brief notes explaining each of the following terms: critical points, critical cooling rate, austenite, tempering, martensite.
2   Describe the method of hardening and tempering a fitter's chisel with a blacksmith's hearth and a bucket of water.
3   A piece of 1·0% carbon-steel bar is 75 mm in diameter. It is heated slightly above the upper critical point, and plunged into cold

water. It is then cut in half with a thin grinding wheel, and the cut surface is tested at various points with the Brinell hardness tester. What results would you expect?

4 A mild-steel pin, 50 mm in diameter and 300 mm long, is subjected to a heavy rubbing action, and lubrication is difficult. Suggest a treatment for improving the surface wearing properties of the pin, and describe this treatment in full.

5 Distinguish between low-temperature and high-temperature tempering, giving the actual temperatures used. Give an illustration of each by naming a part, and stating the temperature at which it should be tempered.

6 It has been said that the annealing of steel is a commencing process, but normalising is a finishing process. Discuss this statement.

7 Make sketches of the appearance under the microscope of correctly normalised plain carbon steel with the following carbon contents: 0·1%, 0·4%, and 0·7%. Explain why these structures differ from each other. If the 0·7% steel is heated to 1000°C, and slowly cooled, would any change in appearance be noted under the microscope?

8 Suggest suitable heat-treatments for the following parts: a chisel which 'snips' at the cutting edge, a spanner which dents easily, a piece of mild-steel sheet which is to be bent up into a bracket. Briefly describe each treatment.

9 Explain what is meant by the term 'critical cooling rate', and discuss its effect on the heat-treatment of plain carbon and alloy steels.

10 What are the factors which determine the time required to heat a piece of steel to its upper critical point?

11 Give the approximate temperatures for each of the following operations: annealing mild steel, heating 1·0% carbon steel for hardening, tempering a carbon steel spring. Briefly outline the method of attaining the correct temperature in each case.

12 Explain briefly the meaning of each of the following heat-treatment terms: carburising, refractory, soaking time, quenching.

13 Explain why steel 'scales' when heated. What are the defects associated with 'scaling'?

Set B (questions requiring further study)

14 How and why is bright annealing performed?

15 Discuss the problem of distortion in the heat-treatment of steel, and explain how it is minimised.

16 Describe the process of case-hardening mild steel, and explain the necessity for the various operations.

17 Describe carefully, with the aid of sketches, how martensite breaks down in the tempering of a high carbon steel.

18 A piece of 0·7% carbon steel is heated steadily to 800°C, and quenched in water. It is then reheated to 800°C, and cooled very slowly. Describe the various structural changes which occur during these processes.

Chapter 6
Alloy Steels

6.1 Service conditions

Engineering parts are subjected to a number of forces in service. These forces may be accompanied by certain special conditions, such as heat in the internal-combustion engine, or in steam plants; or by chemical corrosion by liquids and gases. Tensile, compressive, and shear forces may all be present at the same time, and their intensity may vary slowly or rapidly, and may be produced by sudden shocks. Shear stresses may be produced by abrasion or wear.

The importance of the yield point has already been emphasised, and it is necessary that the designer works with a 'factor of safety', to keep the stresses well below the yield point. If heat, corrosion, or abrasion is expected, then further allowances must be made.

The problem of cracking during hardening has already been discussed in Chapter 5, and may mean that the designer must accept a lower hardness, and also design the component so as to eliminate cracking or distortion as a result of hardening.

A very wide range of alloy steels has been developed to meet varying service conditions, and to reduce heat-treatment problems; it is possible to discuss only a few of the more important types in this book. Some alloy steels are very complex, and contain a number of alloying elements; the reader may have noted slight variations between two apparently similar steels. These variations may or may not have importance, but it cannot be emphasised too strongly that the best guide to the manipulation and use of any particular steel is the literature issued by the manufacturer. All reputable steel-makers are continually testing and trying to improve their products. In buying steel from such firms, the wise engineer takes care to obtain the specialised knowledge which is so freely given.

6.2 The effects of including alloying elements

The effect of alloying depends upon the carbon content of the steel, and upon the other alloying elements present, and their quantities; but the following will give an indication of the effects of the more common alloying elements.

6.2.1 Manganese (chemical symbol Mn). This element is present in all steels as an impurity which counteracts the effects of sulphur; the minimum amount required depends upon the amount of sulphur present. The manganese content of mild steel is usually about 0·5%. A steel with 2·5% manganese has a higher yield point, and a distinctly better resistance to shock; and, since it is not much more expensive, a steel with a low carbon content and about 2·5% manganese is often used as a superior type of mild steel. When about 12% manganese is present, steel has very pronounced work-hardening properties (see section 6.3.4).

6.2.2 Nickel (chemical symbol Ni). About 3% nickel tends to make steel tough, but is normally used on its own only when the carbon content is low, since it tends to change iron carbide into graphite. Up to 5% nickel is used if the steel is to be tough, and has to respond to oil-quenching; if too much nickel is present, martensite will form too readily during quenching, and the steel will be too brittle and hard. Case-hardening steels containing nickel do not suffer grain growth during carburising, and do not always require refining treatment (see section 5.7.2). About 8% nickel is added with chromium, to produce certain stainless and heat-resisting steels, since these two elements prevent the breakdown of austenite during cooling to room temperature.

6.2.3 Chromium (chemical symbol Cr). Chromium and nickel are often found together in steels, because the tendency of nickel to graphitise steel is counteracted by the chromium stabilising the iron carbide. On the other hand, chromium tends to promote coarse-grain structure, and increases the difficulty of heat-treatment. This is counteracted by the nickel, which refines the grain size, and makes heat-treatment easier. The chromium content is increased slightly to produce hardness, and very high percentages of chromium are included if the steel is to be corrosion-resisting or heat-resisting (see sections 6.3.5 and 6.3.6).

6.2.4 Molybdenum (chemical symbol Mo). Steels that contain nickel and chromium suffer from temper brittleness which implies that they become brittle if held at a temperature between 250°C and 500°C. If so heated, the tensile strength remains high, but the shock resistance becomes dangerously low. This trouble can be overcome by the introduction of about 0·25% molybdenum.

6.2.5 Tungsten (chemical symbol W). Tungsten is an important element in high-speed steels, and enables them to cut at high speeds without becoming soft. Plain carbon tool steels cannot be used for high-speed cutting, because cutting generates heat, and these steels tend to soften at about 250°C. High-speed steels can cut at higher speeds because tungsten raises the softening temperature to about 600°C. Cutting and cutting-tool materials are the subject of Chapter 15.

6.3 Some typical alloy steels

The following alloy steels are representative of the many alloy steels in use. They are included here to indicate how the alloying elements are combined to produce special effects.

6.3.1 Case-hardening steels. These steels contain less than about 0·15% carbon, so the core will not respond to hardening. Those with 3% nickel may not require refining after the carburising operation, which tends to produce grain growth, due to the prolonged heating at a high temperature. If the nickel content is increased to 5%, quenching can be in oil.

Table 6.1 Some case-hardening steels

Composition	Description
0·12% C, 3% Ni, 0·45% Mn	Small parts produced from this steel need not be refined after carburising. This is a water-quenching steel, and is used for gudgeon pins, camshafts, etc.
0·12% C, 5% Ni, 0·40% Mn	Small parts produced from this steel need not be refined after carburising. Oil-quenching can be used when hardening. Used for gearbox parts, etc.

Table 6.2 Some nitriding steels

Composition	Description
0·5% C, 1·6% Cr, 1·1% Al	Used when a high-strength core and a high hardness case are required. Oil-quenching can be done when the core is heat-treated.
0·4% C, 3% Cr	Allows a high-core strength and a fairly high case-hardness to be developed. Oil-quenching can be done when the core is heat-treated.

6.3.2 Nitriding steels. These steels contain enough carbon to make them respond to direct hardening, so that a high-strength case is developed as a result of hardening and tempering at about 600°C (the precise technique depends upon the composition of the steel). It is necessary to use an alloy steel so that nitrides are formed. About 3% chromium enables a surface hardness of about 850 HV to be developed, with a gradual variation of hardness from surface to core; but when a total of about 3% of chromium and aluminium is present, the surface hardness developed is about 1100 HV, but with a sudden variation of hardness towards the core.

6.3.3 High-tensile steels. A steel with about 3% nickel is strong and tough, because nickel produces a fine grain structure. If a small amount of chromium is included, the strength is increased; but these steels tend to become brittle if tempered at a certain temperature which depends upon composition. This brittleness is called 'temper brittleness', and can be prevented either by avoiding the temperature which causes it, or by including about 0·25% molybdenum in the steel. An increased quantity of nickel and chromium enables steel to be quenched in a blast of air (air-hardening). About 0·45% vanadium improves the toughness of steels, and is included if they are to be manipulated by drop-stamping, or to be used for forging dies.

Table 6.3 Some high-tensile steels

Composition	Description
0·3% C, 3% Ni, 0·6% Mn	An oil-quenching steel used for crankshafts, connecting rods, etc.
0·3% C, 3% Ni, 0·8% Cr, 0·6% Mn	This is an oil-quenching steel used for highly stressed parts. Care must be taken when specifying the tempering temperature, as it suffers from temper brittleness.
0·3% C, 4·25% Ni, 1·25% Cr	An air-hardening steel that is used for complex shapes, but it suffers from temper brittleness.
0·3% C, 4·25% Ni, 1·25% Cr, 0·25% Mo	This is an air-hardening steel that does not suffer temper brittleness, because of the small amount of molybdenum included.
0·4% C, 5% Cr, 1·25% Mo, 1·0% Si, 0·45% V	An air-hardening steel used for forging dies, die-casting dies, and extrusion-press dies.

6.3.4 Wear-resisting steels. When a high carbon steel contains about 12·5% manganese, austenite is retained as a result of heating and quenching. Solid-solution alloys respond to work-hardening, and so this steel becomes harder as a result of rough treatment. Steels with a high carbon content and about 1·4% chromium become very hard as a result of oil-quenching.

Table 6.4 Some wear-resisting steels

Composition	Description
1·2% C, 12·5% Mn	This is 'Hadfields' austenitic steel. The austenitic structure is produced by quenching from 1050°C. Used for trackwork, dredging equipment, and crushing machinery.
1% C, 1·4% Cr, 0·45% Mn	Oil-quenching steel. Used for roller and ball races, etc.

6.3.5 Corrosion-resisting steels. These steels are classified as follows:
(*a*) Ferritic stainless steels. These have a low carbon content. They cannot be hardened by heat-treatment, but can be work-hardened. They contain a high percentage of chromium, which makes them corrosion-resisting.

Table 6.5 Some corrosion-resisting steels

Composition	Description
0·04% C, 14% Cr, 0·45% Mn	Ferritic stainless steel (also called stainless iron). Can be hardened only by working. Used for spoons, forks, etc.
0·3% C, 13% Cr, 0·5% Mn	Martensitic stainless steel. Hardened by heat-treatment. Used for cutlery, and similarly edged tools.
0·1% C, 8·5% Ni, 18% Cr	Austenitic stainless steel (18/8 type). Will respond only to work-hardening.

(*b*) Martensitic stainless steels. These contain a high percentage of chromium, to make them corrosion-resisting, and sufficient carbon to make them respond to heat-treatment.

(*c*) Austenitic stainless steels. These contain a high percentage of nickel and chromium, and are austenitic, as a result of heating and quenching. They cannot, therefore, be hardened by heat-treatment, but they respond to work-hardening. They are non-magnetic.

6.3.6 Heat-resisting steels. These steels must resist oxidation and attack by vapour and gases at high temperature: They are therefore made corrosion-resisting by the addition of chromium. They must also retain their strength at elevated temperatures, and resist creep. Chromium improves the strength, but other elements, such as carbon, tungsten, and molybdenum, are also included to strengthen the alloy. Some of these steels will respond to heat-treatment, but others can be hardened only by working.

Table 6.6 Some heat-resisting steels

Composition	Description
0·15% C, 1% Mn, 12% Cr, 1% Ni	Can be hardened and tempered. Can be used at temperatures up to 600°C. Used for turbine blades and discs.
0·3% C, 1·5% Si, 16% Cr, 60% Ni	Used in the 'as forged' condition for heat-treatment equipment. Maximum working temperature is 1100°C.

Summary

1 Alloy steels contain iron, carbon, and other alloying additions.
2 Alloy steels have been developed to meet demands for higher strength, better response to heat-treatment, improved heat resistance, improved corrosion resistance, and special properties.
3 Engineers find it convenient to classify alloy steels according to their characteristics and applications.

Questions

Set A
1 Name two articles which you consider would be more suitable in alloy steel than in plain carbon steel. Give the approximate composition of each alloy, and state its outstanding property.
2 Discuss some of the factors that have led to the development of alloy steels.

3 Outline the process of hardening and tempering a nickel–chrome–molybdenum steel. Give approximately the variation in physical properties obtained by alteration of the tempering temperature of this steel.

4 Explain the significance of the grouping of corrosion-resisting steels into three main categories.

5 Name the element that produces 'air-hardening'. What is the advantage of this property?

Set B (questions requiring further study)

6 Explain why ferritic stainless steels and austenitic stainless steels do not respond to quench-hardening. Why are these steels awkward to machine?

7 What is implied by 'grain growth'? How can it be overcome by alloying?

8 Why are nitriding steels always alloy steels?

Chapter 7
Non-ferrous Metals and their Alloys

7.1 Non-ferrous metals

Non-ferrous metals are, by definition, metals other than iron; they can be classified as follows:

  (a) Non-ferrous metals that are used extensively in the unalloyed condition, or as the base of alloys. This group includes aluminium, copper, lead, magnesium, nickel, tin, titanium, and zinc; these metals are the main subject of this chapter.

  (b) Non-ferrous metals that are used in small quantities, either in the unalloyed condition, or as additions in small quantities in other alloys. This group includes metals such as tungsten, chromium, vanadium, cobalt, and silver. Some of them have been mentioned in the chapters dealing with cast irons and steels, and some are mentioned in this chapter.

  (c) The so-called 'new metals': a group which includes beryllium, hafnium, niobium, vanadium, and zirconium. These metals are briefly discussed in this chapter.

7.1.1 Aluminium (chemical symbol Al). Aluminium is very weak and very ductile, and melts at 660°C. It is an important engineering metal because it is light (its density is approximately one-third that of iron) and does not suffer deterioration as a result of atmospheric corrosion, as the oxide film that is set up upon exposure to air insulates it against continued attack. Its tensile strength is only about 60 N/mm², but this can be increased by cold-working. Aluminium has high electrical and thermal conductivity, and a high coefficient of thermal expansion. It can be polished to reflect light and heat. It is used mainly as the base of reasonably strong and light alloys.

Aluminium is produced by treating bauxite to obtain alumina, from which aluminium is extracted by electrolysis.

7.1.2 Copper (chemical symbol Cu). Copper is very weak and ductile, and melts at 1083°C. It has a high thermal and electrical conductivity, and a good resistance to corrosion. Copper has a tensile strength of

about 160 N/mm^2, and an elongation of about 50%: cold-working increases its strength but reduces its ductility. The ductility can be increased at the expense of hardness and strength by annealing; a range of so-called 'tempers' can be produced by controlling the extent of working after annealing. Copper and its alloys can easily be joined by soldering, brazing, and welding; and are used extensively in engineering, in spite of the high cost of copper.

Copper to be used for electrical wiring and for conductors must be very pure, and is produced by electrolytic refining; it is accordingly known as 'electrolytic' copper. Copper that is not to be used for electrical work need not be as pure, and can be refined by fire-refining.

Small quantities of other elements are often included in copper, to produce special properties. For example, up to 0·5% arsenic allows copper to be used at temperatures of up to 300°C without loss of strength, about 0·08% silver prevents it from softening during soldering, and about 0·5% tellurium produces 'free cutting' characteristics. Copper with small additions is sometimes called 'lightly alloyed' copper.

Copper resists the corrosion of a number of corrosive liquids, and is used in chemical works, and food and brewing plants. It is very ductile, and can be heavily cold-worked; sheet copper can be spun, pressed, and drawn into many shapes.

7.1.3 Lead (chemical symbol Pb). Lead is very weak (its tensile strength is about 15 N/mm^2), but very malleable and ductile, and melts at 327°C. It is very heavy, and resists corrosion; it is a good insulator against nuclear radiation. It is used as the base for type metals and bearing metals, and is a major constituent in solders. It is introduced into alloys to produce free-cutting characteristics. Lead is produced from its ores by a fire-refining process.

7.1.4 Magnesium (chemical symbol Mg). Magnesium is very light; it has a tensile strength of about 100 N/mm^2, and melts at about 651°C. It is rather brittle, and so requires careful cold-working: it can be hot-worked easily. It has a poor resistance to corrosion, particularly if the air is humid, and if it contains traces of salt. This poor corrosion resistance is caused by the porosity of the oxide film that forms upon its surface. Corrosion resistance can be improved by priming and painting. Magnesium is used mainly as the base of light alloys. It is produced by treating its ores to obtain magnesium chloride, from which the magnesium is extracted by electrolysis.

7.1.5 Nickel (chemical symbol Ni). Nickel is very similar to iron; it has a tensile strength of about 370 N/mm^2, and it melts at about 1458°C. It is magnetic, and is more resistant to corrosion and to loss of strength due to heating than is iron. It is used as an underplating before chromium plating, to give protection against corrosion, as an alloying addition to steels and cast irons, and as a base for alloys.

Nickel ores contain copper, and the production of nickel is complicated by the awkwardness of separating nickel and copper.

7.1.6 Tin (chemical symbol Sn). Tin is soft and weak, and melts at 232°C. It is extremely corrosion-resistant, and is applied as a thin coating on sheet steel to be used for foodstuff containers. (Tin-coated steel is called tinplate.) Tin is used as a base for bearing metals and low melting-point alloys, as a major constituent in solders, alloyed with copper to form bronzes and gunmetals, and included in brasses if improved corrosion resistance is required. The tensile strength of tin is only about 13 N/mm^2. It is obtained from its ore by a simple refining process.

7.1.7 Titanium (chemical symbol Ti). Titanium has a strength/density ratio that places it midway between aluminium and steel. It has a melting-point of about 1660°C, and is used unalloyed, as the base for a number of alloys, and as a small-quantity addition in other alloys. It has a tensile strength of about 260 N/mm^2, and until recent years was classed as a 'new metal'. The extraction of titanium from its ores is difficult, because of the great affinity of titanium for oxygen.

7.1.8 Zinc (chemical symbol Zn). Although zinc is a weak metal (its tensile strength is about 155 N/mm^2), it is used extensively in engineering, in the form of die-castings. (Die-casting is described in Chapter 9.) The effect of corrosion is resisted by a dense layer of corrosion product that is naturally formed on its surface, so that it is insulated against continued corrosion. It is used in the form of rolled sheets for roofing and battery containers, and as a lining for transportation cases, because it can be made water- and air-tight, and is proof against insects and rodents.

Parts to be rendered corrosion-resistant can be treated by zinc plating, dipping, spraying, and similar treatments; underground lines can be protected against corrosion by connecting them with insulated wires to zinc anodes that are buried near by. Zinc is also used as an alloying addition to strengthen other non-ferrous metals. It is obtained from its ores either by processes that include condensation, or by electrolysis.

7.2 Aluminium alloys
Alloying elements are added to aluminium to produce stronger materials, and to improve its casting properties. Copper, manganese, magnesium, zinc, nickel, and silicon are the most important alloying elements used.

Aluminium alloys are classed according to the method whereby they can be manipulated into shape, i.e. wrought aluminium alloys and casting aluminium alloys. Within these two groups, alloys are further classified according to whether they respond to heat-treatment of the strengthening type.

Wrought alloys of the 'non heat-treatable' type can be made stronger as a result of work-hardening; but it must be appreciated that, when the desired thickness has been obtained, the tensile strength of the material cannot be increased without making the material undersized. Wrought alloys can be softened by annealing before working is started.

7.2.1 The heat-treatment of aluminium alloys. Aluminium alloys of the heat-treatable type can be hardened by a process that is two-part. The first part, called *solution-treatment*, consists of heating the alloy to a temperature of about 490°C, and then quenching it in water or oil. Immediately after this treatment, the alloy will be very soft and ductile, and can be cold-worked with ease.

The second part depends upon the composition of the alloy. Some alloys will start to become harder and stronger a few hours after the quenching, and reach their maximum strength after about three days standing at room temperature. This process is called *age-hardening*, and can be retarded by holding the alloy at a very low temperature. Rivets made from this type of alloy are solution-treated, and kept in a refrigerator until required. The special advantage of using rivets of this material is that they become stronger after the riveting operation without the need to heat-treat the structure. The well-known alloy Duralumin is typical of this type, and contains about 4% copper.

Other alloys do not become stronger unless they are heated at about 180°C for some hours after they have been solution-treated; this second heat-treatment is called *precipitation-treatment*. The alloys are not quenched after they have been soaked at the precipitation temperature.

7.2.2 Casting aluminium alloys. These alloys contain rather large quantities of silicon or magnesium, to produce a lower melting-point alloy. Care must be taken when selecting the alloy and the method of casting, because only certain casting alloys are suitable for die-casting as well as for sand-casting. As in the case of the wrought alloys, some of them 'naturally age' after solution treatment, but others must be given precipitation-treatment.

7.2.3 Protection against corrosion. It has already been stated that the resistance to corrosion associated with aluminium depends upon the thin oxide film that builds up on its surface when exposed to air. This film can be produced artificially by *anodising*, and it is then thicker and more even than the natural film. The parts to be anodised are polished and sand-blasted, and then placed in a bath containing chromic, sulphuric, or oxalic acid. These parts form the anode when electricity is passed through the bath. The film thus produced may be dyed in any one of a number of colours; the smooth, coloured surface is hard-wearing, and has a pleasing appearance.

The corrosion-resistance of aluminium alloys can be improved by *cladding* with pure aluminium. In this process, a slab of aluminium alloy is placed between two much thinner sheets of pure aluminium, and hot-rolled. During the rolling, the pure aluminium alloy becomes welded to the alloy, producing a thin sheet of aluminium alloy with a thin covering of pure aluminium.

7.3 Copper-based alloys

7.3.1 Brasses. Zinc is alloyed with copper to form a range of alloys called *brasses*. Since zinc is cheaper than copper, the larger the amount of zinc, the cheaper the alloy. The properties of brass vary considerably with the zinc content, as shown in fig. 7.1. It will be seen that the ductility is a maximum when the zinc content is 30%, and falls sharply with further increases in the zinc content. The melting-point is lowered by increases in the zinc content. Brasses with less than about 37% zinc are suitable for cold-working, and those with between about 37% and 45% zinc are suitable for hot-working and casting.

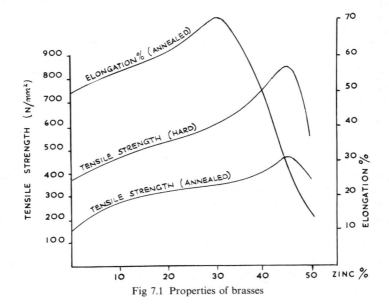

Fig 7.1 Properties of brasses

An important cold-working alloy is known as *70/30 brass,* and contains 70% copper and 30% zinc (this alloy is also known as *cartridge brass*). It is very ductile, and is produced in various cold-drawn and cold-rolled sections, such as tubes, strips, and sheets. It is annealed by heating to 600°C, and then cooling at any desired speed; cooling by quenching is generally used to save time. The amount of cold-work done on the metal after the last anneal has a considerable effect on the mechanical properties.

Sheet brass is supplied in three qualities: hard, for cutting to shape; half-hard, for simple cold-work, such as bending; and soft for heavy cold work, such as drawing. Hard brass has a Brinell number of 200, and annealed brass has a Brinell number of 60. The corrosion resistance of brass is improved by the addition of a small quantity of tin. *Admiralty brass* contains 70% copper, 29% zinc, and 1% tin, and is used for condenser tubes.

Basis brass has a composition of 63% copper and 37% zinc. It is cheaper than 70/30 brass, but is less ductile, and is suitable for press-work. When the properties of this brass are not guaranteed, it is known as *common brass.*

When 70/30 or 63/37 brass has been severely cold-worked, season cracking may occur. This happens when the article is brought into contact with mild corrosives, such as slightly salty water, or air containing traces of acid. Cracks suddenly appear, sometimes after years of service; and, owing to the internal stresses set up by cold-working, these cracks may be wide. The remedy is to anneal at 280°C after cold-working. This treatment relieves internal stresses, but has little effect on the hardness.

Muntz metal is an important hot-working and casting brass, and contains 60% copper and 40% zinc. It is used as hot-rolled plate, forgings, extrusions, and castings, and also as a brazing metal for steels. About 1% tin is added to muntz metal to improve its corrosion resistance; the alloy is known as *naval brass.*

The machining properties of brass are greatly improved by the inclusion of small amounts of lead. If about 3% lead is included, it will be in the form of small globules distributed throughout the brass, and its action is to break up the chips into short pieces, and to act as a lubricant. The tensile strength is almost unchanged, but the shock resistance of the brass is lower.

Various metals are added to brass to improve particular properties, such as corrosion resistance in specific circumstances, tensile strength, hardness, or shock resistance. About 1·5% iron and 0·75% manganese are added to 60/40 brass to improve the tensile strength and resistance to salt water; this alloy, called manganese 'bronze', is used for underwater shafts and fittings. Manganese, aluminium, and iron are added to 60/40 brass to give a tensile strength of 600 N/mm^2. Nickel is added to brass to give a silvery appearance which does not tarnish readily. A typical *nickel silver* contains 20% nickel, 30% zinc, and 50% copper; it is used for ornamental work on motor cars, and shop and house fittings, because of the fine, white polish it will take.

7.3.2 Bronzes. Tin is alloyed with copper to form a range of alloys called *bronzes*. (A number of other strong copper-base alloys are now also called 'bronzes', and so these copper–tin alloys are often called *tin bronzes*.) Tin is even more costly than copper, and so the cost of the alloy increases with the tin content. The melting-point is lowered by the addition of tin, and so the tin bronzes with higher tin content are more suitable for casting, although they tend to be harder and more brittle than those with a lower tin content. These bronzes are classified as wrought bronzes and casting bronzes.

Wrought tin bronzes contain up to about 8% tin, and can be cold-rolled or drawn. They can be softened by annealing, and given a range of properties, depending upon the extent of cold-rolling after annealing. About 0·3% phosphorus is included in wrought tin bronzes to produce *wrought phosphor bronze*; this type of bronze is used for springs, springy electrical contacts, and for the suspension coils of moving-coil instruments.

Casting tin bronzes contain between 10% and 18% tin and other elements. *Casting phosphor bronze* contains 0·05% phosphorus. It is a very good bearing metal, because it combines hardness and toughness; and, if the bearing is to be subjected to heavy loads, the phosphorus content can be increased by up to 0·5%, although the increased phosphorus content reduces the ductility. Small amounts of lead are included to improve the machinability of bronzes; about 5% lead also improves the bearing properties of bronzes.

7.3.3 Gunmetals. Casting tin bronzes containing zinc are called gunmetals; the zinc gives better casting properties. *Admiralty gunmetal* contains 88% copper, 10% tin, and 2% zinc, and is used for naval components, and for valves and similar steam-plant parts. Up to about 5% lead is added to gunmetals, to improve their castability and machinability.

7.3.4 Nickel bronzes. Small amounts of nickel are often added to tin bronzes to improve their mechanical properties. Between 3% and 5% nickel is added to alloys containing between 5% and 10% tin and 2% zinc, so that they resist wear and corrosion, and also retain their strength at elevated temperatures. These alloys can be heat-treated like aluminium alloys; they are solution-treated by quenching from 760°C, and then given precipitation-treatment at 300°C.

7.3.5 Aluminium bronzes. Aluminium bronzes contain copper and aluminium. They have good corrosion resistance, and retain their mechanical properties at reasonably high temperatures. They are classified as wrought alloys and cast alloys.
The *wrought aluminium bronzes* contain between 4% and 7% aluminium. They can be annealed, and then strengthened by cold-working.
The *cast aluminium bronzes* contain about 10% aluminium with 2% iron. They can be sand-cast and gravity die-cast, and are used for pump casings, valve parts, gears, and racks.

7.4 Magnesium alloys
Magnesium is not strong enough to be used structurally without alloying. Magnesium alloys contain elements such as manganese, aluminium, zirconium, zinc, and thorium, and can be heat-treated by solution-treatment and precipitation. They must be machined at high speeds, with sharp tools to ensure that rubbing does not occur, as magnesium is inflammable when in a finely divided form.
Magnesium alloys are classified as wrought alloys and cast alloys. The wrought alloys are used for step-ladders, railings, brackets, and levers. Casting magnesium alloys are sand-cast for engine parts, and pressure die-cast for domestic and office equipment parts.

7.5 Nickel alloys

7.5.1 Nickel–iron alloys. An alloy of iron and 36% nickel has an almost negligible coefficient of expansion at ordinary atmospheric temperatures, and is used for length standards, measuring tapes, pendulum rods, and precision-machine parts. It is also used in thermostats operating at up to 100°C. Iron–nickel alloys with 40% and 42% nickel are used in thermostats, and those with 42% nickel are also used as the core of copper-clad wires used for sealing into the glass envelopes of electric lamp bulbs, radio valves and television tubes.

7.5.2 Nickel–copper alloys. An important alloy in this group is *Monel,** containing 66% nickel and 33% copper, with up to about 2% manganese. This is a wrought alloy that can be strengthened by work-hardening. Casting Monel contains up to about 4% silicon. Monel resists attack by acids, gases, and sea water; it also retains its strength at high temperatures. It is used for pump parts, steam-turbine blades, motor-boat propeller shafts, food-handling equipment, laundry equipment, and surgical apparatus. Because of its excellent corrosion- and heat-resistance, it is used for electrical terminal nuts and bolts, and for electrical water-heater parts.

---

* These are trade names of alloys produced by Messrs Henry Wiggin & Co. Ltd.

7.5.3 Nickel–chromium alloys. *Inconel** is an alloy of 76% nickel, 15% chromium, and mainly iron. It resists corrosion by many inorganic and organic components, and attack by oxidising atmospheres at high temperatures; hence it is used in food, chemical, and textile-processing plants, and also for heat-treatment equipment, and steam-turbine parts.

*Nimonic alloys** are basically 80/20 nickel–chromium alloys that were originally developed for use in gas-turbine engines, where high strength at high temperatures, and resistance to oxidation and creep is required. These alloys can be formed by spinning, rolling, and pressing; they can be joined by argon-arc, and by electrical resistance welding. The casting equivalent of the Nimonic alloys are the Nimocast alloys,* which can be cast by sand-casting, shell-moulding, and investment-casting processes.

7.6 Bearing metals
Phosphor bronze and various brasses have already been mentioned; the structures of the brasses with a high zinc content, and bronzes with a high tin content are typical of many bearing metals. These alloys consist of a hard constituent set in a soft constituent; the hard constituent takes the wear, and the soft constituent acts as a cushion, and allows the bearing surface to 'give' to slight misalignment. Furthermore, the soft spots on the surface are always slightly below the hard spots, and thus form minute oil reservoirs.

Fig 7.2 A typical tin-base alloy

For heavy loads and moderate speeds, the leaded bronzes are very suitable; for light loads, a cheap lead-base alloy will suffice; but for high speeds and heavy loads, a more expensive tin-base alloy is necessary. A typical lead-base alloy contains 80% lead, 15% antimony, and 5% tin. A typical tin-base alloy contains 60% tin, 27% lead, 10% antimony, and 3% copper. The microstructure of this latter alloy is shown in fig. 7.2; the cubes consist of an antimony–tin compound (SbSn), and the needles are a copper–tin compound (Cu_6Sn_5); they are set in a mainly tin and lead eutectic (laminated).

* See footnote on p. 69.

7.7 Solder

Solder is an alloy of tin and lead, to which a little antimony is often added. The melting temperature of an alloy is often lower then that of either of the two metals of which it is composed. Figure 7.3 is a simplified diagram illustrating this point. The melting-point of lead is 327°C. and that of tin is 232°C. In each case, the melting or freezing occurs at this temperature. In the case of lead–tin alloys, the melting-point decreases with increasing tin content, reaching a minimum of 183°C with 62% tin, and then increasing again. The composition which has the lowest melting-point is called the *eutectic* composition for the system. An alloy of eutectic composition solidifies at a specific temperature (in this case 183°C), but alloys of any other composition solidify over a solidification (or freezing) range.

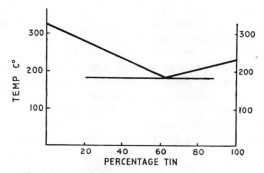

Fig. 7.3 Equilibrium diagram for lead–tin alloys

In fig. 7.3 it will be noted that a horizontal line is shown. Below this line, which is at 183°C, all lead–tin alloys are solid; between this line and the upper V-shaped line is the freezing range. Common solder contains equal proportions of tin and lead, and has a freezing range from 210°C to 183°C, and so solidifies fairly quickly. Plumber's solder has 70% lead and 30% tin, and freezes from 250°C to 183°C; consequently it has a long 'pasty' stage, that enables the plumber to 'wipe' a joint. Tinman's solder has about 40% lead and 60% tin, and consequently solidifies rapidly, because the freezing range is very short.

7.8 'New' metals

7.8.1 Beryllium (chemical symbol Be).
Beryllium is a hard, steel-grey metal that melts at about 1285°C. It is lighter than aluminium, has a good thermal conductivity, good strength at high temperatures, does not react to any marked degree with neutrons which pass through it, but has a poor ductility. Beryllium has been used in small amounts for

some time as an alloying element in copper, but is now in demand in the pure condition in wrought forms as a structural material, because of its low density and high modulus of elasticity; it is likely to be used in high-speed aircraft, and for space vehicles.

7.8.2 Hafnium (chemical symbol Hf). This is a similar metal to zirconium. It melts at 2120°C, is heavy, and is slightly stronger than beryllium. Hafnium is used as a control-rod material for pressurised water-cooled reactors, because it has good strength and corrosion resistance, absorbs neutrons, and is free from radiation damage.

7.8.3 Niobium (chemical symbol Nb). This is a silvery-white metal which is extremely ductile and soft, but is slightly weaker than iron. It melts at 2468°C. Hot-working and heating in air should be avoided, as its ductility is affected by small amounts of oxygen and carbon. Niobium is being developed as a nuclear engineering material, and also as a gas-turbine blade material.

7.8.4 Zirconium (chemical symbol Zr). This is an abundant metal that is difficult to separate from its ore. It is silvery-white in colour, reasonably strong, and melts at about 1852°C. It is very similar to titanium (see section 7.1.7), but is about one and a half times as heavy. It has been used for some time as an alloying element in magnesium alloys; but it is now being developed as a nuclear engineering material, on account of its good strength at room temperatures and moderately elevated temperatures, its resistance in alloy form to corrosion by water, steam, and other reactor coolants, and because it does not react to any marked degree with neutrons which pass through it.

7.8.5. Aluminium, magnesium, and vanadium are also being developed as nuclear engineering materials.

Summary

1 Non-ferrous metals can be classified as (*a*) those used extensively in unalloyed condition or as a base for alloying, (*b*) those used in small quantities, either in unalloyed condition or as alloying additions, and (*c*) the so-called 'new' metals.
2 Aluminium alloys are classified into (*a*) wrought alloys, and (*b*) casting alloys; these groups are further classified according to the response to heat-treatment. Aluminium alloys are heat-treated by annealing, and by a strengthening heat-treatment involving solution-treatment followed either by precipitation heat-treatment or by ageing.
3 Brasses are copper–zinc alloys. They are classified according to

their zinc content; alloys with less than 37% zinc are cold-working alloys, and those with more than 37% zinc are hot-working and casting alloys.

4 Bronzes are copper–tin alloys; they are classified according to their tin content. Those with less than about 8% tin are wrought alloys, and those with more than about 8% tin are casting alloys. Gunmetals are copper–tin alloys which also contain zinc.

5 Aluminium–bronzes are copper–aluminium alloys. Those with between 4% and 7% aluminium are wrought alloys, and those with 10% aluminium are casting alloys.

6 Magnesium alloys are similar in many ways to aluminium alloys. They are classified in a similar way to aluminium alloys, and respond to heat-treatment of the same types.

7 Nickel is used as the base for several important corrosion- and heat-resisting alloys.

8 Bearing metals need to combine hardness with the ability to 'give' to slight misalignment. Certain brasses, bronzes, lead-base, and tin-base alloys have these desired characteristics.

9 Solder is basically a lead–tin alloy. It is a good example of an alloy of the eutectic type.

10 A number of metals that were previously awkward or impossible to extract from their ores, or to manipulate, have during more recent years been developed to suit special requirements. These metals are known as 'new' metals.

Questions

Set A

1 Distinguish between 70/30 brass and 60/40 brass, and state the main properties of each. Which is the more suitable for cold-working?

2 Make a list of the non-ferrous materials suitable for cold-working, and give one example of a cold-worked component in each material.

3 State the approximate composition of a castable alloy of aluminium, and of a cold-working alloy of aluminium. In what forms can the cold-working alloy be obtained?

4 State the composition of plumber's solder, and explain why it is important to have this particular composition.

5 Suggest suitable materials for the following parts, and give brief reasons for your answers: rivets for a water-tank, body of a small water-valve, body of a very large water-valve, spanner, aircraft under-carriage, gas-turbine blade.

6 Describe the uses of manganese in engineering materials.

7 Arrange the following materials in order of ductility: pure iron,

mild steel, cast iron, 80/20 cupro-nickel, 60/40 brass, malleable
cast iron.

8   With what particular type of engineering component do you as-
    sociate the following metals: tungsten, chromium, zinc,
    molybdenum? Give reasons for your answers.

9   Explain what is meant by season cracking, and describe a treat-
    ment for preventing its occurrence. A piece of 70/30 brass sheet
    cracks on bending: what is the remedy for this defect?

Set B (questions requiring further study)

10 Distinguish between a hot-working brass and a cold-working
    brass. Describe carefully the method of annealing 70/30 brass.
    What occurs if this brass is annealed from too high a tem-
    perature?

11 Write a description of the various bearing metals, and give typical
    applications of the various types.

12 Discuss the phenomenon of age-hardening in aluminium alloys,
    and explain how it affects the working of these alloys.

13 Why is nickel important to the gas-turbine industry?

14 Write notes on non-ferrous alloys and their resistance to
    corrosion.

Chapter 8
Heat-treatment Equipment

8.1. The heat-treatment of metals and their alloys has been discussed in the foregoing chapters. Successful heat-treatment depends upon correctly designed furnaces, accurate control of temperature, and correct quenching. Quenching media are discussed in section 5.5.1; furnaces and temperature control are discussed in this chapter.

8.2 Heat-treatment furnaces
Furnaces are available for all the usual heat-treatment processes, and for a wide range of components. The design depends on the use to which the furnace will be put. Not only do the size and shape need designing, but also the source of heat, the method of temperature control and observation, and the size and disposition of the door or doors; and, in the case of large furnaces, the lay-out of the whole heat-treatment department must be carefully planned.

8.2.1 Gas-fired furnaces. In modern practice, gas-fired furnaces are the commonest type. In order to appreciate their use, a little knowledge of combustion is required. Natural gas, and coal gas after purification, as supplied in the usual town's gas main, consists almost wholly of the elements hydrogen (H) and carbon (C). Hydrogen and carbon combine chemically in a number of *hydrocarbons*. One typical hydrocarbon is methane (CH_4), and this gas is present in all towns' gas.

When the hydrocarbons burn, they do so by combining with oxygen (O), thus liberating great heat, and forming a new series of gases. The principal gases formed are carbon monoxide (CO), carbon dioxide (CO_2), and water vapour (H_2O). The relative amounts of carbon monoxide and carbon dioxide depend on the amount of oxygen provided; if enough oxygen is present, all the carbon will form CO_2; but if there is a deficiency of oxygen, then some CO will remain.

The usual source of oxygen is the atmosphere, which consists mainly of a mixture of four parts of nitrogen (N) to one part of oxygen; consequently the combustion is accompanied by large quantities of nitrogen. This nitrogen contributes nothing to the combustion, but nevertheless is heated up to the same temperature as the other gases. Each kg of hydrogen gives out about 140 megajoules when burnt to H_2O; each kg of carbon gives out about 21 megajoules when burnt to CO, or about 46 megajoules when burnt to CO_2. These two gases provide all the heat; the oxygen which is essential to the combustion process, and the nitrogen which is incidental to it, provide no heat—in fact, they have to be heated by the heat energy released by the hydrogen and carbon, and in consequence they lower the final gas temperature very considerably. In order to burn coal gas completely, not less than four volumes of air are required for each volume of gas: it will be obvious to the reader that the volume of nitrogen is very great.

When a hot flame is required, pure oxygen is provided for mixing with the combustible gas, which is usually acetylene (C_2H_2) or pure hydrogen. Since hydrogen has a higher calorific value than carbon, the oxy-hydrogen flame is hotter than the oxy-acetylene flame, but both are much hotter than the air–town-gas flame, due to the absence of nitrogen.

In the ordinary town-gas furnace, if plenty of air is provided, the products of combustion are N_2, CO_2, H_2O, and O_2. Of these gases, the last three, and particularly the free oxygen, will quickly oxidise hot steel, and at the same time extract carbon from the surface of the metal. In consequence, they are termed *oxidising* or *decarburising* gases, and the furnace is said to have an oxidising or decarburising *atmosphere*. Steel heated in such an atmosphere will *scale* rapidly. This scale consists of a layer of iron oxide, under which there will probably be a further layer of decarburised steel. Such a scale may have disastrous consequences. The oxide layer acts as a heat insulator, and prevents quick heat dissipation when the hot steel is quenched; the low-carbon-steel layer cannot be hardened, and the result is that the component has a soft, scaly surface, and may be improperly hardened throughout. Many components have to be ground after hardening, but if they have been allowed to scale, they may require so much grinding as to leave them undersize and useless.

If the air supply to the furnace is cut down, there will be a deficiency of oxygen, and the products of combustion will be N_2, CO, H_2O, and some CO_2, with some unburnt hydrocarbons such as CH_4. The hydrocarbons and the carbon monoxide are *reducing* or *carburising* gases; that is, they tend to extract oxygen from the steel, and to deposit carbon. In these circumstances, the furnace is said to have a reducing or carburising atmosphere. The scaling will be much less than with an oxidising atmosphere, but it will not be eliminated; this can be accomplished only by removing the H_2O.

With either a reducing or oxidising atmosphere, the highest possible temperature is not attained. With the former, the unburnt hydrogen and carbon are wasted; while with the latter, the excess oxygen and nitrogen are heated unnecessarily. By careful control, a *neutral* atmo-

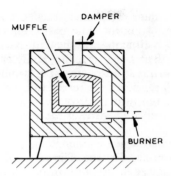

Fig 8.1 Controlled-atmosphere gas-fired furnace

sphere may be obtained; this has neither excess hydrogen nor oxygen. Such an atmosphere is difficult to hold, and in practice the atmosphere is given a reducing bias, to ensure that it will never be oxidising.

In the completely non-scaling atmosphere, which is used for close or bright annealing and similar operations, the H_2O is eliminated as follows. The steel is enclosed in a gas-tight chamber or *muffle* (fig. 8.1). The atmosphere for this muffle is provided by burning gas and air in a separate chamber, and passing the products of combustion through a condenser. In the condenser, the H_2O changes from vapour to liquid, and is drained off. In burning the gas, the amount of air is deliberately restricted, and, to ensure that the gas is reducing, some unburnt coal gas is added after the condenser. The atmosphere thus created is passed to the muffle, and there surrounds the steel. The heating of the muffle is carried out externally, by gas, oil, or coal, whichever is most convenient. Figure 8.2 illustrates the principle of this system.

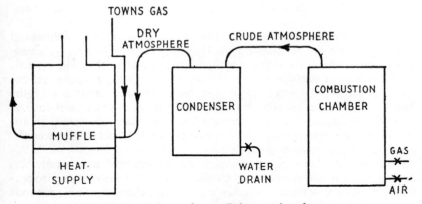

Fig 8.2 Arrangement of controlled-atmosphere furnace

In another type of furnace, the muffle is flooded with 'cracked' ammonia which has been partially burnt. The gas ammonia (NH_3) is treated to separate the two constituents, and the hydrogen is partially burnt in air, thus adding further nitrogen. The H_2O produced is removed by condensation, and the atmosphere for the muffle consists solely of nitrogen, with a small proportion of unburnt hydrogen. This method is rather expensive, owing to the price of ammonia, but the atmosphere can be recirculated, and 'freshened up' with a little new ammonia.

The bunsen burner. The bunsen burner is the apparatus used for providing the flame in the gas furnace. The principle is illustrated in fig. 8.3. The gas is introduced to the bottom of a thin iron tube, and the *primary* air enters at the side. The gas flow is controlled by a valve on the gas-inlet pipe, whilst the air orifice may be equipped with an adjustable shutter. The air and gas mix thoroughly as they rise up the tube, and they burn at the top, with a *duplex*, or two-part flame. The air surrounding the flame provides the oxygen required to complete the combustion, and is therefore termed *secondary* air.

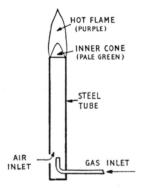

Fig 8.3 The bunsen burner

A very important point about the bunsen flame is its cleanliness. If pure gas is allowed to pass up a tube, it will burn at the top, obtaining its air from the surrounding atmosphere. However, if a metallic surface is placed in the flame, it will be covered in soot from the flame in a few seconds. This soot is, of course, carbon deposited by the gas. In the case of the bunsen flame, no soot will appear, but the surface will oxidise, as has already been described. Oxidisation is, however, quite a slow process compared with the sooting up caused by the pure gas flame. If the gas-tap is opened on a bunsen burner, and the air is not allowed to enter, a long, yellow flame will result; but immediately air is admitted, the flame shortens greatly, and narrows, burning with a purple colour. The gas, already charged with air, burns in a much smaller space, and the heat is much more concentrated.

The simplest type of gas-fired furnace consists of a box-shaped oven, the inside being lined with fire-bricks or other heat-resisting material, termed the *refractory* lining. The heat is provided by one or more bunsens let into the furnace. One arrangement is shown in fig. 8.4. The burners are placed vertically, in recesses or flutes in the vertical sides of the furnace. The flames rise up each side, and play on the roof, before passing up the chimney; a considerable amount of the heat is obtained by radiation from the arched roof. The chimney is provided with a sliding damper, which is opened when the furnace is lit, but is subsequently partially closed, thus conserving some heat. The front of the furnace is provided with a counter-weighted door, which slides up to give access to the inside. Many furnaces have elaborate heat-controls, but the ordinary workshop furnace is often controlled by simply adjusting the gas-taps, by hand.

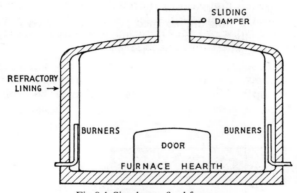

Fig 8.4 Simple gas-fired furnace

The size of these simple furnaces varies widely, and may be very large, but the most popular types have hearth sizes from 600 mm × 600 mm to 1500 mm × 900 mm. The temperature attained is up to 1000°C, so that plain carbon and many alloy steels can be given any standard heat-treatment.

For the hardening of high-speed steel, temperatures of 1300°C are required. Furthermore, slow heating to about 850°C, followed by rapid heating to the quenching temperature, is essential. For this work, special double-deck furnaces are manufactured. Figure 8.5 illustrates the layout of a typical furnace for high-speed steel. The air is supplied at a pressure of about 3500 N/m² (gauge), usually by an air blower, while the gas is supplied at the usual mains pressure. The mixture of air and gas is projected at high speed into the lower chamber, and as this chamber is quite small, with a volume of about 30 litres, and is heavily heat insulated, the temperature of 1300°C is quickly attained. The hot gases rise from the lower chamber, and round the sides of the upper

UPPER CHAMBER

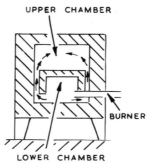

BURNER

LOWER CHAMBER

Fig 8.5 Double-deck furnace

chamber, which is partially protected from the direct flames, and has a temperature of about 900°C.

High-speed steel tools are warmed at the sill, soaked in the upper chamber, and finally transferred to the lower chamber. The air and gas mixture is controlled by an automatic valve.

Figure 8.6 illustrates an automatic air–gas proportioning valve, and also three methods of admitting the flame to the furnace. The gas inlet cock is simply opened full out, and the size of flame is controlled by the position of the air cock. The gas governor automatically admits the

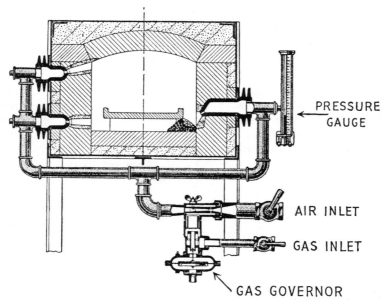

PRESSURE GAUGE

AIR INLET

GAS INLET

GAS GOVERNOR

Fig 8.6 Air–gas proportioning (*British Furnaces Ltd*)

correct amount of gas, according to the air pressure, several burners being controlled by one governor.

The three burners shown would not normally be used on one furnace, but each has its own application. The one on the right is arranged to direct the flame on to a heap of broken refractory. The large surface accelerates the completion of combustion, and radiates an enormous amount of heat. The 'tunnel' burners, shown on the left, are usually fitted in the side wall of the furnace. The flame may play on the furnace arch, or can be directed under the hearth, to provide 'bottom' heat, where this is required.

The muffle furnace has been mentioned earlier. Simple muffles are frequently made in the workshop by capping the ends of a suitable piece of wrought-iron pipe, and placing the steel inside the pipe before insertion in the furnace. It should be realised that a certain amount of air is present inside the muffle, and the results obtained are not equal to those produced in a proper muffle furnace, with a controlled atmosphere. However, uneven heating and excessive scaling are minimised.

8.2.2 The continuous furnace. The furnaces already described soon attain a fixed temperature, depending on the amount of air and gas admitted. If a part is to be heated or cooled at a certain rate, the furnace must be heated or cooled with the component. The continuous furnace is long compared with its width; the temperature is kept low at the entrance, and rises steadily along the length. If annealing is to be done, the temperature falls towards the exit; if hardening is required, the temperature is kept high up to the exit. If prolonged soaking is required, a suitable length of the furnace is held at that temperature. It only remains to traverse the components at the correct speed, and the heating cycle is performed automatically. This traversing may be done by pushing the components through the furnace by mechanically operated rods (the pusher furnace), or by carrying them on a conveyor belt made of heat-resisting metal (the travelling-hearth furnace).

Figure 8.7 shows diagrammatically a continuous furnace and quenching bath for the mass heating and quenching of small parts.

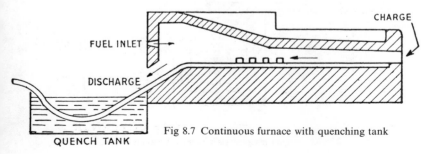

Fig 8.7 Continuous furnace with quenching tank

8.2.3 The salt-bath furnace. These furnaces, which may be heated by gas or electricity, consist essentially of a suitably shaped container of molten salt, in which the components are immersed. The mixture of salts used is varied according to the working temperature. The salt-bath furnace has several advantages: the heating of the components will be rapid and even, due to their being surrounded by a liquid; no oxidising will take place, as air is excluded from the work; very accurate temperature control is possible; and distortion of the hot component is unlikely, as it can be suspended or held in a suitable metal basket. Disadvantages are that they are rather expensive; the component cannot be seen; and some salt will cling to the component, and will drip off during subsequent handling, or will contaminate the quenching bath.

8.2.4 Electric furnaces. The electric furnace is a chamber of refractory material, supported by a suitable steel casing on the outside, and heated inside by elements which work on the same principle as the ordinary domestic electric fire, giving their heat to the charge by means of radiation. The heating elements are commonly made from an alloy of nickel and chromium; which has great heat-resisting powers. In small furnaces, these elements are made from wire; but, in larger equipment, strip, rod, or tube is bent to a suitable shape. These elements may be placed on the side walls, base, and roof; and arranged to give even heating of the furnace charge. Figure 8.8 shows the disposition of the elements in a box-type furnace.

In the gas-, oil-, or coal-fired furnace, the flame is actually inside the chamber, and thus decides the atmosphere content: there is also danger that the flame impinging on the component may cause local overheating. Also flues must be arranged to carry away the products of combustion. In the controlled-atmosphere furnace, heated by gas, coal, or oil, the charge must be placed in a separate gas-tight muffle, which

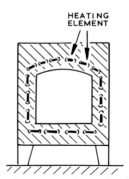

HEATING
ELEMENT

Fig 8.8 Heating elements in an electric furnace

is surrounded by the heating flames. In the electric furnace, the atmosphere consists simply of the air of the atmosphere; or, if this is detrimental, a suitable atmosphere is manufactured, and fed directly into the furnace chamber.

The disadvantages of electric furnaces are that, for very high temperatures, the heating elements have a rather short life, and are liable to be damaged by careless work. It is also usually stated that gas-fired furnaces cost less to run, due to gas being cheaper than electricity in most towns; but this is a controversial subject, as electric furnaces would appear to have a higher thermal efficiency per unit of energy supplied. Either type can be accurately controlled as regards temperature.

8.2.5 Forced air-circulation electric furnace. This type of furnace is used for heat-treatment demanding accurate and uniform heating (for example, when heat-treating aluminium-based alloys). Figure 8.9 illustrates a typical forced air-circulation electric furnace, and it will be seen that the air-circulation is increased by the action of a fan.

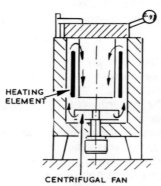

HEATING ELEMENT

CENTRIFUGAL FAN

Fig 8.9 Forced air-circulation furnace

8.2.6 Induction heating. In Chapter 4 (fig. 4.6), the high-frequency induction furnace was sketched and described. The same process is used to heat metal for other purposes besides melting. For example, a long bar can be passed quickly through a high-frequency induction coil, and immediately quenched in a spray of oil or water (fig. 8.10).

The process may be described as that of passing metal parts through a coil of wire which carries an alternating current. The greater the frequency of the supply, the smaller the distance the heat penetrates, but the more rapid will this heating be. Components or bars of medium-carbon, high-carbon, or alloy steel can be heated and quenched at the surface, while remaining normalised at the core. The frequency varies from 1000 to 500 000 hertz, the lower frequencies being used for

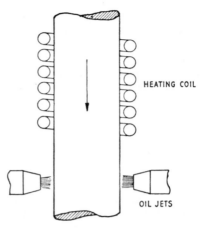

HEATING COIL

OIL JETS

Fig 8.10 Induction heating

'through' heating of fairly large components. The advantages of the system may be summarised as follows.

1. The heat can be applied exactly where it is required, for the correct length of time.
2. The surface heating of a component may take only two or three seconds, and thus the oxide film formed is infinitesimal. However, the process can be performed in a reducing atmosphere, if necessary.
3. The interior of the material may remain cold and rigid, thus minimising distortion.
4. The method lends itself to mass production, and in fact this heat-treatment process is not very different from a machining process; hence it can take its place in the production line.

The principal disadvantage is the rather expensive electrical equipment required.

Besides the 'through' and surface heating of parts, induction heating is suitable for heating for brazing, as in the 'tipping' of machine cutting-tools.

8.3 Pyrometry

Temperature observation and control is of great importance in heat-treatment processes. In some cases, an error of 20°C can lead to serious defects in the heat-treated component. There are a number of instruments for the measurement of temperature; most of them give a scale reading, while some produce a chart which gives a record of temperature over a period of twelve or twenty-four hours. Some furnaces are fitted with an automatic recorder. Certain special instruments not only record the temperature of the furnace, but also control the temperature, by governing the amount of fuel fed to the furnace. Pyrometry is the term used for the technique of temperature measurement.

8.3.1 Liquid mercury thermometers. These include the familiar mercury-in-glass thermometers, which can be used up to 500°C, and also the mercury-in-steel thermometers. The latter, which operate a pressure-gauge mechanism, can be used as indicators, or, by means of a revolving chart, can operate as recorders. Furthermore, the fine-bore tube connecting the mercury bulb to the pressure gauge may be up to 30 metres in length. When the pressure-gauge mechanism is operated by expansion of liquid mercury, the maximum working temperature is about 600°C.

8.3.2 Vapour-pressure thermometers. These thermometers use mercury vapour instead of liquid mercury. They have a steel bulb which is immersed in the hot substance, and which is connected by fine-bore tubing to the pressure gauge. The pressure gauge, which is calibrated in degrees Celsius, may be placed at any convenient position up to 30 metres distant from the bulb. Vapour-pressure thermometers may be used up to a temperature of 800°C.

With mercury-in-steel thermometers, it is essential that the bore of the connecting tube should be very small relative to the mercury bulb. When this precaution is taken, the connecting tube may be heated to some extent without affecting the reading appreciably.

8.3.3 Fusible cones. These cones are about 12 mm in diameter at the base, and about 25 mm high. They are made from various salt mixtures, each of which has its own melting temperature. The cone is mounted on a small porcelain or fire-clay dish, and placed in the furnace—preferably on or near the part being heated. The cones are marked with the melting temperature. Incipient fusing can be detected as the cone starts to bend over from the apex.

If a certain temperature is to be attained, say 780°C, then two cones are inserted: one with a melting-point of 750°C, and another with a melting temperature of 800°C. The 750°C cone is melted, but the 800°C cone is left intact. One serious limitation of this method is that no continuous record of furnace temperature is obtained; the only information gained is that at a certain time the furnace temperature was between two limiting values, and that at no time was the upper limit exceeded.

8.3.4. Thermo-electric pyrometers. Most of the furnaces in the heat-treatment shop are fitted with this type of pyrometer. If two dissimilar wires are brought into intimate contact at one end (by twisting together, and welding), and this end is heated, then a small electric potential is set up across the contact. Such a pair of wires is called a *thermo-couple*. The electrical circuit is completed by a millivoltmeter, as shown in fig. 8.11. We owe this discovery to Le Chatelier, who used one wire of pure platinum, and another of platinum alloyed with 10% of rhodium. Since that time, the platinum alloy has been altered to one containing 13% rhodium.

The platinum/platinum–rhodium thermo-couple is satisfactory up to a temperature of 1400°C. It is known as the *rare-metal* thermo-couple, and is expensive. For temperatures up to 1100°C, *base-metal* thermo-couples are quite satisfactory. Since the metals used are fairly cheap, the wires can be of thick section, thus giving a more robust

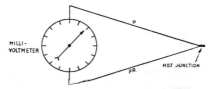

Fig 8.11 Thermo-electric pyrometer

instrument. The rare-metal wires are usually about 1 mm in diameter, while the base-metal wires are commonly 3 mm in diameter. In the case of the iron/constantan base-metal couple, a constantan rod may be welded at one end to the base of a closed iron tube; this is a very stout construction.

The common base-metal couples are the copper/constantan (up to 500°C), the iron/constantan (up to 900°C), and the chromel/alumel (up to 1100°C).

Referring to fig. 8.11, it is usually impracticable to connect the millivoltmeter directly to the wires of the thermo-couple, as it would be heated up by the furnace. Such heating would upset the reading, since it is the temperature *difference* between the hot and cold junctions which determines the readings. Consequently, the millivoltmeter and the cold junctions are installed in a place which does not suffer from wide variation in temperature. The modified circuit is shown in fig. 8.12. It will be noted that *compensating leads* have been added. If copper leads were used, the junctions between the copper wires and the wires of the thermo-couple would themselves introduce additional thermo-couples, and heating of these extra junctions would upset the reading. Consequently, the compensating leads must be made from suitable alloys of copper and nickel which will not cause a potential difference across the junction of the lead and the thermo-couple wire. The instrument is calibrated after the compensating leads have been fitted. It will be appreciated that the leads must not be shortened when the pyrometer is fitted to the furnace.

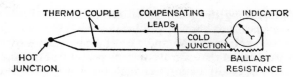

Fig 8.12 Thermo-couple with compensating leads (*Foster Instruments Ltd*)

To obtain the most accurate readings the cold-junction temperature should be kept constant. This may be done in several different ways, one of which is by bringing the cold junctions to a depth of a few metres in the earth under the building. However, in industrial plants the millivoltmeter can usually be placed at some point where the temperature variation is not very pronounced in relation to the high temperature to be measured.

The millivoltmeter may then be set to read correctly with the cold junction at room temperature—say 20°C. If the cold junction is likely to suffer from excessive temperature variation, then an automatic compensating device can be fitted to the millivoltmeter.

The reader will have noted the *ballast resistance* shown in fig. 8.12. The resistance of the thermo-couple circuit changes with temperature, but the ballast resistance is made from material which has a constant resistance. The ballast resistance has a value of at least four times the resistance of the rest of the circuit; consequently, changes in resistance of the circuit are 'swamped' by the ballast resistance, which is sometimes termed a *swamp resistance*.

The inclusion of this large extra resistance reduces the amperage of the thermo-couple circuit. The millivoltmeter used must, therefore, be an extremely sensitive instrument. Figure 8.13, which is a plan view, is

Fig 8.13 The millivoltmeter
(*Foster Instruments Ltd*)

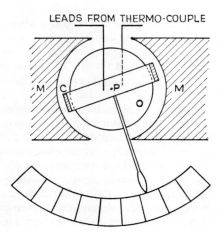

a diagram illustrating the working principle of the millivoltmeter. A
permanent magnet (not shown) produces a magnetic field in the air
gap between two pole pieces M, and a central core O. A moving coil C,
which can rotate about the central core, has pivots P at top and bottom.
The leads from the cold-junction terminals are brought to the coil C by
light hair-springs. Changes in electromotive force cause the coil to rotate.
This rotation is registered on a temperature scale by a finger attached
to the coil. In practice, the scale would be vertical to the paper.

There are many interesting problems involved in the design of these
instruments, but they are too complex to be discussed here. The reader
is referred to specialist books on the subject.

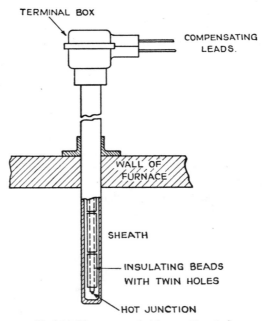

Fig 8.14 Thermo-couple (*George Kent Ltd*)

Figure 8.14 shows a thermo-couple mounted in the wall of a furnace.
The two wires are protected by a porcelain sheath, made from special
fireclay which is impervious to the furnace gases. They are insulated
from each other by being passed through beads with twin holes. The
wires are brought to two terminals in the head of the instrument: the
compensating leads are fixed to these terminals. The head of the instrument should be some little distance from the furnace wall, so that
the compensating leads are at a temperature lower than 100°C.

The thermo-couple shown has a single sheath of refractory material.

For temperatures up to 1100°C, the refractory sheath may itself be enclosed by a nickel–chromium-alloy sheath, which protects the refractory sheath from accidental damage. A disadvantage of this double sheath is that the response of the pyrometer to temperature change is slowed down.

8.3.5. Recorders. Many thermo-electric pyrometers are fitted with a recorder. The recorder moves a paper chart under a pen which periodically makes an ink dot on the chart. Over a period of time, a line is made on the chart, which has a suitable temperature scale ruled upon it. The usual method of conveying the pyrometer reading to the chart is as follows.

Let us suppose that the last mark on the chart is at 900°C. Subsequently, the millivoltmeter reading has risen to 910°C. Two clamps grip the finger of the millivoltmeter for a short time, while two prongs move together and 'find' the new position. The movement of the prongs operates an electrical relay system, which in turn moves the pen to the new correct position, and dips the pen to make a fresh mark on the chart. The finger of the millivoltmeter is now released by the clamps, so that it can move in accordance with any further temperature change.

8.3.6 Electrical resistance thermometers. When a conductor made from a pure metal, such as nickel or platinum, is heated, its electrical resistance varies. The principle of the resistance pyrometer is based on this phenomenon.

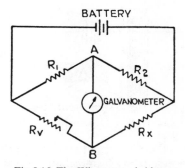

Fig 8.15 The Wheatstone bridge

The measuring device for the pyrometer is based on the *Wheatstone bridge*. As shown in fig. 8.15, this device consists of four resistances, R_1, R_2, R_V, and R_X; a galvanometer; and a battery, which supplies current to the circuit. The resistances R_1 and R_2 are of known value, while the value of R_V can be varied as required. The value of R_X is unknown.

The galvanometer is a sensitive instrument which records any difference in electrical potential between the points A and B. If A and B are at the same potential, the galvanometer reads zero, and the bridge is said to be 'in balance'. When the bridge is in balance, the following relationship holds good:

$$\frac{R_1}{R_V} = \frac{R_2}{R_X}$$

or

$$R_X = \frac{R_2 R_V}{R_1}$$

In using the Wheatstone bridge, the resistance R_V is varied until the bridge is in balance.

Knowing the values of R_1, R_2, and R_V, it is possible to calculate the value of R_X. If R_1 and R_2 are equal to each other, then $R_X = R_V$. Alternatively, R_2 might have a value of, say, $10R_1$, in which case $R_X = 10R_V$. The relative values of R_1 and R_2 determine the relationship of R_V to R_X. The Wheatstone bridge can be used, therefore, to determine the value of an unknown resistance, whether the value is large or small.

The application to the electrical resistance pyrometer is shown in fig. 8.16. As before, we have the known resistances R_1 and R_2, which, in this case, are of equal value; and also the variable resistance R_V. The platinum coil R_p now forms the unknown resistance.

The compensating leads are platinum wires, with a length equal to

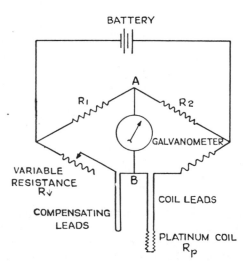

Fig 8.16 The resistance pyrometer (*Cambridge Instrument Co.*)

that of the leads to the platinum coil. The coil leads and the compensating leads, which are insulated from each other, are enclosed in the porcelain sheath which contains the platinum coil. This sheath is exposed to the hot substance, such as the atmosphere of a furnace.

When the furnace temperature rises, the resistance of the platinum coil, and of the two pairs of leads, increases. As regards the four leads, since two are on each side of the bridge, their change of resistance has no effect; but the increasing resistance of the coil unbalances the bridge, and deflects the galvanometer. The slider of the variable resistance is now moved until the bridge is in balance. The change in resistance of R_V is equal to the change in resistance of the platinum coil.

The relationship between change of temperature of a platinum wire and change of resistance is complicated, but it need not concern us. In the industrial type of resistance pyrometer, the scale for the slider of the variable resistance is marked in degrees.

This method of restoring a zero reading on an instrument is termed the *null method*; it usually leads to very accurate readings. The resistance thermometer, which may be used at temperatures up to 1200°C, is a very accurate instrument. It is sometimes used to calibrate thermo-electric pyrometers.

8.3.7 Radiation pyrometers. All the instruments previously described must be exposed to the hot substance whose temperature is to be measured. None of them is suitable for continous use at temperatures exceeding 1400°C. However, the heat or light emitted by the hot body may be used to measure its temperature. Before proceeding further, we must consider the emission of heat by hot bodies.

Not all hot bodies at the same temperature radiate the same amount of heat energy per unit area. The heat energy radiated by carbon at a particular temperature is about twice that emitted by polished platinum at the same temperature, when both are in the open. In other words, the condition of the radiating surface influences the amount of heat energy radiated.

It is very common to speak of 'black-body' conditions when discussing the emission of heat energy. A perfect black body is one which radiates the maximum amount of heat energy at a particular temperature. As noted in the last paragraph, platinum in the open is far removed from a perfect black body; the same remarks apply to other metals when viewed in the open. If the quantity of heat radiated by a certain surface area is taken as a measure of temperature, allowance must be made according to how far the particular metallic surface deviates from the ideal 'black-body' surface.

In heat-treatment practice, the main concern is with temperatures inside an enclosed space. It can be shown that a metallic surface when completely enclosed (e.g. by a furnace) radiates energy under conditions which approach those of a black body. Even more important is the fact that the inside wall of a furnace is almost equal to a perfect black body, as regards the radiation of heat energy.

It can be shown that the heat energy received by a cool body from a hot body varies as the difference between the fourth powers of the absolute temperatures. In heat-treatment furnaces, the temperature of the furnace is very much higher than that of the receiving body, i.e. the radiation pyrometer. Consequently, small changes in temperature of the pyrometer are unimportant.

The radiation pyrometer is usually arranged to collect the heat energy passing through the peep-hole of a furnace. In other words, the instrument 'views' that part of the inside wall of the furnace which is opposite the peep-hole.

Figure 8.17 illustrates the principle of the *variable-distance* instrument. Heat from the hot body AB enters the tube, and is focused, by a concave mirror, on to a small sensitive thermo-couple. The temperature of the thermo-couple will be much lower than that of the hot body, but its temperature will vary in accordance with variations in the hot-body temperature. The millivoltmeter attached to the thermo-couple is calibrated in terms of the temperature of the hot body. Temperatures up to 2000°C may be measured in this way.

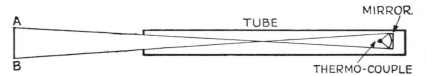

Fig 8.17 The radiation pyrometer

The line AB represents a circular portion of the hot surface being viewed. Now the heat collected by the mirror from unit area of the hot surface diminishes in proportion to the square of the distance between the hot body and the mirror. On the other hand, the area of the body from which the mirror is receiving heat (i.e. the area 'seen' by the mirror) increases as the square of the distance. Consequently, within certain limits, the distance of the mirror from the hot body is immaterial. It is essential that the area of the hot body 'covers' the mirror. Since most of the observations are made through a peep-hole in a furnace, this sets a practical limit to the distance at which the instrument can be used.

A lens-focus instrument is shown in fig. 8.18, together with the necessary moving-coil galvanometer or millivoltmeter. This instrument is normally set for use at a distance of about 700 mm from the hot body, but it can be set for other distances when required. These instruments are fixed at a set distance from the furnace peep-hole. If necessary, the peep-hole can be fitted with a short search-tube and a mica screen; the pyrometer is then calibrated with the screen in place.

It will be noted that the radiation from the hot body is focused by the lens A, is passed through the orifice plate B, and falls on the thermo-couple unit C. Four thermo-couples, which are enclosed in a

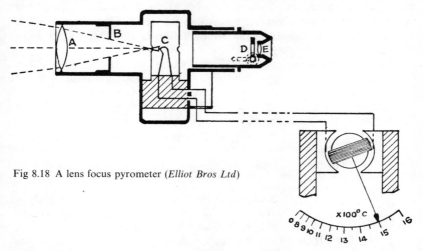

Fig 8.18 A lens focus pyrometer (*Elliot Bros Ltd*)

glass envelope, are provided. These are coupled in series, in order to increase the sensitivity of the instrument. The glass envelope is filled with inert gas. The radiation is focused on to small plates of blackened platinum, attached to the thermo-couples. On looking through the eyepiece E, and the absorption screen D (which is used only for high temperatures), the view is as shown in fig. 8.19. The dark strips are the thermo-couples. The white circle, which is an image of part of the hot surface, must completely surround the thermo-couples.

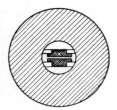

Fig 8.19 View through pyrometer eyepiece

In addition to the instruments which can be adjusted for distance, *fixed* distance instruments are made. These instruments are fixed permanently to the wall of the furnace. A water-cooled tube protrudes through the furnace wall, and the tube of the pyrometer is fixed to the outer end of the wall tube.

8.3.8 Optical pyrometer. There are two distinct types of optical pyrometer. The more important type, which is called the *disappearing-filament* pyrometer, will be described first.

Light from the hot body is compared with the light emitted by the filament of a lamp. The brightness of the lamp filament can be varied; the operator alters the current flowing through the lamp, until the filament has the same brightness as the hot body. The temperature is then read off the scale of a rheostat, which is calibrated in degrees Celsius.

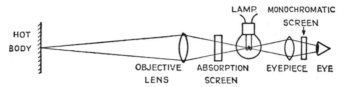

Fig 8.20 Disappearing-filament pyrometer (*Foster Instruments Ltd*)

The optical principle is shown in fig 8.20. Light from the hot body is picked up by the objective lens. After passing through an absorption screen, it is focused on the lamp filament, and passes to the eyepiece lens. The light then passes through a monochromatic screen, which reduces the dazzle, and eliminates colour difference between the hot body and the filament. The operator looks through the eyepiece, and sees the dark filament of the lamp against the bright background of the hot body (fig. 8.21). The lamp current is now increased, and eventually the lamp filament shows bright against the background. The current is adjusted until the filament disappears: this is the correct setting. The absorption screen behind the objective lens reduces the intensity of light from the hot body; in consequence, the filament brightness has only to equal the apparent brightness of the hot body. This allows the lamp to be run at reasonable temperatures, thus increasing the life of the filament.

An external view of the pyrometer is shown in fig. 8.22. The knurled

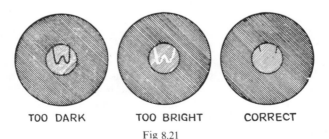

TOO DARK   TOO BRIGHT   CORRECT

Fig 8.21

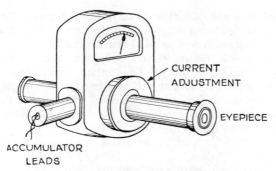

Fig 8.22 Disappearing-filament instrument

ring controls the filament temperature; the reading is taken on the curved scale near the top of the instrument. The twin leads are connected to a small accumulator.

The electrical circuit is shown in fig. 8.23; it will be noted that a Wheatstone bridge is used. The resistances A, C, and D are adjusted so that the bridge is in balance, and the millivoltmeter M is at zero when the lamp filament is at, say, 800°C. The rheostat R, taking current from

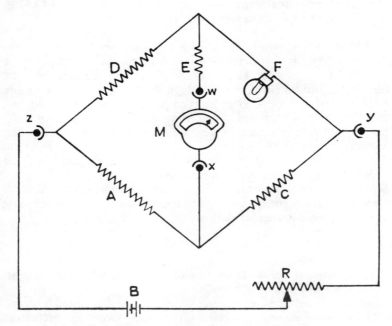

Fig 8.23 Disappearing-filament pyrometer circuit

the accumulator B, is adjusted so as to raise the filament temperature. The resistance of the lamp filament will increase with increasing temperature, but resistances A, C, and D remain unaltered. Consequently, the milliammeter will register an increasing out-of-balance of the current flowing through the bridge. The 'ballast' resistance E is put in when calibrating the instrument; it is also used as a 'swamp' resistance against temperature changes of the whole of the instrument. The lamp and resistances can be detached at points w, x, y, and z, and removed as a single unit from the body of the instrument.

The disappearing-filament pyrometer is suitable for temperatures between 800°C and 3000°C.

The *Wanner* optical pyrometer, which is named after its inventor, may also be noted. This instrument is not very widely used, and a brief description will suffice. The light from the hot body is optically matched with the light from a constant-comparison lamp. The light from the lamp is polarised in one plane, and the light from the hot body is polarised in a plane at right angles to the first plane.

The two beams are passed through a Nicol prism, which is rotated. Rotation of this prism causes an apparent increase in light from one source, and a diminution of light from the other source. The prism is rotated until the two beams appear to give light of equal intensity. The device for rotating the prism has a scale marked in degrees Celsius. The maximum temperature which can be measured is 4000°C.

8.3.9 Choice of pyrometer. The choice of pyrometer for a particular application depends on several factors. Direct-contact instruments are limited to about 1400°C. The accuracy of reading required must be taken into account. Instruments of a high degree of accuracy are more expensive. The grade of attendant employed must be considered: where the labour is unskilled, a recording instrument is most suitable. When the temperature must be kept constant within close limits, the pyrometer should be connected with a fuel-control system. In this connection it should be noted that the optical pyrometer cannot readily be coupled to a recorder or a fuel-control system.

Since there are a number of firms who specialise in the field of temperature measurement, it is wise to consult them before purchasing a pyrometer for a particular purpose.

Summary

1   Heat-treatment demands control of furnace temperature and atmosphere, and accurate quenching.
2   Heat-treatment furnaces can be classified into (*a*) gas-fired furnaces, (*b*) salt-bath furnaces, (*c*) electric furnaces, (*d*) forced air-circulation electric furnaces, and (*e*) induction furnaces.

3 Thermometers can be classified into (*a*) liquid mercury thermometers, (*b*) vapour-pressure thermometers, (*c*) fusible cones, (*d*) thermo-electric pyrometers, (*e*) electrical resistance thermometers, (*f*) radiation pyrometers, and (*g*) optical pyrometers.

4 The choice of pyrometer depends upon the temperature to be measured, the accuracy of measurement required, the need for temperature-control, the location of the pyrometer, and the degree of skill needed to operate the quipment.

Questions

Set A

1 Explain what is meant by a continuous furnace. What would be the temperature arrangements in such a furnace (*a*) when heating steel for quenching, (*b*) when heating steel for annealing?

2 Describe the principle of the thermo-couple, and explain how it is applied to the observation of high temperatures. How can a thermo-couple be tested for accuracy?

3 Discuss the relative advantages of fusible cones, thermo-electric pyrometers, and optical pyrometers.

4 Outline the essential properties of a good oil for quenching steel.

5 Why is it important to control the temperature of a furnace very closely? If the temperature of a furnace could not be controlled to closer limits than $\pm 100°C$, what difficulties would be introduced into the heat-treatment of plain carbon steels?

Set B (questions requiring further study)

6 Make a sketch of a salt-bath furnace, explain its function, and give the composition of the salt used.

7 Make a sketch of an industrial thermo-couple. What are the relative merits of the different materials used for thermo-couples?

8 Make a lay-out for a small heat-treatment shop to cater for ferrous materials. What additional equipment would you require if aluminium alloys were to be heat-treated?

Chapter 9
Casting

9.1 Introduction

When a metal or alloy is produced it is usually in the molten state. It is poured into a suitable mould where it is allowed to cool and solidify before being removed; it is then said to be *cast*. This may be done to produce a convenient simple shape that is either further manipulated by hammering, rolling etc. (see chapter 10), or machined to produce the desired shape; this simple cast product is called an *ingot*, *billet*, etc., depending upon its size. The cast shape may be complicated, and be so accurate that little or no machining is required; such a cast product is called a *casting*.

9.1.1. The three basic casting methods are *sand-casting*, *die-casting*, and *investment-casting*. Sand-casting is done using a sand mould produced with the aid of a pattern, die-casting uses a metal mould that is machined from a block, and investment-casting uses a refractory mould that is produced using a pattern (but unlike sand-casting, the pattern is melted to remove it from the impression). The casting method used depends upon a number of factors, including the metal to be cast, the shape to be produced, the allowable costs and the quantity to be produced.

9.2 Sand-casting

In this method, the metal is poured into a mould or cavity that is formed in a special sand; the metal to be cast is melted in a suitable furnace and brought to the mould in a ladle, from which it is poured into the mould. When the metal is solid, the mould is broken up, and the casting removed. Apart from the pouring technique, the main problem associated with sand-casting is the removal of the pattern from the completed mould so that the metal can be poured in. In some cases this can be overcome by making the pattern of several pieces; but as a new mould is made for each casting, the casting should, if possible, be designed so that the pattern is of one piece, so minimising the moulding time.

9.2.1 The simplest mould consists of a box of sand with a depression at the top, into which the molten metal is poured; the 'top' horizontal face of the casting being controlled by the quantity of metal that is poured into the mould, and the inclination of the mould relative to the 'horizontal'. This *one-part* open mould is suitable for casting billets and similar shapes.

When a more complicated and accurate casting is required, a *multi-part* mould consisting of two, or occasionally three sections, placed one on the other, is necessary; three-part moulds are not used as often as two-part moulds because they are more expensive to make, and consequently castings are designed with a view to using two-part moulds. The sand-casting process is best introduced by describing the production of a casting using a simple two-part mould.

9.2.2 Sand-casting using a simple two-part mould. Figure 9.1 shows a bracket that can be cast using a simple two-part mould; this method can be used because the pattern will have a suitable flat face that can be placed on the moulding board at the start of the moulding operation (this will be evident when fig. 9.3 is presently studied). The pat-

Fig 9.1 Bracket

tern used to produce the mould will be almost a replica of the casting to be produced, but it will be overall larger than the casting to allow for the contraction that will occur when the metal cools. To avoid tedious calculations, the pattern maker uses a suitable *contraction rule* when making the pattern (a contraction rule resembles an ordinary rule, but all the lengths are increased to produce the desired oversize; a range of contraction rules is available). When only one or two castings are required the pattern may be made of plaster-of-Paris, but wood or metal is usually used; wood is used for up to about 100 moulds where hand moulding is used (machine moulding has a sand-blasting effect, and would damage a wooden pattern), and metal is used for large quantities and when machine moulding is used (the metal used is usually that most readily available in the foundry). Sand moulds are contained in metal *moulding boxes* (or 'flasks') that have four sides but no top or bottom; fig. 9.2 shows a pair of moulding boxes. During the moulding operation the boxes are located together by pins so that they

COPE

DRAG

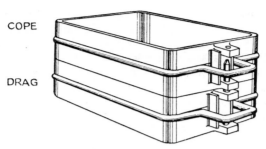

Fig 9.2 Moulding boxes

can be separated to remove the pattern, and replaced in the correct position before the metal is poured in; the boxes are clamped together, or the *cope* (top section) weighted down when pouring to prevent the cope from 'floating away' from the *drag* (lower section) when the mould is full of molten metal.

Figure 9.3 illustrates the sequence when moulding the simple two-part mould to cast the bracket shown in fig. 9.1.

At stage 1 the pattern is seated on the moulding board (this could not be done if the casting, and therefore the pattern also, did not have a suitable flat surface); the pattern is covered with *facing sand*, which is a specially prepared sand of good quality which can take a clean and smooth impression, and can resist the heat from the molten metal that will be in contact with it. The facing sand is backed up with *moulding sand* (also called *floor sand* and *backing sand*), which is old facing sand from previous moulds; the moulding sand is carefully rammed up so that it is fairly tight around the pattern to produce a good solid mould, yet permeable enough to allow the gases produced during casting to escape; the sand is finally levelled off.

The mould with the pattern still in position is inverted (see stage 2), the exposed sand lightly covered with *parting sand*, and the exposed pattern with facing sand; parting sand has no cohesion, and is introduced to permit a clean separation when the mould is opened up (stage 3) to remove the pattern. The second moulding box is located in position on the first box and filled with moulding sand. Two or more plugs are introduced when the second box is being filled (these are removed later, leaving channels in the sand); one of these plugs is positioned to one side of the pattern as shown. The sand is rammed up and levelled off.

The boxes are now separated (stage 3) to allow the pattern to be removed. This is done by screwing a bar with a threaded end into a suitable insert in the pattern, damping the sand around the pattern, and gently rapping the bar in all directions so that the pattern can be carefully withdrawn. To facilitate the removal of the pattern without

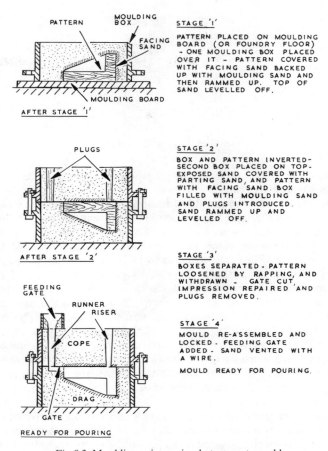

STAGE '1'

PATTERN PLACED ON MOULDING BOARD (OR FOUNDRY FLOOR) – ONE MOULDING BOX PLACED OVER IT – PATTERN COVERED WITH FACING SAND BACKED UP WITH MOULDING SAND AND THEN RAMMED UP. TOP OF SAND LEVELLED OFF.

STAGE '2'

BOX AND PATTERN INVERTED– SECOND BOX PLACED ON TOP– EXPOSED SAND COVERED WITH PARTING SAND, AND PATTERN WITH FACING SAND. BOX FILLED WITH MOULDING SAND AND PLUGS INTRODUCED. SAND RAMMED UP AND LEVELLED OFF.

STAGE '3'

BOXES SEPARATED – PATTERN LOOSENED BY RAPPING, AND WITHDRAWN – GATE CUT, IMPRESSION REPAIRED AND PLUGS REMOVED.

STAGE '4'

MOULD RE-ASSEMBLED AND LOCKED – FEEDING GATE ADDED – SAND VENTED WITH A WIRE.

MOULD READY FOR POURING.

Fig 9.3 Moulding using a simple two-part mould

scuffing the sides of the impression, all surfaces that lie in the direction of pattern removal are inclined slightly by a small amount (the *draw angle*) as shown in fig. 9.4.

A groove called a *gate* is cut in the sand face to allow the channel produced by the plug that is outside the pattern to connect with the impression (see stage 4 illustration); the metal is poured through this channel (called the *runner*), and the gate prevents it from dropping straight into the impression and damaging it; the cross-section of the gate is slightly smaller than that of the channel so that a full runner will always supply metal to the gate at a slight pressure.

If necessary, the impression is 'repaired' using hand tools, and dusted with plumbago to prevent the sand from fusing with the hot metal.

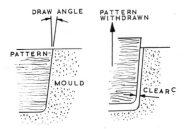

Fig 9.4 Application of draw angle

The plugs are removed from the second (the top) box, leaving the channels already mentioned.

Finally, at stage 4 the mould is reassembled, carefully locating and securing the two sections; the top section is known as the *cope*, and the lower section is known as the *drag*. The sand in the cope is *vented* (using a venting wire which is pushed into the sand, almost to the impression); these vents allow the sand to be rammed up more tightly at the earlier stages without the risk of gases being trapped in the molten metal and forming blowholes in the solid metal. A sand feeding-gate is added to make it easier to pour the metal into the runner. The illustration (stage 4) shows the mould ready for pouring. The molten metal is poured through the *runner* and the air will escape through the *riser*, which will be filled with molten metal when the impression is completely filled. Gases can escape through the runner and the riser, which also act as headers to supply the impression with more metal to compensate for the contraction of the metal when cooling in the molten state.

Additional risers would be necessary if the casting shape was such that air would otherwise be trapped in the impression; they would also be necessary above large sections to provide an extra supply of molten metal. Additional runners would be necessary when large or awkward

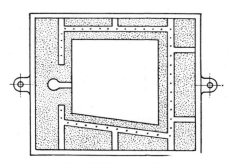

Fig 9.5 Vent channels

castings demand simultaneous pouring from more than one direction so that the impression is completely filled before the metal is solid. In many cases additional venting is done; the centre joint of the mould is a suitable place for this (see fig. 9.5). While the pattern is still in position in the mould, a number of channels are cut; these being about 10 mm wide, and roughly semicircular in section. The sand around the pattern is then vented by pushing a venting wire vertically downwards from the base of the surrounding channel into the sand. Other channels are cut from the main vent channels to carry away the gases to the edge of the box.

When the metal has solidified, the mould is broken open to remove the casting, which will be as shown in fig. 9.6. The *runner* and the *riser*

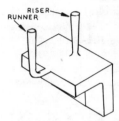

Fig 9.6 Unfettled casting

shown are produced by the metal that solidifies in the runner and riser channels. Before the casting is despatched from the foundry it is *fettled*; this involves the removal of the runner and riser by sawing or grinding, and the removal of any sand adhering to the casting by sand-blasting it.

9.2.3 Sand-casting using a core and a split pattern. Figure 9.7 shows a hollow casting; the hollow feature is produced by placing a *core* in the impression to restrict the molten metal. The casting illustrated introduces further complications because although it has two flat surfaces, neither would be suitable as a seating face for the pattern because its shape prevents it from being removed from the mould. One

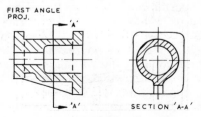

Fig 9.7 Hollow casting

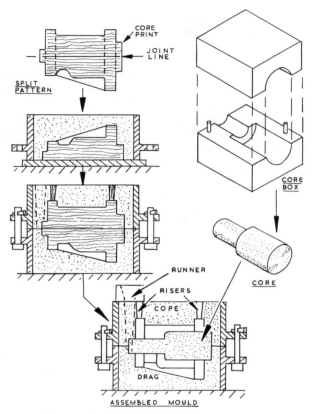

Fig 9.8 Moulding using a two-part mould, split pattern and core

method of overcoming this problem is to use a *split pattern*, one section of which is treated like the simple pattern shown in fig. 9.3 (see stage 1).

Figure 9.8 shows the principal stages in the production of the mould for this casting. The pattern is of two sections (the joint between them being a plane surface), located by dowels (see fig. 9.9); it has a projection at each end, called a *core print* to produce location points in the mould, ready for the core.

At the first stage in moulding, one section of the pattern is treated like a simple pattern (compare this with fig. 9.3, stage 1); when the drag has been rammed up, it is inverted, with the pattern in position. The second moulding stage is similar to that shown in fig. 9.3, except that the other section of the pattern is put in position before the cope is rammed up. The remaining stages are the same as for simple moulding,

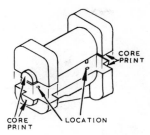

Fig 9.9 Split pattern

until the mould is assembled, when the core is introduced to produce the hollow feature.

The core is made in a *core box*, and is stiffened if necessary by introducing a rod, called a *core iron*, on its axis. The venting problem is acute because the core is almost completely surrounded by molten metal; it is therefore necessary to make it from a special sand, called *core sand*, that when given some further treatment becomes strong but porous.

Further venting of the core is usually arranged. One method being to bury a vent wire in the core, and to draw it out after the core has been rammed up. If the core is made from a core sand that requires heating to develop its strength and porosity, a waxed string is inserted in the core; during the heating process, the wax is melted, leaving a hole. Large cores are vented by a 'cinder vent' consisting of small pieces of coke, rammed up in a continuous line through the core to form a vent passage. Another method is to use a vent pipe; this is a length of perforated pipe placed on the axis of the core (like a core iron), giving support to the core, and at the same time acting as a vent; the vent pipe projects from the ends of the core and on to the edge of the moulding box to allow the gases to escape.

The core can be further supported by introducing a *chaplet* or a number of chaplets when the mould and core is assembled; chaplets are also introduced to prevent the core from bending upwards when the molten metal is poured into the mould. Fig 9.10(*a*) shows two types of chaplet and their application; chaplets are made of steel, galvanised to avoid rusting, which would prevent it from being welded to the molten metal. The chaplet shown supporting the core can also be used to prevent the core from lifting; in this application, the stem of the chaplet is wedged against a bar (see fig. 9.10(*b*)) which is supported by the edges of the box, and weighted down if necessary. Part of the chaplet is removed when the casting is machined, but the stem remains embedded in the wall of the casting.

Figure 9.8 shows the assembled mould, with the core in position (chaplets are not shown in the illustration); it will be seen that two

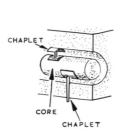

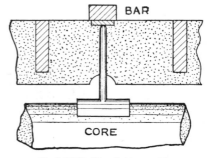

Fig 9.10(*a*) Application of chaplets   Fig 9.10(*b*) Chaplet in position

risers are necessary to prevent air from being trapped, causing the two flanges to be incomplete.

When the mould is broken open to remove the casting, the sand that formed the core is removed through the holes in the casting wall produced by the core; these holes are called *cored holes*. If the casting shape is such that it would be difficult to remove the sand, additional cored holes are necessary; they are also essential if additional core prints are necessary to locate or support the core. If cored holes are not required, they are plugged up later using *core plugs*. A typical core plug is shown in fig. 9.11; the head may be square as shown, hexagonal

Fig 9.11 Core plug

or have a screwdriver slot in it for tightening purposes. Figure 9.12 shows the stages involved in the fitting of a core plug. The cored hole is drilled, tapped, and counterbored; the core plug is screwed into the hole so that a good seal is obtained, and if necessary the casting is pressure tested. The core plug is locked in position by drilling a hole, partly in the casting and partly in the core plug, into which a dowel is fitted. Finally, the head of the core plug is machined off so that the core

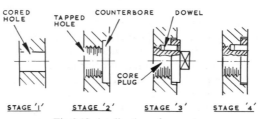

Fig 9.12 Application of core plug

plug cannot be removed. Core plugs of this type should not be confused with those fitted to a motor-car engine cylinder block, which are discs or 'cups' that are forced into the cored holes, but allowed to be pushed out by the cooling-water in the event of it freezing; this usually prevents the cylinder block from becoming cracked by the expanding ice.

9.2.4 Odd-side moulding. In the example just described, the use of a moulding board and a split pattern ensured that the mould was split across a diameter. It is essential to split a mould so that the pattern can be removed without damaging it. If a circular pattern is buried rather too deeply in a half-mould, it cannot be released from the box without breaking the mould away. To embed a solid pattern so that the face of the mould coincides exactly with a diameter on the pattern is not easy, as it cannot be rammed up in the normal way. To overcome the difficulty, *odd-side* moulding may be used.

A suitable cope is rammed up lightly, the right way up, and levelled off. The shape of half the pattern is then cut out of the mould, and the pattern is tried in: further cutting of the mould and bedding of the pattern is carried out until the pattern lies solidly in the top part, with the maximum diameter exactly level with the joint face. The drag, with the centre joint downwards, is then placed in position, and rammed up. The two half-boxes are clamped together, and the whole mould is turned over. The cope is now removed—this is the 'odd side'. Another similar cope is then put on the drag which contains the pattern, and the mould is rammed up and completed in the normal way. The 'odd side' may be used to place the pattern for a number of moulds; in fact, it takes the place of the moulding board. Where a large number of castings are required, the 'odd side' may be made semi-permanent by using sand with a special bond which will set very hard. Alternatively, an odd side may be made up in plaster of Paris.

9.2.5 Floor moulding. For large castings, it becomes very difficult or impossible to turn over a rammed drag; furthermore, a drag of sufficient size may not be available. Consequently, most of a very large mould is made in the floor sand; with a little ingenuity, two or more boxes may be used to form the cope. To register the joint of the mould, a number of stout wooden stakes are driven firmly into the sand. These guide the cope to the correct position. The problem of venting is sometimes troublesome in floor moulds; to overcome the difficulty, a *coke bed* is often used. A coke bed is shown in fig. 9.13. A hole is dug out in the sand, and the bottom is rammed as hard as possible. Alternatively, an iron plate may be laid on the bottom of the hole as a foundation. These iron plates may be prepared for bolts, which help to clamp the assembled mould together.

The coke is laid on the solid foundation, large pieces being placed

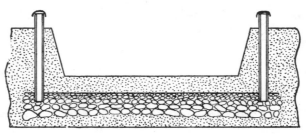

Fig 9.13 Coke bed

down first, followed by smaller pieces. At the sides, *vent pipes* are arranged to lead away the gases. These are 40-mm or 50-mm bore, mild-steel pipes, placed so as to clear the cope. Rag caps are tied over the vent-pipe tops, to prevent loose sand falling down and choking the vent. A thin layer of straw is placed over the roughly levelled coke. Floor sand to a depth of about 250 mm is rammed fairly tightly over the straw. The surface is levelled with straight edge and spirit level, and the whole body of sand is thoroughly vented down to the coke bed. To close the upper end of the vent holes against the metal, a layer of facing sand is now spread, lightly rammed, and strickled off level. The work of ramming up the pattern can now proceed. The sides of the mould can be vented in the usual manner, by passing the vent wire down near the sides of the pattern, and leading the gases away by channels cut in the joint face, as shown in fig. 9.5.

9.2.6 Loose pieces and drawbacks. When a casting has a projecting feature, such as a boss (see fig. 9.14) the pattern cannot be withdrawn without damaging the impression. This can be avoided by changing the design of the casting; the boss could be placed at the joint line (as shown in fig. 9.15(*a*), or be extended to the joint line as shown in fig. 9.15(*b*); but if these modifications cannot be done, it is necessary to employ special moulding techniques—usually increasing the cost of moulding. One such method is to use a loose piece dovetailed to the main body of the pattern, as in fig. 9.16(*a*), which is loose enough to remain in position when the main body of the pattern is withdrawn, but which can then be removed separately as shown in fig. 9.16(*b*).

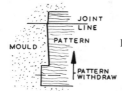

Fig 9.14 Projecting feature preventing removal of pattern

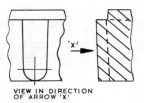

Fig 9.15(*a*) Boss at joint line allows pattern removal

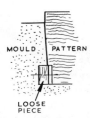

Fig 9.15(*b*) Extended boss allows pattern removal

VIEW IN DIRECTION OF ARROW 'X'

Fig 9.16(*a*) Loose piece applied to pattern

Fig 9.16(*b*) Loose piece allows pattern to be withdrawn

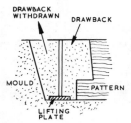
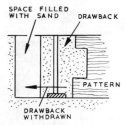

Fig 9.17 Drawback that can be removed easily

Fig 9.18 Drawback that must be removed horizontally

Another method is to use a drawback; this is a separate section of the mould, rather like an 'external core'. The pattern is shaped like the required casting, including the projecting feature. When the drag has been rammed up, part of the sand is cut away to allow the drawback to be positioned so that the cope can be rammed up. When the boxes are separated, the drawback is moved back to allow the pattern to be removed. The shape of the casting shown in fig. 9.17 is such that this can be done easily; but the casting shown in fig. 9.18 requires the drawback to be moved back horizontally, and so there must be a clearance between the drawback and the main mould—this space must be filled up with sand when the mould is assembled ready for casting. The drawback must be supported by a lifting plate and located in position in the mould.

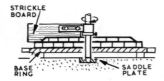

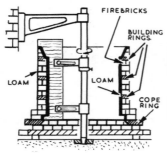

BUILDING THE BASE
SADDLE PLATE BURIED IN FLOOR NEAR WALL. BASE RING PLACED IN POSITION. TWO COURSES OF BRICKS LAID ON BASE RING, ABOUT 20 MM BETWEEN AND OVER BRICK. TOP OF LOAM STRICKLED OFF.
RING AND BASE REMOVED AND DRIED IN STOVE. SURFACE COATED WITH BLACKWASH (PLUMBAGO, WATER AND BINDER MIX) TO FORM PARTING FACE.

BUILDING THE COPE
BASE REPLACED. CAST IRON COPE RING PLACED ON BASE. COPE BUILT UP WITH BRICKS AND LOAM, STRENGTHENED WITH RINGS — THE STRICKLE BOARD USED AS GUIDE. INSIDE PLASTERED WITH LOAM AND STRICKLED OFF.
RING AND COPE REMOVED AND DRIED. INSIDE COATED WITH BLACKWASH.

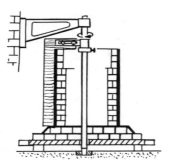

BUILDING THE CORE
CORE BUILT DIRECTLY ON BASE IN SIMILAR WAY, USING THE STRICKLE BOARD ON OUTSIDE. SOME BRICKS ARE MADE OF LOAM TO 'GIVE' WHEN CASTING CONTRACTS
CORE REMOVED AND DRIED. OUTSIDE COATED WITH BLACKWASH.

Fig 9.19(*a*) Loam moulding

9.2.7 Skeleton patterns. Where a single casting of large size is required, the cost of a complete pattern may be prohibitive. There are several ways of minimising the pattern cost. *Skeleton patterns* may be used: a skeleton pattern formed by light wooden ribs is made, and the shape of the mould is worked up from this.

9.2.8 Loam moulding. Large castings of simple shape are often produced by loam moulding using swept-to-shape moulds as an alternative to those produced by patterns. This method is known as loam moulding because the sand that is used is purchased as 'loam moulding sand'. This sand is of comparatively small grain size and has a relatively high clay content; it is mixed with various additives to pro-

PREPARING THE TOP PLATE.

THIS IS NECESSARY TO CLOSE THE MOULD. DABBERS (SHORT FINGERS) CAST ON TO KEY THE LOAM.
LAYER OF LOAM PLASTERED ON AND SMOOTHED OFF. RUNNERS AND RISERS FORMED IN HOLES IN THE PLATE.

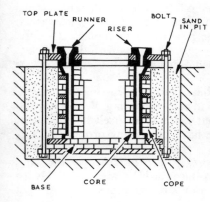

ASSEMBLING THE MOULD

BOTTOM PLATE AND CORE LOWERED INTO PIT IN FOUNDRY FLOOR.
FOLLOWED BY THE COPE.
THE PIT FILLED WITH SAND AROUND COPE AND RAMMED UP.
TOP PLATE FITTED AND SECURED TO BOTTOM PLATE BY LONG BOLTS.

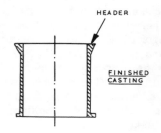

CASTING
METAL POURED INTO MOULD. AFTER A MINUTES, 'KEY' BRICKS REMOVED, CONTRACTING CASTING CRUSHES THE CORE INWARDS – LOAM BRICKS GIVING WAY GRADUALLY.

Fig 9.19(*b*) Loam moulding

duce a range of mixes, from semi-solid, which can be handled, to a thin paste ('slurry') which is applied using a brush.

The manufacture of a large pipe, say of 2–2·5 m diameter and of similar length is typical of this method, and is illustrated in figs 9.19(*a*) and 9.19(*b*). The mould is of four sections—the base, the cope, the core (these three are produced using a strickle board to 'sweep' the loam to shape), and the top plate. When a foundry is designed to produce castings by this method, large pits are built into the floor; the mould is either assembled in one of these pits, or is constructed directly in a pit.

More complicated moulds can be produced by using skeleton patterns, cores, and drawbacks.

Core stripping is often practised in the loam-moulding shop. The core is first prepared by means of a skeleton pattern, by strickling, or by a combination of both methods. It is then dried and blackwashed. Clay or wooden strips of a depth equal to the thickness of metal are placed on the core, which is then built up all over with loam, to the metal thickness. After drying and blackwashing of the core, the cope is built up over the core. The cope may be jointed as necessary, so that it can be drawn off. When completed, the cope is drawn off, and dried. The 'thickness' of loam is now broken off the core; the thickness strips are removed, and the true core surface is repaired and blackwashed afresh. After stripping the thickness, it is usual to replace the cope over the core, trying the thickness at various points with dabs of clay: if the 'metal' is thin, the core is rubbed down, if it is too thick, the face is built up with a little loam.

The mould can then be reassembled ready for casting. Venting is just as essential in loam moulding as in sand moulding. Vent pipes and cinder vents are sometimes used, but dried loam itself has excellent venting properties. Bricks, of course, have no venting properties; consequently, a good thickness of loam is required between the bricks.

Thickness stripping from loam cores is also practised in the sand foundry. When large pipes are produced which are not likely to be repeated, a loam core is made. For straight pipes, with straight branches, the cores are built up on *core barrels*, which are perforated pipes. The core barrel is laid in V-blocks and a handle is fitted at one end. Straw rope is wrapped on the barrel, and a good thickness of loam is added. The core barrel is longer than the core; consequently, the roughly built core may be rotated in the V-blocks while a flat strickle is held up against it, to bring the surface to a true cylindrical shape. The size is tried by calipers, and the length is measured off. The core is then dried out, and blackwashed. More straw rope, followed by a layer of loam, is used to produce the 'thickness'. Wooden flanges are added, and the 'pattern' is used to make a sand mould; it is then removed from the mould, the thickness is broken off, the wooden flanges are removed, and the 'pattern' becomes a core again, ready for placing in the mould.

A very similar technique is used for bent pipes, but the core cannot be rotated. Instead the pattern shop provides curved templates for the core and pattern surfaces. With unusual shapes of pipe, the pattern-maker acts in a supervisory capacity, checking the core and pattern for correct shape and size. The pattern-maker is usually more adept than the moulder at this type of work, which involves the reading of drawings.

9.2.9 Plate moulding. The moulding processes considered so far have all been concerned with the making of only a few articles; when large numbers of parts are required, other methods are often used. In figs 9.1

and 9.3, the moulding of a small bracket was illustrated. If considerable numbers of this bracket were required, then the loose wooden
pattern could be fastened to the turnover board by screws. After the
drag has been turned over, the turnover board and pattern are withdrawn together. This entails a truly vertical lift, which may be aided by
having guide bars. It is best performed by a mechanical lifting and
vibrating device, working in vertical guides.

When the mould is part in the drag and part in the cope, then a
board can be made for each half-mould, with a half-pattern attached.
The cope and drag can now be rammed up separately, and brought
together. With this procedure, one difficulty which must be overcome
is that of ensuring that the two half-moulds coincide at the parting
face. Each board must be dowelled to the half-box on which it is
used, so that the mould is always made in exactly the same place.
Alternatively, a double-sided board may be used, with one-half of the
pattern fixed to each side. The board is then placed between the cope
and drag, which are rammed up at each side of it. The pins of the two
half-boxes may then be used to register the half-moulds. It is necessary,
of course, to make sure that the two half-patterns are fixed in the
correct positions on each side of the board.

Wooden patterns wear rapidly when continually rammed up in
sand. Instead of a wooden board and pattern, the moulding shop can
prepare a metal 'plate' pattern. Originally, these plate patterns were
invariably made in cast iron, but modern practice is to use aluminium,
on account of its lightness. With small castings, a number of patterns
may be mounted on a single plate, which also carries the shape of the
'gates' or 'sprues' through which the metal is to run from a single
runner. Figure 9.20 shows a plate for producing half-moulds for a
small casting. Plate moulding in the modern foundry is essentially a
machine process.

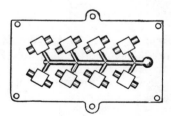

Fig 9.20 Plate pattern

9.2.10 Shell moulds. In making a mould, the flasks in common use are
round, square, or rectangular, according to the shape to be cast.
Usually the space occupied by sand greatly exceeds the actual mould
space. If the mass of the flask is added to the mass of sand in it, it will

be realised that a mould is a heavy article. Owing to the comparative weakness of sand structures, care is necessary when moving a mould; consequently, all but the smallest moulds are made and cast up in one place; apart from turning over, they are not moved. The pattern and core boxes are used and then put at one side, possibly for days, while the mould is smoothed, built up, cored, cast up, and broken away.

In the mechanised foundry, expensive conveying machinery is installed for moving the moulds to the casting station, and a continuous flow of moulds is required.

These difficulties can be reduced considerably by the use of 'shell' moulds. The metal pattern is placed in a convenient place, and is heated to a suitable temperature. It is sprayed with a mixture containing sand and a suitable plastics binder. When a thin shell has been built up, it is baked and hardened, and the pattern is then removed. The shell mould can now be stored until required. Obviously the shell must be capable of being stripped from the pattern. Many shell moulds are made in a number of pieces, which are built up prior to casting, and held together with binding tape or suitable steel clamps. If required, the mould can be partially buried in sand when being cast up, to give support against the pressure of molten metal.

The shell mould is quite permeable, so that air and gas can escape readily, and there is little risk of porosity in the finished casting. When the casting has solidified, the shell mould is easily broken away from the casting.

Shell moulding requires only a small fraction of the sand used in conventional moulding. The moulds, which are light, can easily be trans-

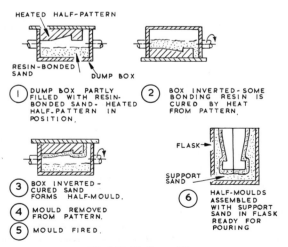

Fig 9.21 Shell moulding

ported to the pouring station, instead of the molten metal being carried to the moulds in ladles, as is the practice in most moulding shops.

Figure 9.21 illustrates shell moulding using a dump box.

9.2.11 Moulding sands. Moulding sand may be left 'green', or damp; this is the common practice for castings of reasonably plain shape, without complicated cores. For complicated castings, the mould may be dried out in a stove, and is then called a 'dry sand' mould. Large moulds made in the shop floor are 'skin dried' by coke braziers or hot-air blowers. These varying methods call for sands of rather different composition; for example, the 'green strength' is important in the first type, while 'dry strength' is important in the two latter types.

The essential properties of moulding sand are as follows:

Permeability. The sand must allow the steam and other gases generated by the heat of casting to escape freely. If there is insufficient passage through the body of sand, then the gases will try to bubble through the solidifying metal, and will leave holes in the casting. The moulder has some control over permeability; hard ramming lowers the permeability, but this is relieved by liberal venting.

Plasticity. This is the ability to take up an intricate shape, such as a figured face. Fine-grained sands have better plasticity than coarse-grained sands, but the plasticity of a sand is chiefly a question of the content of clay, which retains moisture when the sand is damped.

Flowability. This property is allied to plasticity. It is the ability of the sand to take up the desired shape.

In ramming up, the blows of the rammer must be transmitted through the body of sand, which should respond readily to the packing action.

Cohesion. The sand must hold together when the pattern is withdrawn, and the mould is moved about. Cohesion must be retained when molten metal enters the mould, and washes the heated mould surface; this property is often termed *bond strength*. According to the type of mould, green bond strength or dry bond strength may be required. The bond strength of moulding sand is determined largely by the alumina (clay) content. The clay should be present as a thin, tenacious film on each grain of sand. Generally, angular grains with a roughened surface are the best base for the alumina film; 'sharp' sands have smooth oval grains, and are not so easily bonded. Clay, when slowly baked to a reasonable temperature, gives up the free water with which it is associated, but retains the water with which it is chemically combined. In this state, which is that of a dry sand mould, the cohesion remains. However, at high temperatures the chemically combined water is driven off. The *burnt sand* which remains has no powers of cohesion, and is of no further use as moulding sand, since the clay cannot be induced to take up water again.

Refractoriness. The sand should resist the heat of the molten metal, without fusing. It is the silica content of the sand which has the best refractory properties, the clay being the first to fuse. To prevent the metal from making too close contact with the sand face, up to 10% of coal dust is added to facing sand. The first effect of the molten metal is to burn this coal dust, which forms a gaseous 'blanket' between the metal and the mould face. In addition, the finished mould face is coated with plumbago, so that the sand cannot fuse on to the casting face, and produce a rough, hard skin.

Composition of sand. Certain natural sands have suitable compositions for use as moulding sand: Erith, Mansfield, Belfast, and Clyde sands are typical. However, there is a growing tendency to add artificial bonding agents, thus producing what are termed synthetic sands. In these, part or all of the bonding agent may be added to the sand. *Bentonite* is one of the best known of the binders added to the sand used in iron founding. This is a natural clay, which is pulverised to a colloidal state; it then has an extremely fine particle size and remarkable water-holding properties. Fireclay is also used in the pulverised condition.

Core sands are almost invariably made up with an artificial binder. Core sand is usually a clean, sharp, silica sand, to which is added a compound binder. These binders usually contain dextrin (a starchy substance) and linseed oil, sometimes mixed with other oils and water. The core is made, and dried out by stoving; it is then hard and strong, and will stand rough usage, but has very high permeability. Permeability is a most important property, since cores are often almost entirely surrounded by molten metal. When it has served its purpose, the core must be easily removable from the finished casting, and, therefore, must disintegrate readily when 'picked'.

The principal constituents of moulding sands are as follows: silica (SiO_2) 86–90%, alumina (Al_2O_3) 4–8%, iron oxide (Fe_2O_3) 2–5%, with smaller amounts of the oxides of titanium, manganese, and calcium, and some alkaline compounds. Coal dust and water are, of course, added substances.

The water content of moulding sand needs controlling. Green-sand moulding requires to be carried out with sand of low moisture content (3–5%); but in dry-sand moulding, more water may be present when making the mould, as this is beneficial in promoting dry bond strength after stoving.

A more recently developed core sand is produced by mixing sand with sodium silicate solution, so that the grains are coated. When the core is completed, CO_2 gas is passed through it, causing the sodium silicate to bond the grains together. This core sand produces very strong cores.

The testing of sand. This has become an important side of the foundry metallurgist's work. There are instruments for testing all the main properties of sand.

Grain size may be tested by washing the sand free from clay and impurities, and then passing it through a series of sieves of different mesh, thus obtaining the proportion of the total amount which falls into each range of particle size. Another test for grain size is by *elutriation*. The sand is acted on by a rising column of water, the velocity of which can be controlled. With low velocities, only the smaller particles will rise with the water, and these are collected. The water velocity is then increased in steps, and larger particles are collected in a series of grades.

Green and dry strengths are tested by preparing a cylindrical specimen, 25 mm^2 cross-sectional area, and approximately 55 mm long. The ramming is done under standardised conditions. In the case of dry specimens, suitable stoving is necessary. The specimen is then placed on end in a machine which applies a gradually increasing compressive force until collapse occurs. The crushing force is read from a scale attached to the machine.

Permeability is determined by noting the time, in seconds, which is required to pass a known volume of air through a standard test piece, the air being maintained at a standard pressure.

9.2.12 Defects in sand-castings. In most engineering processes, a mistake can be seen as soon as it is made; unfortunately, this does not always apply in the moulding shop. The moulder is often faced with a defective casting, but can only conjecture how the defect has arisen. He must then proceed by trial and error, guided by his previous experience. Here lies much of the skill of the craft of moulding. It must be emphasised that the approach of the average moulder is anything but scientific, and prejudice is allowed too much scope. An elementary knowledge of physics is a great virtue in a moulder; it is a pity that it is so rare.

Blowholes are caused by gas trapped in the metal. They are smooth, round or oval holes, with a shiny surface. Trapped gas is caused by insufficient venting of mould or cores, the incorrect placing of risers, too great a moisture content in green-sand moulding, or insufficient stoving in dry-sand moulds. It is sometimes caused by bad pattern and core-box arrangements, which lead to trapping of gases in 'blind' places in the mould.

Scabs are formed when sand breaks away from the mould face, thus leaving a rough lump on the surface of the casting. They may be caused by slack ramming, or metal washing heavily on the mould face. The hidden danger in scabbing is the fact that the loosened sand is *washed into the metal*, and may turn up at some other point when the casting is machined. Smooth lumps on castings are due to the pressure of the metal forcing out the mould face where the ramming has been slack.

Fins are due to badly fitting mould parts, or cores which do not fit snugly in the core prints. They are easily removed, but the result is unsightly in places where a smooth cast surface is desired.

Displaced cores are generally due to the buoyancy of cores in molten metal: cores must be firmly anchored. In long cores, bending must be guarded against by using stiff core irons, and seeing to the correct placing of chaplets.

Misplaced cores are due to the moulder not checking up the various thicknesses when finally assembling the mould and cores. Both displaced and misplaced cores can be extremely dangerous, as the checking of thicknesses in the finished casting may be difficult. Fatal accidents have occurred due to castings having a thin side and a thick side, when everyone thought that the thickness was equal all round.

Drawing is a defect associated with the contraction of the metal in the mould. It is prevalent in thick bosses which remain liquid after the surrounding metal has solidified. Drawing may take the form of minute or fairly large holes with a black surface. The remedy is to 'feed' such places, or to chill the metal, to speed up the rate of cooling to that of the rest of the casting.

Distortion of the casting is due to contraction stresses, and is a symptom that should not be ignored. Designs which lead to distorted castings require modification.

Cold shuts usually occur in thin places where two streams of metal meet. The cooling action of the mould lowers the temperature, and makes the metal sluggish, so that it fails to unite.

9.2.13 The characteristics and application of sand-casting. It will be recalled that the mould must be opened to remove the pattern before the metal is poured in, but that it is broken open to remove the casting; therefore the main limitation of shape, is that associated with the removal of the pattern. The accuracy produced by sand-casting is limited because sand is used for the mould, and by the removal of the pattern (the easing of the pattern from the impression produces 'rapping error' and the separation and reassembly of the mould sections causes 'parting error').

Sand can withstand very high temperatures, and therefore the process is not limited by the melting temperature of the metal to be cast.

The process is rather slow because a mould must be made for every casting that is made, but the capital costs are low compared with other casting methods; the moulding process can be speeded up by mechanisation and by employing shell moulding.

9.3 Die-Casting

When large quantities of very accurate castings are required, die-casting can be used.

This process employs a metallic mould, called a *die*, and so produces good accuracy and finish. There are two methods of die-casting: *gravity die-casting*, in which the metal is poured into a metallic mould, and *pressure die-casting*, in which a machine is used to inject the metal into the metallic mould. The gravity die-casting method is now often called *permanent-mould casting*, and the pressure die-casting method called simply *die-casting*. Both methods of die-casting are suitable for low and medium melting-point metals and alloys.

9.3.1 Gravity die-casting. The gravity die-casting method is very similar to sand-casting, except that the mould is made of metal, and is called a die. Hollow sections can be produced by using cores made of sand or metal; if they are made of metal, it may be necessary to make them in sections for removal. The die faces are usually coated with a refractory material such as French chalk, graphite, or powdered asbestos, to protect them from erosion by the hot metal.

This method produces castings that can be large (maximum mass about 60 kg), and of much better quality than those produced by pressure die-casting. The range of metals that can be cast by this method is wider than that associated with pressure die-casting, as there is no injection system to be contaminated by the metal being cast.

9.3.2 Pressure die-casting. The basic stages in pressure die-casting are:
  (*a*) the forcing of the metal at a suitable temperature and pressure into the closed die, so that it is completely filled,
  (*b*) the opening of the die, and the ejection of the casting and,
  (*c*) the closing of the die, in preparation for stage (*a*).

There are three methods of pressure die-casting. These are (i) the hot-chamber system, (ii) a variation of the hot-chamber system, called the gooseneck system, and (iii) the cold-chamber system.

9.3.3 The hot-chamber system (fig. 9.22). This system is used for alloys of zinc, lead, tin, and similar low melting-point alloys. Of these metals, zinc alloys are the most popular. The most suitable casting pressure is about 10 MN/m^2, with a casting temperature of about 400°C. Under these conditions, since zinc has no affinity for iron, the hot-chamber system is very suitable. From the fig. 9.22, it will be seen that the injection cylinder is immersed in the molten metal. The plunger forces a 'shot' into the die on each down-stroke. The plunger stroke and the die opening and closing movements are synchronised, thus giving a high rate of production (about 200 shots per hour). The die may be such that one large, or several small casting are produced at each shot;

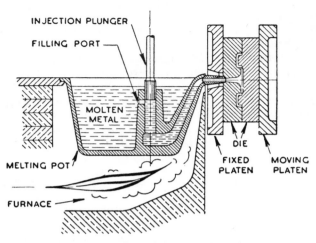

Fig 9.22 Hot-chamber die-casting (*Birmingham Al. Casting Co.*)

when several small castings are produced, they may be identical, or be a 'set' of castings (the reader will no doubt be familiar with the latter, as plastics model kits are of this arrangement).

9.3.4 The gooseneck system (fig. 9.23). This is a variation of the hot-chamber system, developed to offset the limitations associated with

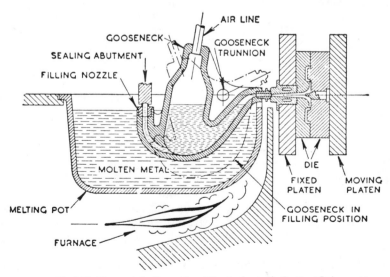

Fig 9.23 Gooseneck die-casting (*Birmingham Al. Casting Co.*)

that system due to the injection system being immersed in the molten metal. The machine is direct-air-operated, and uses a gooseneck pressure chamber that is trunnion-mounted, and operated by a crank mechanism, so that the filling nozzle dips into the molten metal. When the pressure chamber is returned to the casting position, the filling nozzle is sealed, and the injection nozzle makes contact with the entry to the die. Air pressure up to 4 MN/m² inside the vessel forces the metal at high velocity into the die cavity. It is necessary to have the metal in a very fluid condition for satisfactory operation. This type of machine is not so widely used today. It is not suitable for certain alloys—notably aluminium, which has a strong affinity for iron, and tends to 'pick up' this metal from the machine. Castings made by this system tend to be porous, as the injection is less readily controlled than it is in the other die-casting systems.

9.3.5 The cold-chamber system (fig. 9.24) The cold-chamber system is now much favoured. It is the most suitable system for casting aluminium alloys. The cold-chamber is a cylinder into which a plunger is

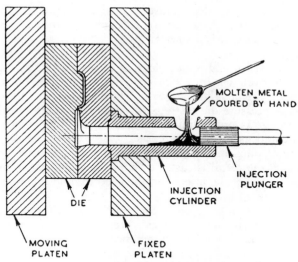

Fig 9.24 Cold-chamber die-casting (*Birmingham Al. Casting Co.*)

fitted. The plunger is operated by a hydraulic press. Molten metal, sufficient for a single shot, is poured into the cylinder, through the aperture at the top, and is then forced into the die by means of the plunger. Pressures between 20 and 180 MN/m² may be used. In the diagram, the metal is being poured by hand, but automatic machines are equipped with mechanical means for ladling the correct charge for each shot. The metal is melted in a separate pot, which can be of graphite or other suitable refractory material; thus there is little risk of metal 'pick-up', as with the other systems. The dies used in this system must be extremely well jointed, and of substantial design, to resist the pressures employed. Castings can be produced by this system at a rate of about 100 shots per hour, and they are of very high accuracy, because of the high pressures that are employed.

9.3.6 Design for die-casting. Components to be die-cast must be very carefully designed to suit the process. It must be realised that the dies cannot be broken to extract the finished casting in the same way that the sand mould is broken to extract the casting in sand-casting, and so the shape must be such that the casting is easily ejected from the dies. The shape must also be such that the dies are easily produced; it should always be borne in mind that the dies are usually cut by rotary cutters, and so the use of standard radii will help the die-sinker. Narrow recesses in the casting mean narrow projections on the die, which will be difficult to machine, and fragile in use. In order to obtain a sound casting, sudden changes of section should be avoided, and, if a heavy boss is unavoidable, it must be placed close to the sprue. It is usual for the casting and the dies to be designed by the same person, to ensure that the casting is a success.

9.3.7 Characteristics and applications of die-casting. Die-casting produces very accurate castings with good surface texture, but the shape must allow easy removal from the die. The dies are costly to make and, in the case of pressure die-casting, the equipment is also costly; therefore this process is only suitable for large quantities, where the time saved will compensate for these costs.

Die-castings often include inserts such as studs and plain bearings around which the metal is cast; this eliminates the cost of machining the casting to accept the insert and the need to hold fine tolerances to obtain the required fit.

This process is only suitable for fairly low melting temperature alloys because metal dies are used; pressure die-casting introduces limitations associated with 'contamination'.

9.4 Investment-Casting
This process is used to produce accurate and complicated castings, and is not limited by the melting temperature of the metal to be cast; it employs an expendable pattern, around which the mould is built up (the pattern is said to be 'invested'). The temperature of the mould is raised, causing the mould to become hard, and the pattern material to be melted, so that it runs from the mould. Figure 9.25 illustrates the stages involved in the production of a casting by this method.

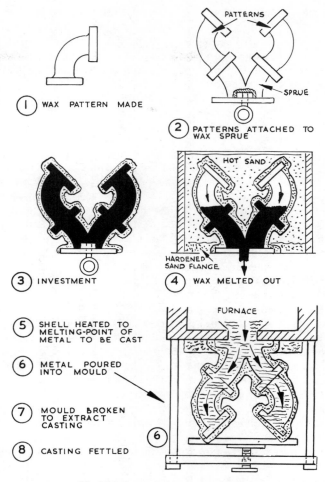

① WAX PATTERN MADE

② PATTERNS ATTACHED TO WAX SPRUE

③ INVESTMENT

④ WAX MELTED OUT

⑤ SHELL HEATED TO MELTING-POINT OF METAL TO BE CAST

⑥ METAL POURED INTO MOULD

⑦ MOULD BROKEN TO EXTRACT CASTING

⑧ CASTING FETTLED

Fig 9.25 Stages in investment casting

9.4.1. As already stated, a pattern is required for each casting. It is made from a low melting-point material, usually wax, and is produced by injecting the material into a metal die, using a machine. The die is in sections, so that it can be 'peeled' from the pattern. The pattern is cleaned up, and is attached to a wax runner (called a 'sprue'). Several small patterns may be attached to one sprue; the joining of the patterns and sprue is done by local melting of the patterns and sprue. The assembly is mounted on a base-plate for ease of handling. A refractory shell is gradually built up around the pattern(s) and sprue, first using a

Table 9.1 *Comparison of Casting Methods*

	Sand-Casting	Die-Casting	Investment-Casting
Shapes that can be cast	Limited by removal of pattern from mould (but pattern can be made in sections). Hollow shapes can be cast	Limited by removal of casting from die. Hollow shapes can be cast by the 'gravity' method but not by the 'pressure' method (sand would collapse)	Not limited
Accuracy	Rather poor due to sand. Parting error and rapping error (because of pattern removal) also present	Good, but parting error (because of casting removal) also present	Good—no parting error because mould is one-piece
Finish	Poor—due to sand	Very good	Very good
Choice of metal	Not limited by melting temperature	Limited by melting temperature and by injector contamination	Not limited by melting temperature
Economics	This is slow and therefore costly, but is suitable for small quantities	This is costly due to die costs and equipment cost, but economical for large quantities	Very costly, but may be the cheapest, or only method of manufacture of awkward shapes

liquid refractory, and then spraying on a fine-grain solid refractory. The investment is dried, and the process is repeated several times, so that a thick shell is produced around the pattern.

The investment is then heated to about 350°C, to melt out the pattern material, and to harden the shell. There are several methods of heating the investment at this stage, and in the version shown it is done by surrounding the investment with hot sand. The sand may be kept in place around the mould, if support is needed during the casting operation. The mould is finally fired by heating it to a higher temperature; this heating also prevents chilling during the casting operation that follows.

9.4.2. The metal to be cast is melted in a small carbon-arc furnace that is trunnion-mounted, so that it can be inverted during the pouring operation. The hot mould is clamped to the mouth of the furnace, which is then inverted (stage 6 in fig. 9.25). Compressed air is used to ensure that the molten metal is packed into the mould. The mould is removed from the mouth of the furnace, and is set aside to cool. Finally, it is broken open, to remove the casting, which is then fettled.

9.4.3 Characteristics and Applications of Investment-Casting. The investment-casting process is expensive, but as there is no problem regarding the removal of the pattern (it is melted out) or of the casting (the mould is broken open), it can be used to produce components that are of awkward shape. The accuracy of casting produced by this method is very high, and so little or no machining is necessary; this process is therefore suitable for materials that are difficult to machine, and for shapes that are difficult or awkward to machine.

This process was originally used in ancient China, and was later used in dental work, and in the manufacture of jewellery. It was more recently developed for the production of gas-turbine parts, because of the need to minimise or eliminate machining, on account of the shapes or the material being difficult to machine. It is now also being used for certain motor-car engine parts, and for high-class castings for model engineers.

9.5 Comparison of Sand-, Die-, and Investment-Casting
When selecting the casting method to be used, the shape, accuracy, finish, material and economics must be taken into account as indicated in table 9.1

9.6 Centrifugal-casting
Centrifugal-casting involves the casting of metal into a rapidly rotating mould; this usually produces a denser and more homogeneous casting than is obtained when other methods are used. Figure 9.26(*a*) illus-

trates 'true' centrifugal casting; in this method, a thin-walled cylindrical casting is produced without using a core (long castings are
produced by rotating about a horizontal axis, and pouring from two
runners that start half way along the axis, and move outwards, in opposite directions). Figure 9.26(b) illustrates semi-centrifugal casting—this
is very similar to 'true' centrifugal casting except that a core is used. The
variation shown in fig. 9.26(c) is called centrifuging; in this method, the

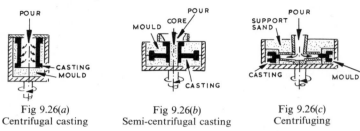

Fig 9.26(a)	Fig 9.26(b)	Fig 9.26(c)
Centrifugal casting	Semi-centrifugal casting	Centrifuging

runner is 'spoked', like a wheel, and a mould is attached to the end of
each 'spoke', so that each is filled under centrifugal force (this method
is often used in conjunction with investment casting).

9.7 Full mould (or cavity-less casting)
In all the casting processes so far described, the pattern is removed
from the mould before casting, or else no pattern is used to produce
the mould. In the full mould method the pattern is not removed from
the mould before the metal is poured in, but is burned out by the hot
metal. This enables extremely awkwardly shaped castings to be produced without loose pieces and cores, and the mould can be in one
piece. The pattern is made from expanded polystyrene (this is the
material from which domestic insulation tiles and packaging is made);
it can be cut and joined using a suitable adhesive, and the mould is
produced using ordinary foundry methods. So far, full mould casting
has been used only for small-quantity work.

Summary
1 The casting process consists of pouring molten metal into a suitable impression, allowing it to solidify, and then removing it from
   the impression.
2 In the sand-casting process, the impression is made in sand.
3 The sand-casting process is a three-stage process: (a) the moulding
   stage (manufacture of the impression), (b) the pouring stage, and
   (c) the fettling stage (cleaning the casting ready for machining).
4 The impression may be made 'freehand', but more usually a pattern is used. The pattern is similar to the finished casting. The

casting must be designed so that the pattern can be removed after the impression has been made.

5 Hollow castings can be produced using 'cores' made from a suitable sand.

6 The sand-casting process can be speeded up by the use of plate moulds, and mechanical moulding machines.

7 Casting defects can be caused by faulty casting metal, poor casting design, faulty pattern and moulding, or by incorrect pouring.

8 Sand-casting is a slow process that does not produce very accurate castings. Die-casting and investment-casting produce very accurate castings. Investment-casting can produce more intricate castings, but is slower.

9 Die-casting uses a permanent mould made of metal. Die-casting is limited by the melting-point of the mould metal, and by the need to be able to remove the finished casting from the metal mould.

10 Die-casting processes can be classified as (a) gravity die-casting, and (b) pressure die-casting. Gravity die-casting is similar to sand-casting, except that a metallic mould is used. Pressure die-casting uses a machine to inject the molten metal into the mould (die).

11 Die-castings must be carefully designed to suit the process.

12 Investment-casting uses a pattern for each casting. The pattern is invested (covered with the mould material), and melted out to produce the mould.

13 The investment-casting process can be used to produce castings that would not be produced by other processes, and can be performed with a high degree of accuracy and finish. The casting process is expensive, but must be evaluated in conjunction with the cost of the possibility of producing the part by other methods.

14 Centrifugal-casting involves pouring into a rapidly rotating mould and produces denser and more homogeneous castings than when other methods are used.

15 Full mould casting uses a pattern that is burned away when the molten metal is poured into the mould with the pattern still in there.

Questions

Set A

1 Describe the process of making the complete mould for a large cast-iron elbow pipe, the lower half of the mould being in the shop floor.

2 What are the essential properties of a good moulding sand? Describe the tests which may be applied to moulding sand to determine (a) its green strength, (b) the grain size.

3   Describe (*a*) odd-side moulding, (*b*) the use of chaplets. What is a
     core print? Describe an application of a 'loose piece' on a pattern.
4   Write brief notes on the following moulding-shop operations:
     withdrawing the pattern, feeding, venting.
5   Discuss the advantages and limitations of plate moulding.
6   Describe the process of making a loam mould for a large rect-
     angular pipe.
7   Describe the following defects in a casting, and briefly explain
     how they are prevented: scabs, drawing, cold shuts.
8   What are the advantages of shot-blasting over hand-fettling of
     castings? Describe the main points of a small shot-blasting
     cabinet.
9   Reducing the dimensional tolerances on a die-casting almost in-
     variably increases the cost. Suggest reasons for this.
10   By means of suitable examples, discuss the relative merits of die
     castings and drop forgings.
11   What are the advantages claimed for die-casting, compared with
     sand-casting?
12   Under what circumstances would gravity die-casting be used
     rather than pressure die-casting?
13   What are the circumstances that brought about the development
     of investment-casting as an engineering process?

Set B (questions requiring further study)
14   Describe the method by which a simple iron casting is made with
     the aid of a loose pattern.
15   Contrast the relative merits of iron and steel castings.
16   Write notes on designing for sand casting.
17   Write notes on designing for die-casting.
18   Discuss the factors that must be examined when selecting the
     casting process to be used for a component.

Chapter 10
Working Methods

10.1 Introduction to working methods

A metal or alloy is usually produced in the molten state, and then solidified in a mould. If the solidified metal is in the finished—but unmachined—shape, it is called a *casting*; but, if in a simple form, it is called an *ingot*, *slug*, or *blank*. (These terms refer mainly to the size, but the usage of the terms varies from locality to locality.)

The ingot, slug, or blank is usually manipulated into a form nearer to that of the finished material, by rolling, hitting, squeezing, etc. These processes are known as working processes, and the material is said to be wrought. Material to be wrought must be ductile or malleable, or be made so, either by heating during the working process, or by heat-treatment before the process.

10.1.1. Working processes are broadly classified as (*a*) *hot-working processes*, and (*b*) *cold-working processes*. Hot-working is done at a temperature high enough to ensure that there are no residual stresses after the working has been completed (each metal or alloy has a temperature range within which it should be hot-worked); and cold-working is done at a lower temperature (usually room temperature), so that the material becomes work-hardened as a result of distortion of the grains of which the material is comprised.

10.1.2. When a metal or alloy is wrought, a so-called *fibre* or *grain flow* is produced, by elongation of the impurities between the grains, and orientation of the grains; the direction of the fibre is at right angles to the direction of the stresses which act upon the material during the working. Working produces directional properties that can be likened to the directional properties associated with the grain of wood (fig. 10.1). Figure 10.2 shows the grain fibre developed when a crankshaft is forged—this produces the variation in the directional strength demanded by the crankshaft if it is to be strong enough to resist the high stresses that will be applied to it when in service.

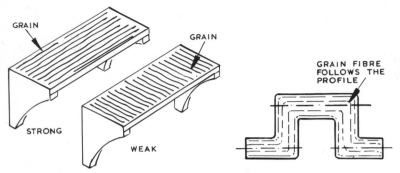

Fig 10.1 Grain fibre   Fig 10.2 Grain fibre in forged crankshaft

10.2 Wrought forms

Before considering working methods, it will be as well to study some of
the common wrought forms.

10.2.1 Bar. Bar is a common rolling-mill product, and may be obtained
in round, square, rectangular, and hexagonal sections. Round bar
ranges from about 5 mm to 250 mm in diameter; rectangular bar from
9 mm × 12 mm to 50 mm × 300 mm; square and hexagonal sections
up to 150 mm across are typical. Mild steel, medium carbon steel, and
alloy steel are commonly supplied in the form of black bar; the surface
of black scale is due to the oxidisation of the steel by the atmosphere,
during the hot-rolling. Generally, the corners of all black bar are
slightly rounded.

Another form that is similar to bar is the billet used for forging
down. Small billets are merely suitable bar cut off to length, but larger
sizes are rolled to dimensions requested by the customer.

10.2.2 Bright-drawn bar. This is produced by drawing bar through
shaped dies, to produce bar with a smooth surface, and of accurate
size. Material in this form is particularly useful because small parts are
commonly turned using capstan, turret, or automatic lathes. These
machines use a self-centring chuck which feeds the bar forward as
required, and which can be used with success only upon accurate bar.
Many parts can be designed with a considerable length of parallel
cross-section, and if the other portions are of smaller size, and turned
down from bright bar, there will be a considerable saving in machining
time. A part with a hexagonal or square portion, and the remainder
round, may be turned from hexagonal or square bar; similarly, nuts
are produced from hexagonal bar that is drilled, tapped, and parted off
to length.

The drawing operation work-hardens the surface of bright-drawn bar, the depth of this hardening depending on the severity of the drawing. This work-hardening is sometimes a disadvantage if the bar is to be heated during a joining operation, because distortion will probably occur; and the same difficulty may arise if the work-hardened surface is machined away at certain points. When distortion must be avoided, the bar may be annealed, and the bright surface retained, if necessary, by bright annealing. It should be noted that bright bar is stronger but less ductile than black bar.

High carbon and alloy tool steels can also be obtained in round and square bar, for machining, and for forging into tools of various shapes. Of particular interest is the precision centreless-ground high carbon steel bar, which is produced to within about 0·005 mm of specified size. This bar is used for dowels and guide-pins, particularly in jig and press-tool work.

10.2.3 Rolled sections. The commonest rolled sections are angles, channels, and joists of steel with about 0·25% carbon. The sizes produced range from 120-mm × 120-mm angle to 600-mm × 200-mm joists. The principal use of rolled sections is in constructional work, but many engineering parts which were formerly cast in iron are now being built up by welding rolled sections and plate.

10.2.4 Sheet. Hot-rolled and cold-rolled sheet is available in a range of metals and alloys, and over a wide range of sizes. The type of rolling used, and also the accuracy and finish, depends upon the use to which the sheet will be put. Tin-coated steel sheet (tin-plate) has a thin coating of tin on each side, and is used extensively for food canning, and small semi-ornamental articles, such as kitchen equipment and fancy goods. The finish is rust-proof with normal usage, and joints may readily be soldered—this is a useful point for sealed food cans. Tin-terne steel sheets have a coating of tin–lead alloy, and are cheaper than pure tin-coated steels; lead-coated steel sheets are cheaper still. Lead-coated steel sheet is used for machinery guards, and fairly large press work; it can be painted or enamelled after the part is shaped, as it is free from rusting.

The most suitable steel sheet for outside use is galvanised sheet, but if this sheet is worked or heated for bending, welding, or riveting, the zinc surface will be damaged; so many articles are produced from ordinary mild steel sheets, cleaned after the working or joining is completed, and then dipped in a bath of molten zinc. Aluminium alloy sheet is often clad with pure aluminium during the hot-rolling process, to give an improved corrosion resistance.

10.2.5 Plate. Mild steel plate is hot-rolled to a thickness between 3 mm and 80 mm; the thickest plate normally stocked, however, is about 30 mm. Plates are used in shipwork, boilers, heavy tanks, and vessels of all descriptions; and, as already mentioned, they are increasingly being used as a substitute for cast iron.

10.2.6 Tube. Tube is produced in three ways: solid drawn, for heavy duties; seam welded; and close jointed. The solid-drawn mild steel tube is used for hydraulic, high-pressure steam, and oil services. Seam-welded tube is made from a strip of suitable width, which is hot-drawn to circular form, and the joint, which may be lapped or butted, is pressure-welded. It is used for water and gas services at moderate pressures. Electric conduit is made from a thinner strip, which is brought to a circular form, and the joint well closed, but not usually welded.

10.2.7 Wire. Wire is usually cold-drawn through dies. The drawing operation work-hardens the material, and so the wire is finally annealed if it is to be bent at a later stage.

10.2.8 Extruded sections. The extrusion process is used to produce lengths of material with very simple or very complicated cross-section. Extruded sections are used for light alloy window frames, banisters and similar architectural applications, as well as for aircraft spars and stringers. Until recently, the extrusion process was applied only to light alloys, and other suitable non-ferrous metals and alloys; but the extrusion of steel is now becoming more common.

10.2.9 Forgings. The forms already described are 'lengths' of material of uniform cross-section: forgings differ from these forms in that a forging is associated with one part, such as a crankshaft, connecting-rod, or driving-shaft.

10.3 Hot-working processes
As already stated, hot-working is done within a temperature range to suit the material, so that there will be no residual stresses in it after the working is completed. This implies that hot-working does not produce the same strength as does cold-working; similarly, because of the heating, hot-working produces less accurate and rougher parts than does cold-working. Hot-working enables a greater and more rapid deformation to be achieved; sometimes material is first hot-worked, and later cold-worked to develop the required strength and accuracy—hot-rolling followed by cold-rolling, and hot-rolling followed by drawing are typical examples of this.

10.3.1 Hot-rolling. Plates, angles, channels, sheets, bars, and rails are typical hot-rolled products; they are all produced by passing the materials between rotating rollers (called 'rolls') so that it becomes longer and thinner. The thickness of the material is progressively reduced by passing it between the rolls several times, reducing the gap between them before each pass. The shape of the material is controlled by the shape of the rollers (see fig. 10.4). The assembly of rolls, framework, motor, drive, and controls is called a 'stand', and a 'mill' is a collection of stands. The shape may be produced by one stand, or by passing the material through several stands in turn.

Figure 10.3 shows some typical roll arrangements. Figure 10.3(*a*) is the simplest arrangement, but requires either that the material be taken to the front before each pass, or that the rotation of the rolls be reversed to allow it to pass backwards between the rolls. The three-high arrangement shown in fig. 10.3(*b*) enables the material to be fed back through a different 'gap' between the rolls, which may therefore be non-reversing. The amount of stress acting upon the material being

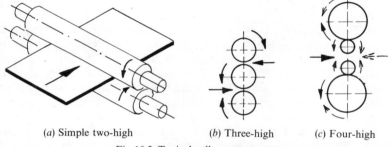

(*a*) Simple two-high   (*b*) Three-high   (*c*) Four-high

Fig 10.3 Typical roll arrangements

rolled depends upon the force on the rolls, and upon their diameter (the stress increasing with reduction of roll diameter); if the rolls are of small diameter, they will tend to deflect—but this can be prevented by introducing 'backing rolls', as shown in the four-high arrangement in fig. 10.3(*c*). The four-high arrangement is a reversing system—the non-reversing equivalent requires seven rolls.

All the material to be rolled starts as an ingot, which is rolled on a cogging mill (with an arrangement as shown in fig. 10.3(*a*)) to reduce its

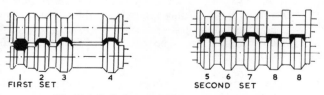

FIRST SET   SECOND SET

Fig 10.4 Rolls for producing a channel section

thickness, and to start to develop grain fibre. The rolled 'bloom' is reheated, and then re-rolled to produce the final shape. Plane sheets are rolled between plain cylinders; but angles, channels, etc., require special rolls which are grooved to produce a series of 'gaps' between which the material is rolled. Figure 10.4 shows the 'gaps' between the two pairs of rolls to be used when rolling a channel section.

10.3.2 Extrusion. Long lengths of continuous section can be produced by extrusion, in which the heated billet is placed in a heated container, and pushed through an orifice (called the *die*) by a hydraulic ram. Figure 10.5(*a*) illustrates the principle of extrusion. Tubular and similar sections can be extruded by using a mandrel that restricts the space in the die. The billet may be pierced by the mandrel as shown in fig.

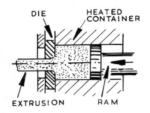

Fig 10.5(*a*) Principle of extrusion

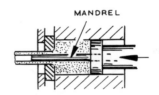

Fig 10.5(*b*) Extrusion of a tubular section using a mandrel

10.5(*b*), so that the latter can take up its position within the die opening; or, alternatively, the billet may be bored before it is heated.

10.3.3 Forging. In hand-forging, the heated metal is hammered, in conjunction with simple tools. The basic operations are *upsetting*, in which the section thickness is increased at the expense of length, and *drawing down* (and *setting down*), in which the length is increased at the expense

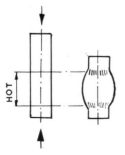

Fig 10.6 Upsetting

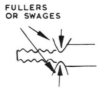

Fig 10.7(*a*) Drawing down

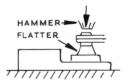

Fig 10.7(*b*) Setting down

of section thickness. These operations are illustrated in figs 10.6 and 10.7. Large but simple forgings are also produced by using simple tools, but the force is supplied by a machine-hammer or press. Smaller parts can be produced in quantity by *die-forging* (or *drop-stamping*), in which the material is struck many blows between *dies* that are mounted in a machine. The blows are continued until the faces of the dies meet.

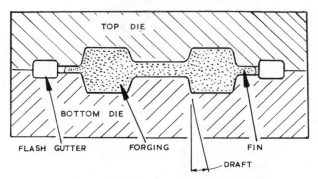

Fig 10.8 Forging dies

Figure 10.8 shows the section through a typical pair of forging dies; it will be seen that the excess metal flows into the flash gutter around the impression, to form a 'fin'. It also illustrates that the part to be forged must be designed with a 'draft', so that the dies can also have a draft, to assist in freeing the forging. Figure 10.9 shows two stages in the production of a forged part; the 'fin' is removed to leave a 'flash'. When designing a forging, it must be remembered that the die faces must lie along the section with the largest 'area', and also that the flash must be easily removed, or be in such a position that it can be allowed to remain without detriment to the function or appearance of the part.

(a)   (b)

Fig 10.9 Two stages in the production of a forged part

10.5 Cold-working processes

Many metals have sufficient ductility to be worked cold. Cold-working may vary from a simple bend to the great deformation produced by deep pressing and tube drawing; in all cases, work-hardening occurs to some extent, depending upon the material and the amount of cold work. The phenomenon of work-hardening is illustrated by fig. 10.10.

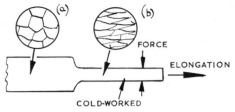

Fig 10.10 Work-hardening

The structure of metals is crystalline, the size of each crystal (or grain) being between 0·25 mm and 3 mm across. After cold-working, the crystalline structure is deformed—the grains are elongated in the direction in which the metal is drawn out.

The result of cold-work is to increase the hardness and tensile strength, but to decrease the ductility and shock resistance: the structure shown at (*b*) in fig. 10.10 is typical of a cold-worked metal. During cold-work, therefore, the metal becomes more difficult to work, and the danger of cracking increases. If the duty of the component is light, and the cold-working is not severe, then the work-hardening produced is unimportant, and in fact the greater strength and hardness may be an advantage. However, where considerable cold-work is to be performed, the part may be softened by annealing, so that the original crystal structure is restored, and the metal regains its original softness and capacity for cold-work. (Annealing consists of heating the metal to a suitable temperature, holding it at that temperature, and then cooling it at a suitable rate. In the case of steels, the cooling must be very slow, but in other cases it is not of special importance.)

10.4.1 Cold rolling. Strips and sheets are cold-rolled in a four-high mill (see fig. 10.3(*c*)). The thickness can be maintained to very close limits, and the surface is very smooth, and may even be polished.

10.4.2 Pressing. Sheet metal can be pressed to shape between formers, as shown in fig. 10.11: the production of car bodies is a typical example of pressing.

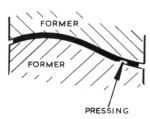

Fig 10.11 Pressing sheet metal

10.4.3 Deep drawing. Sheet metal can be drawn and stretched into cup-like shapes by a process called deep drawing, using press-tool techniques, fig. 10.12.

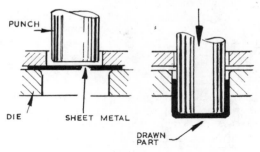

Fig 10.12 Deep drawing

10.4.4 Wire drawing. Rod or wire can be pulled through a die (fig. 10.13) to produce improved accuracy and finish, as well as improved mechanical properties, which arise as a result of the combined squeezing and pulling.

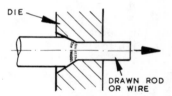

Fig 10.13 Wire drawing

10.4.5 Tube drawing. A tube that has been cast or hot-worked to a suitable bore, outside diameter, and length, can be drawn to improve its accuracy and strength. The material is supported internally by a mandrel, and drawn through a series of hardened dies, each 'draw' reducing the wall thickness, and increasing the tube length. This process is illustrated by fig. 10.14.

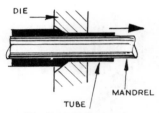

Fig 10.14 Tube drawing

10.4.6 Impact (or cold) extrusion. In this process, a slug of metal, pre-formed as required, is placed in a die, and struck by the punch. The metal can be extruded forwards (fig. 10.15(*a*)), backwards (fig. 10.15(*b*)), or in both directions at once.

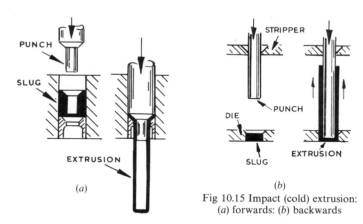

(*a*)

Fig 10.15 Impact (cold) extrusion:
(*a*) forwards: (*b*) backwards

10.4.7 Embossing and coining. These are similar processes, using a punch and die set. In the embossing process (fig. 10.16), thin sheet is located in the die, and then locally bent and formed by the punch, without very much alteration to its thickness. In the coining process (fig. 10.17), a thin slug of metal is struck by the punch, so that the die and punch shapes are filled by local extrusion and indentation.

Fig 10.16 Embossing

Fig 10.17 Coining

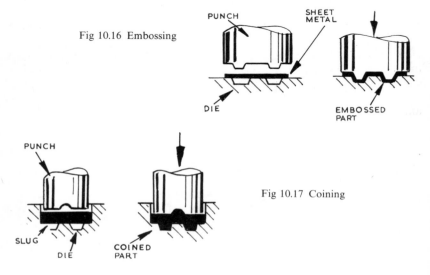

10.4.8 Spinning. Sheet metal can be made into hollow shapes of circular cross-section by spinning. This process is cheaper than pressing, when a small number of thin parts is required, since a simple high-speed lathe, a wooden former, and a set of simple tools is the only apparatus required. Figure 10.18 illustrates the principle of spinning, and shows

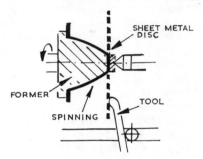

Fig 10.18 The principle of spinning

the rotating former, and the sheet held against it by a 'pallet' in the tail-stock. The sheet and the tools are kept well lubricated with tallow, and the sheet is gradually eased to the shape of the former by the tool held either under the arm or over the shoulder of the operator, and pivoted on the round pin. The pin is placed in a suitable hole in the rest, at the front of the lathe, and moved to 'follow up' the shape being produced. The spinning tools are about one metre long, and the fulcrum point is about 200 mm from the operating end of the tool, so that there is a good leverage. Necked parts can be spun using a collapsible former, so that the sections of the former can be withdrawn in turn through the neck. With special tools, various beads and ornamental edges can be formed.

10.4.9 Cold-heading. This is a method of forging heads on small and medium-sized screws, bolts, etc. The blank is usually a piece of wire of suitable length and cross-section (fig. 10.19); one end is cold-forged in dies, to form the desired shape of head. The part may need to be annealed after cold-heading.

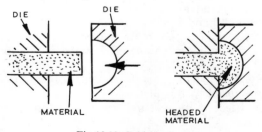

Fig 10.19 Cold-heading

Summary

1 A metal or alloy is usually produced in the molten state, and solidified in a mould. If the cast shape is then manipulated in the solid state, the product is said to be wrought.

2 If the working produces residual stresses, the process is said to be cold-working; but if it does not produce residual stresses, the process is said to be hot-working. Cold-working is not necessarily a room-temperature operation, and hot-working is not necessarily done at a high temperature.

3 Cold-working produces increased strength and hardness, known as 'work-hardening'. It is produced by distortion of the grains during the working, which is not relieved by heat.

4 Working produces grain fibre, by orientation of the grains, and elongation of impurities; this results in directional properties. The direction is related to the shape of the part, and so the material and its shape must be considered against the properties required.

5 Wrought forms can be grouped into those that are long lengths, and those that are individual components. Drawn bar, rolled sections, sheet and plate, tube, wire, and extruded sections are typical 'long length' forms. A forging is an 'individual component' form.

6 Hot-rolling, extrusion, and forging are hot-working processes.

7 Cold-rolling, pressing, deep drawing, impact extrusion, embossing, coining, spinning, and cold-heading are typical cold-working operations.

8 The choice of manipulation process depends upon the material to be manipulated, the shape required, the accuracy required, and the quantity involved.

Questions

Set A

1 (a) What is the difference in action between the power hammer and the hydraulic press?
(b) Discuss the advantages and disadvantages of drop-forging compared with hand-forging.

2 (a) Name two articles which are shaped by cold-working.
(b) What properties of a material make it suitable for cold-working?

3 (a) Briefly describe the process of drop-forging, and name two articles produced by this method.
(b) What defect would occur if steel were forged at too low a temperature?

4 Why is sheet metal annealed before it is cold-worked? If a sheet

has to be heated for annealing, why should it not be hot-worked to shape?

5 Explain what is meant by galvanised sheet-steel, and describe some of its uses.

6 Name four types of sheet-steel, explain briefly how each is prepared, and give one use for each type.

7 What is bright-drawn bar, and how is it used? Discuss its advantages and limitations.

8 Give brief definitions of the following terms: billet, terne plate, seam-welded tube, free-cutting steel, rolled section.

9 Complete the following table, using one of the following terms in each case: good, fair, poor, none. Each material is in its softest state.

Material	Machining	Cold-working	Hot-working	Harden by quenching
grey cast iron				
mild steel				
1·0% carbon steel				
70/30 brass				
60/40 brass				
aluminium				

Set B (questions requiring further study)

10 Compare a hot-rolled section with a cold-rolled section, with respect to (*a*) dimensional accuracy, (*b*) finish, and (*c*) mechanical properties.

11 In what way does extrusion give better freedom of design than does rolling? What are the limitations associated with extrusion?

12 Explain why forging produces better mechanical properties than does casting.

Chapter 11
Powder Metallurgy

11.1 Introduction to powder metallurgy

It has been stated in Chapters 9 and 10, that when a metal or alloy is manipulated it is usually heated to make it molten, and then it is poured into a mould where it is cooled so that it solidifies. The cast shape may be the finished shape (or very near to the finished shape), or it may be a convenient rough shape that is further manipulated into shape in the solid state. Powder metallurgy differs from other processes in that at the very start of manipulation the metal or alloy is solid, and remains completely solid, or in some cases almost completely solid during the manipulation process.

11.1.1. Powder metallurgy was originally developed because manipulation processes involving melting were unsuitable in the following circumstances:

(a) When metals were required to be 'mixed' to produce special properties, but could not be alloyed because they will not form a liquid solution.

(b) When alloying is impossible because the difference between their melting points is such that one would become a gas before the other had melted.

(c) When melting and solidification causes the quality to be poor.

(d) When melting causes the loss of identity of the constituents (for example, when a cutting material consisting of a mixture of tungsten-carbide and cobalt is produced, powder metallurgy must be used because melting would cause the tungsten-carbide to break down).

One problem associated with the manufacture of shapes by using powder metallurgy has been that of high porosity. This problem has been overcome; however, by controlling the extent of porosity, the process is also used to produce porous parts such as plain bearings that are later impregnated with oil for use where the application of oil would cause trouble; more recently, the combination of large particles and controlled porosity has been used to produce filters.

As the powder metallurgy process is very rapid and can produce parts with excellent dimensional accuracy and surface finish, it is now used for the manufacture of parts of suitable shape, where the quantities required make this process more economical than other methods. Powder metallurgy does not produce such a high strength as that obtained by processes involving melting, but provided the product is strong enough for the application, this does not cause any great difficulties.

11.1.2. Figure 11.1 shows the sequence of operations involved in the manufacture of parts using powder metallurgy. The basic operations are (1) the *preparation* and *blending* of the powders, (2) the *pressing* (or

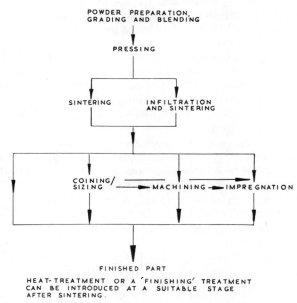

Fig 11.1 Sequence of operations involved in powder metallurgy

compacting) of the powders, and (3) the *sintering* of the compacted powders. The sintering process consists of heating the compacted powders at a temperature that is usually lower than the melting point of the metals or alloy involved (but in certain cases one of the constituents is allowed to become molten). A part produced by powder metallurgy is often termed a 'sintered part'.

11.2 The preparation, grading, and blending of the powder
Before being made into powder the metal is extracted from its ore using the usual processes or converted into an oxide; if appropriate,

the metal is further treated to make it into an alloy. The method used to produce the powder depends upon the metal to be powdered and the required shape of the powder particles; the properties of the product depend to a large extent upon the shape and size of the particles.

11.2.1 The preparation of the powder. The principal preparation methods are:

Mechanical disintegration. Mechanical methods such as hammering, milling, and grinding can be applied to the more brittle metals and alloys; the particles so produced are directed into the separator unit in a stream of gas.

Atomisation. In this process, a stream of molten metal is broken down into solid spherical or tear-shaped particles by high pressure jets of air, steam, gas, or liquid, and collected in a dust collector. This is the most commonly used method.

Electrolytic deposition. The metal to be powdered by this method is put into solution in an electrolyte, through which current is passed, and metal powder is deposited on a suitable cathode, from which it is removed. Powders produced by this method are of high purity, have a regular shape and are easy to compress; they are used extensively in the production of porous bearings.

Chemical methods (including reduction, condensation, and precipitation). The reduction process involves reduction from the oxide using a reducing gas and produces very fine particles. In the condensation process, the metal is boiled and the vapour condensed; in the precipitation process, the metal is caused to become displaced, in the form of powder, from a solution.

After the powder is made it is washed before grading.

11.2.2 Grading. The powdered metal is carefully graded according to particle size to suit the application. The particles may be as small as 0·001 mm diameter.

11.2.3 Blending. Graded powders are weighed out according to the properties required of the mix, and thoroughly blended by tumbling for several hours. At the blending stage, a solid pressing lubricant such as fatty acid, stearic acid, or metal stearate is added to allow the metal powder to be compacted without galling or excessive die wear.

11.3 The pressing (or compacting) operation
The blended powders are cold pressed by extrusion, rolling, or, more commonly, by pressing between a punch and die set (similar to presswork—see chapter 13); this produces the required density and shape, and causes the particles to become joined together by cold-welding.

The pressure required for cold-welding depends upon the metal and the properties to be produced, but may be as low as 75 N/mm^2 or as high as 900 N/mm^2. Figure 11.2 illustrates pressing using a punch and die set to produce a plain bearing; a double acting press is used

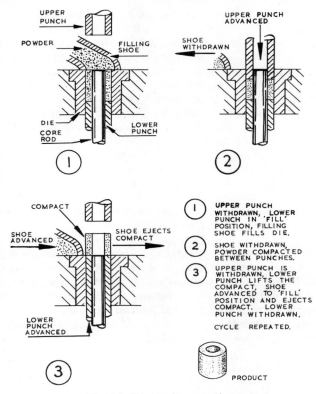

Fig 11.2 The pressing operation

to obtain uniform pressure and to eject the compact (pressing or briquette). This is usually a very rapid process; up to 300 parts are produced per hour using a hydraulic press, and up to 1500 parts are produced per hour using a mechanical press. The punch and die are usually made from hardened steel, but sometimes a tungsten carbide punch and die may be used.

When designing a part to be produced by powder metallurgy, great care must be taken to ensure that its shape is such that the powder will receive uniform pressure during the pressing stage, that the pressing can be removed easily and intact from the die, and that the punch and die can be easily made and do not wear out too rapidly.

11.4 The sintering operation

The compact is strong enough to be handled, but not strong enough for service; it must therefore be subjected to a further operation, called sintering, to develop additional strength.

The sintering operation consists of heating the compact to a temperature that is usually below that of its constituents so that grain growth occurs, combined with diffusion across the surfaces that were joined by cold-working during the pressing operation. Sometimes the compact is heated to a temperature that is high enough to cause one of the constituents to melt and flow between the particles of the other constituent or constituents, to 'cement' them together (an example of this is the manufacture of cemented carbide cutting tool materials; these consist of tungsten carbide set in a matrix of cobalt—the latter being melted during the sintering operation). Sintering is done in a controlled atmosphere because oxidation would cause the bond to be weak; the duration of the heating depends upon the constituents and the properties that are to be developed, and may take only a few minutes or, in special cases, very many hours. Special materials such as magnet materials usually require a low temperature sintering (called *pre-sintering*), followed by a number of further sintering operations at various temperature and for various durations.

11.4.1 Infiltration. It has been stated earlier that the problem of porosity has been overcome. Infiltration is one of the methods used to overcome this problem; it consists of filling the pores with a lower melting point metal by capillary action. This is usually done by passing the compact with the infiltrant laid on top, through the sintering furnace, (typical examples of infiltration are iron and steel, strengthened by using copper as the infiltrant).

11.5 Sizing and coining

The sintered part may be cold-worked to improve its accuracy and mechanical properties; this is done by repressing it in a die that is similar to the original pressing die. Sizing produces better dimensional accuracy without significantly increasing the density. Coining significantly increases the density, improving the mechanical properties, and also improves the dimensional accuracy and surface finish.

11.6 Impregnation with lubricant

A suitable high porosity part can be impregnated with a lubricant to produce a self-lubricating bearing for use where usual lubrication would cause contamination of parts in the vicinity (for example, in food mixers and washing machines), or where a 'maintenance-free' part is required. The lubricant can be lubricating oil, lanolin, lanolin lubricating oil mixture, or a solid lubricant such as P.T.F.E., molybdenum disulphide, or graphite.

11.7 Machining
When a part includes features that cannot be produced directly by powder metallurgy because of shape or because an extremely high degree of accuracy is required, the sintered part can be finished using conventional metal-removal operations.

11.8 Heat-treatment
A sintered part that is produced from a powdered heat-treatable alloy, or is produced from a mixture of metals that responds to heat-treatment, can be subjected to heat-treatment in the same way as a part produced by casting or working; such treatment is usually followed by machining to remove distortion caused by quenching.

11.9 Advantages and limitations of powder metallurgy as a production process

11.9.1. The advantages can be summarised as follows:
1. Shapes can be produced that would be impossible or very awkward to produce by machining.
2. Costs are reduced because, by careful design, machining is eliminated or reduced.
3. A number of parts can often be combined as a single part.
4. Controlled porosity can be obtained.

11.9.2. The limitations can be summarised as follows:
1. The tooling costs for the pressing operation are high, and the production quantity must be in excess of 10 000 to make the process economical.
2. The shape of the part must be such that the powder is subjected to uniform pressure at the pressing stage and so produce uniform properties, and it must be such that the compact is readily removed from the die (awkward features can be machined later).
3. Not all metals and alloys are suitable for powder metallurgy.
4. The strength and toughness of a part produced by powder metallurgy is lower than that when casting or working is done.

Summary

1 Powder metallurgy differs from other metal manipulation processes in that the metal or alloy is solid at the start of the process and remains so.

2   Powder metallurgy was originally developed to overcome alloying problems, but is extensively used for the production of large quantities of small and medium size parts.
3   The basic operations are: the preparation and blending of the powder, the pressing of the powder and the sintering of the pressed powder (the pressed powder is usually called the 'compact').
4   Additional operations are included to improve the strength and accuracy of the product.
5   The product may be machined if required and given heat-treatment if the powder or 'blend' is suitable.
6   The product is weaker and less tough than that produced by casting or working because the powder 'units' that make up the part are huge compared with atoms that are the units when the initial shape is produced by melting.
7   The tooling costs are high, making the process economical only when large quantities are required.

Questions

Set A
1   Explain why a part that is produced by powder metallurgy is less strong and tough than one produced by casting or working.
2   'A process originally developed to overcome a problem is often used more extensively for another reason.' Comment upon this statement with reference to powder metallurgy.

Set B (questions requiring further study)
1   Write notes on designing for powder metallurgy.
2   Examine parts produced by powder metallurgy and discuss the reason why powder metallurgy was adopted (for example, because machining was impossible, to reduce costs, to obtain special properties).

Chapter 12
The Joining of Engineering Materials

12.1 Selection of joining method
When a designer selects the method to be used for joining engineering
metals and components, he must take many factors into account.
These include:
  (a) the composition and the properties of the metals to be joined,
  (b) the size and the shape of the parts to be joined,
  (c) the required joint strength, and the degree of permanency
     required,
  (d) the limiting conditions (for example, the effect of heat upon ad-
     jacent parts in the assembly), and
  (e) the allowable cost of the joint.

12.1.1. Joining methods may be classified as mechanical joining, metallurgical joining, and adhesive joining.

12.2 Mechanical joining methods

12.2.1 Fastening. Fastening methods include nut and bolt, stud and
nut, and set bolt. When nut and bolt fastening is used, both parts must
be drilled so that the bolt can pass through, and the parts be secured
by the nut. When a stud and nut fastening is used, the stud must be
attached to one part, and the other part must be drilled so that it can
pass over the stud, and the parts be secured by the nut. The stud may
be attached to one part by screwing it into a drilled and tapped hole,
or, alternatively, the part may be 'cast around' the stud, which is specially shaped so that it neither rotates nor is pulled out when the nut is
tightened. (This latter method is used extensively in die-cast components; the technique is also used in the moulding of plastics components.) When a set-bolt fastening is used, one part is drilled so that
the set bolt can pass through it, and the other part is drilled and
tapped so that it acts like a nut, into which the set bolt is screwed. In
all these methods, the parts can be easily separated for repair or main-

tenance. The parts of the fastening system are locked by spring washers, tab washers, locking plates, or locknuts. Pipes can be joined by attaching nipples to the pipes, and the nipples secured by nut against a seating in a pipe union, producing a tight joint.

12.2.2 Riveting (fig. 12.1). This is a semi-permanent joining method in which the parts to be joined are drilled to accept each rivet. In the conventional method, the rivet has one head at first, and the second

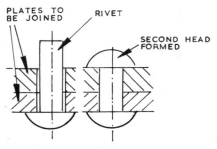

Fig 12.1 Riveting

head is formed when the rivet is struck, using special tools, when in position. The riveting action effects joining by causing the rivet to completely fill the holes in the plates being joined, and by compressing the plates between the rivet heads. A range of special rivets is available which enable riveting to be done from one side of the assembly only.

12.2.3 Folded joint. Sheet metal may be joined by folding, to produce a self-locking joint; but if the joint has to be liquid-proof, the seam is also soldered. There are a number of variations of the folded joint, but fig. 12.2 illustrates the principle of this joining method.

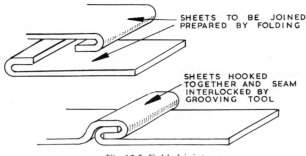

Fig 12.2 Folded joint

12.3 Metallurgical joining methods

All the methods in this group produce local casting, alloying, or crystal growth across the joint line, but they differ greatly in the way the joint is made.

12.3.1 Welding. The welding of two pieces of metal is the permanent joining of them. The oldest method of welding is to heat the metals to a soft and sticky state at the proposed joint, and hammer them together to form one homogeneous piece. This ideal was not always realised in practice: the joint often remained a source of weakness, due to the work being done at too low a temperature, or to the inclusion of metallic oxides in the joint.

Before the introduction of cheap steel, wrought iron was the common material for forged parts. Wrought iron is a very suitable material for forge-welding. The blacksmith prepares the ends to be joined, and heats them until white hot. The heated ends are fluxed with clean sand, and thoroughly forged together. Wrought iron has a high melting-point, and the full heat of the blacksmith's furnace is just sufficient to bring the metal to the welding temperature. The limitations of this method are obvious. It is not possible to weld long edges, such as two plates, and tubes and shaped sections present very serious difficulties. Metals which do not have a 'sticky' stage cannot be joined. The whole process calls for considerable skill, and is slow.

Resistance-welding

For metals which will stick together when heated to a suitable temperature, the various *resistance-welding* processes have largely superseded the blacksmith's methods. When an electric current is passed through a metal conductor, the resistance to its passage depends mainly on the surface area of the conductor and on the electrical conductivity of the material. If the resistance is high, the metal will be heated. The commonest example of this is the fine wire which forms the filament of an electric lamp: this is heated to whiteness when the current is switched on. However, unless the conductor is of very small size, or the current extremely great, the resistance will be almost negligible, and little heating will occur. The conditions become quite different if there is a discontinuity in the conductor. For example, if two metal parts are touching, there will be a distinct break at the point of contact, and if electric current is passed through them, considerable resistance will occur at the joint, and great heat will quickly develop at this particular place.

The electricity supply in most works is alternating current at about 200 to 400 volts. This is a dangerous voltage to use on bare metal parts which may be touched accidentally by the workers. Furthermore, these high-voltage currents do not have the best heating effect. For any normal welding process, 100 volts is ample for all purposes; and for the resistance-welding processes, 10 volts is usually quite sufficient. Accordingly, resistance-welding machines usually incorporate a step-down *transformer*. The principle of this device is shown in fig. 12.3. The high-voltage current is brought to a soft iron core by means of in-sulated cables. The cable passes a large number of times round one arm of the core. The take-off side of the transformer consists of an-

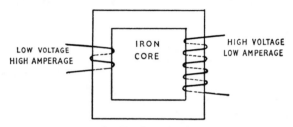

Fig 12.3 Transformer

other cable which has a few turns round the opposite arm of the core. When the high-voltage mains current is switched on, a low-voltage current is induced in the cable at the opposite side of the core. The ratio of the two voltages is determined by the ratio of the number of turns round each of the arms. The practical transformer is more com-plicated than this, but it works on the principle outlined.

The power of an electric current is measured in watts, and watts = amperes × volts. With the exception of certain losses, the fall in voltage at the outlet of a transformer brings about a proportionate rise in the amperage output. It is the amperage which largely determines the heating value of an electric current when it passes along a conductor.

The principle of the *flash-butt welding machine* is shown in fig. 12.4; it is designed for butt-welding bars, tubes, and similar sections. The machine has two compressed-air-operated jaws for gripping the parts to be joined; the jaws are plainly seen at the front of the machine. The jaws are connected by cables to the output side of a transformer. One

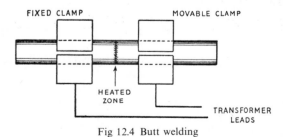

Fig 12.4 Butt welding

jaw is fixed, and the other is movable, mounted on a slide through which the forging pressure is applied. The components to be welded are mounted in the jaws, and the ends are brought lightly in contact with each other; simultaneously, the current is switched on. An arc is struck between the parts, and intense heat develops rapidly at the joint. The two end faces soon begin to melt, but a 'creep' action of the movable jaw keeps them close. The current is switched off, and the creep movement is instantly transformed into a sharp blow, this action forging the two weldable ends together into a homogeneous joint.

There is a typical 'flash' round the finished joint, where overheated metal has been forced out by the final blow. The actual welded zone is at about 70°C below the melting temperature. The flash serves the purpose of protecting the weld from the atmosphere at the instant of welding, and contains the overheated metal unsuitable for welding.

The advantages of this method are as follows. The whole process is automatic, and can be done at a very high speed with comparatively unskilled labour. Except at the joint, the metal is cold, and thus not distorted. It is not necessary to take great care in preparing the faces to be welded; they may be sawn off, for example, and during the 'creep' action they will be melted away uniformly. In this connection it should be noted that the faces to be joined should have an equal cross-section. The solid plate and tube shown in fig. 12.5 would be unsuitable for the process; instead, the plate should be prepared with a spigot, as shown.

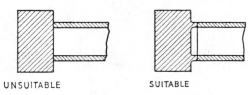

UNSUITABLE   SUITABLE

Fig 12.5

It would then be quite suitable. Solid pieces of equal size can, of course, be welded quite easily. Many very intricate components can be made in simple parts, and the whole brought together by flash-butt welding, thus saving a complicated forging operation. Sheet steel pressings (such as motor-car body-work) are made in convenient pieces, and are then assembled rapidly by flash-butt welding or by spot welding.

Figure 12.6 shows the principle of *spot welding*, which is used to join two plates together at their joint surface. The transformer takes a.c. current at the mains voltage, and provides a high-amperage, low-voltage current to the two electrodes. When the plates are in place, and the two electrodes are seated firmly on them, the current is switched on. Care is taken to have the electrode tips in close contact with the

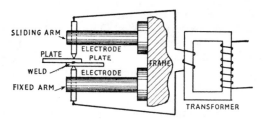

Fig 12.6 Spot welding

outsides of the plates; consequently, the principal resistance is on the *insides*, and it is here that most of the heat is developed. When the spot in the middle reaches welding temperature, the current is switched off, and the electrode pressure is simultaneously increased. The plates are pressed firmly together, and a weld is made at this spot. To prevent heating of the electrode tips, cooling water is circulated through the core of each electrode.

Spot-welding machines work on an adjustable time cycle. The top electrode is moved upwards, to allow the plates to be inserted, and is then brought down. At the same time, the current is switched on, and the welding is completed; the top electrode then moves upwards again, and releases the plates. The complete cycle is performed by the operator pressing a foot pedal. The heating period is given automatically, and is pre-set for the particular type of component.

The spot weld is an excellent substitute for a rivet on light plates. There is no hole to drill or rivet to fit, and, apart from a very slight mark left by the electrode tip, the outer surface is quite smooth.

A variation of spot welding is *seam welding*, in which the plain electrodes are replaced by rollers. The plates pass between the rollers at a fixed speed, and the time cycle of current, heat, and weld pressure goes on automatically producing spot welds as long as the plate is fed along. If the pitch of the welds is less than about 3 mm, the weld edges will overlap, and produce a continuous seam. Figure 12.7 illustrates the principle of seam welding.

When it is desired to weld a fairly thick object to a thin plate—say a nut to receive a screw—*projection spot welding* may be used. One or more projections are made at the points where a weld is desired (fig.

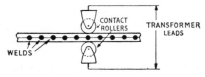

Fig 12.7 Seam welding

Fig 12.8 Projection spot welding

12.8). When the welding current is switched on, the projection collapses under the heat and pressure, and a weld is made at this point.

Fusion-welding

The welding processes described so far are known as *pressure-welding* processes. The *fusion-welding* processes are based on the principle of melting the edges to be joined, and adding further molten metal, to form a pool joining the two edges. The pool is then allowed to solidify and form a joint. Fusion welding, therefore, is a melting and casting process. The metal recast may have a different composition from the parent metal; in fact, one of the important points in fusion welding is to provide a filler metal best suited to make the joint. It is obvious, of course, that the filler metal must be capable of alloying with the two parent metals. In welding, certain constituents may be fused out under the intense heat. These can be replaced by having an excess in the filler metal.

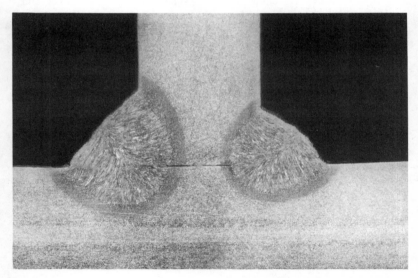

Fig 12.9   *Murex Welding Processes Ltd*

Figure 12.9 shows a weld made between two plates. The undisturbed structure can be seen, and the recast metal shows plainly. The original shape of the plate edges is obvious; but the pool has not been confined within these edges; it has penetrated the parent metal at both sides. This factor of *penetration* is of great importance. A sound welded joint should have even penetration into both the parent metals. The skill of the welder influences the penetration obtained; poor penetration is often due to bad workmanship, such as unequal heating of the plates to be joined.

Three common plate welds are shown in fig. 12.10. There are many variations on these welds; principally, it is a question of plate preparation. Four different preparations are shown in fig. 12.11. The U-shape requires less filling metal than the V-shape, and the double-U and double-V are necessary on thick plates, to prevent distortion, minimise the amount of filler, and ensure good penetration throughout the weld. Figure 12.12 shows a plate welded mainly from one side, but with a 'sealing' run on the opposite side. The various shapes are generally prepared on a special plate edge-planing machine, or by 'gouging'.

Except for light work, it is not possible to fill up the joint with a single pass of the welding apparatus. A number of 'runs' are made, superimposed on each other. Figure 12.13 shows a weld made in a number of runs from both sides. This method has certain advantages. The first layer of molten metal cools rapidly, and is liable to be hard and brittle; however, each succeeding run reheats the lower ones, which will then be insulated from the atmosphere, and will cool more slowly. It is important to clean the weld surface before each fresh run is made, otherwise dirt may be trapped in the weld, and will be a source of weakness.

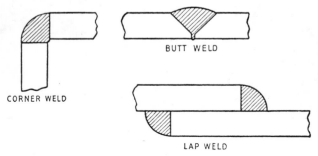

CORNER WELD

BUTT WELD

LAP WELD

Fig 12.10 Common plate welds

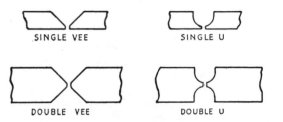

SINGLE VEE

SINGLE U

DOUBLE VEE

DOUBLE U

Fig 12.11 Plate preparation

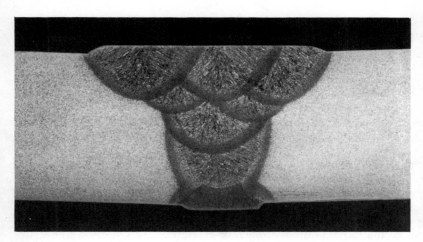

Fig 12.12 *Murex Welding Processes Ltd*

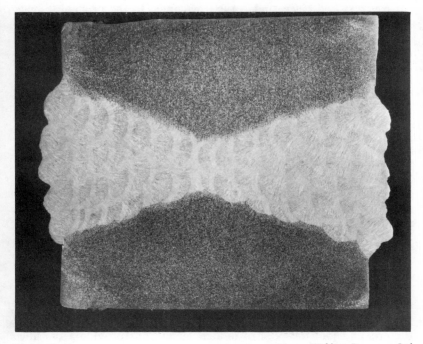

Fig 12.13 *Murex Welding Processes Ltd*

Owing to the intense local heating, welded structures are liable to be distorted when complete. This distortion can be minimised by 'tacking' components together at selected spots by short runs, and then filling in the intervening spaces judiciously. It is also common to provide fixtures for holding the work while welding proceeds. These fixtures hold the components in the correct relative positions, and may also be able to turn round so as to present the working faces to the welder at a convenient height. Fixtures that can revolve or swivel are sometimes called manipulators. In the best class of work, the finished welded structure is placed in a furnace, and is given a thermal stress-relieving treatment, to remove internal strains.

Distortion and cracking in welded work are sometimes prevented by *preheating*. This is particularly important when broken iron castings are being repaired by welding, since cast iron has very little ductility. If a portion of a casting is expanded due to heat, the rest of the structure is cold and rigid, and will warp or crack. However, if the whole structure can be heated, the broken portion can be welded, and the whole casting can cool and contract together.

Besides the repair of castings, worn parts, such as shaft journals, are often built up by welding. A deposit of suitable depth and hardness is put on the worn place, and is then machined to the original dimensions.

However, the principal field of fusion-welding is in the building up of structures from mild-steel plates and other sections. These are cut and bent to shape, and welded up. Welding has largely replaced riveting on vessels of all descriptions, from small water-tanks to ocean-going ships, and is now quickly eating into the field covered by the iron-casting process.

The two main methods of fusion-welding are the *electric-arc* process and the *gas-torch* process.

Arc-welding

In arc-welding, the metal is melted by the heat from an arc struck between an electrode and the work. The electrode may be carbon, with a separate filler rod being used (fig. 12.14), or it may be a metal which is melted locally during the welding operation, to become the filler (fig. 12.15).

The principle of the electric-arc process is shown in fig. 12.16. An electrode of suitable material is brought close to the parent metal. Current of low voltage and high amperage passes across the gap, thus forming an electric arc from the electrode to the parent metal. The metal on the circumference of the arc is rapidly melted by the intense heat developed. Globules of metal from the electrode are forced across the arc, and join the pool of molten metal, thus providing the filler already mentioned. As the electrode moves along the work, the pool

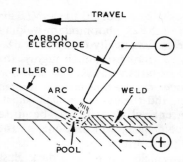

Fig 12.14 Carbon electrode arc-welding

Fig 12.15 Metal electrode arc-welding

solidifies. Bare electrodes may be used, but the deposit is liable to be hard and brittle: for the best work, covered electrodes are used, and it is a covered electrode that is shown in fig. 12.16. It will be noted that the coating projects beyond the tip of the electrode, thus protecting it from the atmosphere. The coating produces a gas which shields the arc, and prevents air reaching the molten pool; it also contains a flux which cleans the joint, and leaves behind a slag-coating on top of the solidifying metal. This slag-coating protects the metal from oxidation, and slows down the cooling process. The slag must be brushed off with a wire brush before another 'run' is made, so that it will not be trapped

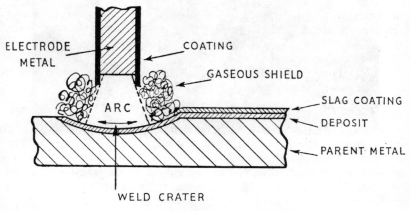

Fig 12.16 Covered electrode arc-welding

in the weld. Welds made with covered electrodes are stronger, tougher, and more ductile than welds made with bare wire electrodes.

To start up the arc, the electrode end is lightly scratched on the work; a pressure of about 70 volts is required to break down the resistance, and start the arc; this is termed the *striking voltage*. Once the arc has been struck, the voltage falls to about 20 to 30 V. This *working voltage* depends on the length of the arc, but modern welding machines are designed to compensate automatically for slight variations in the distance of the tip from the molten pool. Roughly, the correct distance is 2 to 7 mm, but this requires great skill to maintain because the tip is melting. If the electrode actually dips into the molten pool, the resistance will be almost nil, and the system will be short-circuited. At this point, maximum current will flow. It may be up to 400 amperes at almost zero voltage. No harm will be done, as the welding machine is designed to cover this contingency.

The operator is provided with a face-shield which has a dark glass through which he can watch the process. The electrode is held in an insulated holder, as shown in fig. 12.17. One wire is brought to the

Fig 12.17   *Murex Welding Processes Ltd*

base of the electrode holder, and the circuit to the machine is completed by a second wire, which is clipped to the work, and returns the current to the machine.

D.C. current may be used for arc welding. It is provided by a special generator with a drooping characteristic. Figure 12.18 shows a typical characteristic curve. When the generator is on open circuit—i.e. when no current is passing—the amperage is nil, and the voltage is at a maximum: this is point A on the curve. When the arc is struck, the voltage falls almost instantaneously to the part of the curve marked B–C. If the electrode end contacts the metal being welded, then the short-

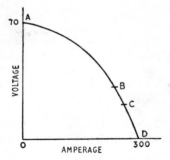

Fig 12.18 Welding generator
characteristic curve

circuit position D is reached. It is important that the generator should steady itself very quickly in any of these positions, as they may arise very frequently when welding is being carried out; if the changes cannot be accommodated in a few hundredths of a second, the welder will have difficulty in working steadily.

The d.c. generator may be driven by a d.c. or a.c. motor, or by a petrol or heavy-oil engine. A portable, engine-driven d.c. plant, independent of a supply of electricity, can be constructed, and such sets may be mounted on trailers or railways trucks, if desired. In the workshop, the commonest type is the a.c.-motor-driven set, which may be mounted on wheels, or more or less fixed in one position, according to circumstance.

Figure 12.19 shows a typical a.c.-motor-driven d.c. generator set. The a.c. motor with its starter is on the right, and the d.c. generator with its switchboard is on the left. Three current ranges are available, from 15 to 300 amperes, by connecting to terminals 1, 2, or 3, and the regulator (4) permits fine adjustment within each range. The actual amperes used are registered on the ammeter (5). The lower current ranges are used for thin electrodes and light plates, although the type of metal being welded also has an effect on the correct current value. The terminal (10) is the negative pole of the generator, and the return cable (11) is fixed to this. The other end of the return cable is fixed to the work, or to a metal table, on which the work is placed.

Welding may be carried out directly with an a.c. current, the voltage being reduced by a transformer. The drooping characteristic is obtained by means of a choke coil connected in series with the transformer output side and the arc. A choke coil is a coil or wire on an iron core. As the current passing through increases, the coil causes a drop in voltage. There are no rotating parts in an a.c. welding set, and both first cost and maintenance cost are lower than for a d.c. set. There are certain disadvantages to the a.c. set, however. It can be operated only where a.c. current is available, and certain metals are welded more readily with a d.c. set. It must be added that the great bulk of production welding is done on mild steel, and on this metal a.c. welding is

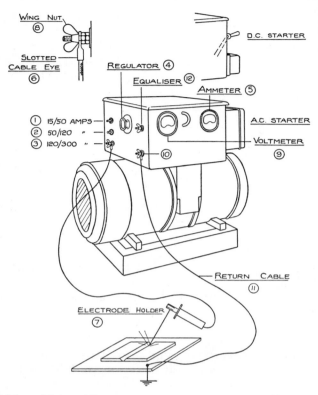

Fig 12.19 Motor-driven welding set   *Murex Welding Processes Ltd*

quite as good as d.c., providing the correct type of electrode is used. Most types of automatic arc welding are now done with a.c. current. In damp situations, the d.c. method is often preferred, chiefly because the maximum striking voltage of the a.c. method is about 100 volts, against the 70 volts of the d.c. system.

Gas-welding

In gas-welding, a flame is used to melt the filler rod and the metal to be joined (fig. 12.20).

It has been pointed out (see section 8.2.1) that the oxy-acetylene flame is much hotter than the air-acetylene flame, owing to the absence of nitrogen. If oxygen and acetylene under a slight pressure are properly mixed, and burnt at the outlet of a suitable nozzle, the flame produced has a maximum temperature of 3100°C, and will quickly melt the surface of any of the normal metals or alloys encountered in engineering. The oxy-acetylene welding torch is shown in fig. 12.21. A

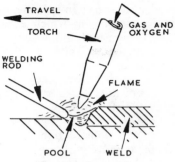

Fig 12.20 Gas-welding

nozzle is fixed to the outlet end of the torch, and the bore of this nozzle determines the gas consumption and the size of the flame. A selection of nozzles is shown, and also the spanners for changing nozzles. The larger the flame, the quicker will melting proceed. The two gases are brought to the two connections by separate rubber tubes, and are thoroughly mixed in the torch. A neutral flame is obtained by supplying the correct gas proportions to the nozzle by means of regulating knobs on the torch.

The oxygen and acetylene are stored under high pressure in steel

Fig 12.21 Welding torch and nozzles   *British Oxygen Co. Ltd*

'bottles' (coloured for identification). In the case of acetylene, the bottle contains a liquid called acetone, in which acetylene dissolves very readily. As the pressure is increased, more acetylene will be dissolved: for example, 1 volume of acetone will absorb 25 volumes of acetylene at atmospheric pressure; but, at 15 atmospheres pressure, 375 volumes may be dissolved. It follows, therefore, that as acetylene is withdrawn from the bottle, and the pressure falls, more of the gas will emerge from solution. To assist in even distribution of acetylene in the acetone, the bottle also contains 'kapok' fibre, which gives a cellular construction to the chamber. The cellular construction also prevents too rapid a discharge of gas. A reducing valve with pressure gauges is fitted to the head of the bottle.

The parts to be welded are prepared in the manner already described. The torch-flame is adjusted and played on the joint, and at the same time the end of a welding rod is held in the flame. The edges to be joined and the welding rod are melted simultaneously, and a pool of molten metal is formed. The operator moves steadily along the joint, building up a weld between the two parent metals. Two methods are practised: *leftwards* welding and *rightwards* welding (see figs 12.22 and 12.23).

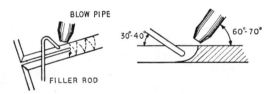

Fig 12.22 Leftwards welding

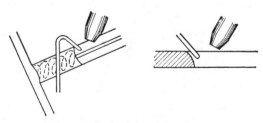

Fig 12.23 Rightwards welding

When using the leftwards method the welding is started at the right-hand end and proceeds towards the left-hand end. The blow pipe is oscillated as it is moved, to ensure that the edges of both the plates being welded melt at the same time, and the filler rod precedes it. Once a molten pool has been obtained, the filler rod is melted by being fed into the pool. This method is used for welding thin steel plates, cast iron, and some non-ferrous metals.

When using the rightwards method the welding is started at the left-hand end and proceeds towards the right-hand end; the filler rod follows the blow pipe and is given a circular motion. The flame is directed on to the newly deposited metal, giving better control of the cooling rate. This method is used for welding thick plates because it is quicker, produces less distortion and allows a better view of the weld that does the leftwards method.

As in the electric-arc process, there are many different types of welding rod to suit the various metals to be joined. The rod is not of quite the same composition as the metals to be joined; for example, it is usual to add a deoxidising agent, such as silicon, to improve the quality of the weld metal.

Flame-cutting
Plates are often cut to shape by means of the oxy-acetylene flame. The part to be cut is first heated to a high temperature, known as its 'ignition point', and a jet of pure oxygen is then played on to the hot surface. Violent oxidation or burning immediately commences, and will continue as long as oxygen is supplied. A narrow groove is formed, the force of the jet blowing out the burnt metal in a shower of brilliant white sparks. The speed at which the groove is formed depends on the plate thickness; the following speeds are typical of mild steel plate.

Plate thickness (mm)	25	75	150
Speed of cutting (metres per hour)	21	13	7

The flame-cutting nozzle is rather different from the welding nozzle: the oxygen and acetylene for the heating flame emerge through an annular nozzle which surrounds a central nozzle through which the pure oxygen of the burning jet is discharged.

Hand torches may be used for flame-cutting, but much work is now done on special cutting machines. These have a well-balanced double-jointed arm, on the end of which is placed the torch, directed vertically downwards. The path of the torch may be guided by hand round a template, or along a straight-edge mounted above the head of the torch, and contacted by a roller. Other machines are equipped with rollers which automatically traverse the torch around the template at a pre-set speed.

The flame-cutting machine is extremely useful in shops where plate is welded up into various components. It is also very convenient for cutting large holes in plates. Previous to its advent, this was a laborious business, involving the drilling of many holes, and the subsequent breaking out of the unwanted piece, often with hammer and chisel.

Even when this was done, the scalloped edge left by the holes had
to be trimmed up, either by boring or by further hand chipping and
filing.

Inspection of welds
The view afforded to the welder through the darkened window of his
shield or goggles is far from perfect, and one defect which occurs as a
result of this is that of 'undercutting', shown in fig. 12.24. Metal from
the vertical plate is brought down into the pool, and is not replaced by
deposited metal. The actual size of the fillet may not be correct, or may
vary along its length. This defect can be checked with radius gauges.
Other visible defects are burnt metal—caused by undue 'dwelling' at
one spot—cracking, and porosity of the weld surface.

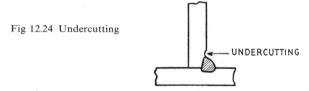

Fig 12.24 Undercutting

The quality of welding can be controlled by the regular production
of test welds that can be given a destructive test so that the standard of
workmanship of each welder can be appraised.

Welded joints can be tested by non-destructive methods; the method
used depends on the material and the amount of information required. A
part may be subjected to a series of non-destructive tests, starting with
a simple visual test and concluding with an expensive X-ray test to prevent spending money checking a part not 'worthy' of an expensive test.

Surface defects can be revealed by a dye-penetrant method in which
the surface of the part is cleaned and then immersed, swabbed, or
sprayed with a dye penetrant that will enter any fine surface cracks;
after a short time, the surface is cleaned and dried, and a powder
dusted on to it, drawing out any penetrant that entered surface cracks,
to reveal their presence by staining the powder.

Certain cracks at or near the surface of magnetic materials can be
revealed by magnetic particle testing. In this method a magnetic flux is
set up in the workpiece by direct or induction method, and iron filings
in suspension in water or paraffin are applied to the surface and allowed to float away. They remain attracted to the surface of the workpiece near cracks or defects because these cause 'spillage' of the flux,
and the material locally to behave like two magnets with their opposite poles near each other.

Ultrasonic testing can indicate the presence of internal flaws, and
the depth at which they lie.

In this method ultrasonic vibrations are transmitted through the material using a probe, and reflected back to the probe when they reach an interface. The transmitted and received vibrations each produce a 'blip' on the screen of a cathode ray tube; if the material is free from flaws, the distance between the two 'blips' represents the thickness of the material. If a flaw is present, some of the energy will be reflected by it, and be received by the probe before that which is reflected by the opposite side of the material, and the cathode ray tube display will show three 'blips' – the third one lying between the transmission 'blip' and that produced by energy that travelled to the opposite side of the material. The spacing of the three 'blips' produced by a faulty material can be compared with the spacing of the two 'blips' produced by a fault-free material to indicate the depth at which the fault lies.

The shape of an internal flaw can be revealed by X-ray examination in which the rays are passed through the material to act on a photographic plate on the opposite side. As in ordinary photography, the picture so produced depends upon the extent of the 'attack' on the plate; this depends upon the amount of energy that passes through the material being tested, and which, in turn depends upon the presence of internal flaws which are therefore seen on the photograph.

12.3.2 Soldering. This is a method of producing a permanent joint. The parts to be joined are carefully fitted, so that there is only a small clearance between them, and then the clearance is filled with an alloy of tin and lead, called solder. The solder alloys locally with the metal to be joined. One difference between fusion-welding and soldering is that in fusion-welding there is a large gap between the parts to be joined, which is filled with the filler metal; but in soldering, the gap between the parts is very small. The surfaces to be joined must be chemically clean, if the soldered joint is to be satisfactory, and a suitable flux must be applied to attack and dissolve the oxide film that forms on the surface of the metal and the molten solder; the flux also screens the region of the joint against oxidation during the soldering operation. The metal to be joined is heated, using a heated bit, or a blow lamp; and then the solder, in the form of wire, rod, or fine particles, is melted into the clearance between the parts. A range of solders is available, to suit the metals to be joined, and the conditions in which the joining is to be done. For example, tinman's solder is basically 62% tin and 38% lead, and melts at about 183°C; plumber's solder is basically 33% tin and 67% lead, and solidifies over a temperature range from 260°C to 183°C, enabling the plumber to make a 'wiped' joint. Soldering with a lead-tin alloy is often called 'soft soldering', in contrast to brazing (see below) which is called 'hard soldering'.

12.3.3 Brazing. Brazing is a similar operation to soldering, but is done at a higher temperature than soldering, and produces a stronger joint. For general work, the joining agent is brass with about 50% copper and 50% zinc (hence the name 'brazing'). Silver solders contain between 10% and 80% silver, with copper and zinc, and have a melting-point of between 625°C and 870°C, according to composition. The preparation of the parts and the joining technique are similar to those used when soldering.

12.4 Adhesive joining methods

Synthetic adhesives of the 'impact' type, and adhesives of the thermosetting type (see section 14.1.2), which require a combination of heat and pressure to 'cure' them, are used to join metals as well as non-metals. The 'Redux' process, used to fabricate parts of aircraft, is an example of the latter method of joining.

Summary

1   The joining method used depends upon the metal being joined, the size and shape of the parts to be joined, the required joint strength, the limiting conditions, and the allowable cost.
2   Joining methods can be classified as (a) mechanical, (b) metallurgical, and (c) adhesive.
3   Fastening, riveting, and folding are mechanical methods of joining.
4   Welding, soldering, and brazing are metallurgical methods of joining.
5   Adhesives may be of the impact type, or be thermosetting plastics.

Questions

Set A
1   Examine a number of assemblies, to determine the joining methods used. Consider also the factors that determined the methods used.
2   List the various welding methods, and indicate how they are similar, and how they differ.
3   Compare soldering and brazing, and explain how they differ.

Set B (questions requiring further study)
4   Write notes on designing for welding.
5   Discuss how mechanical joining can be used to advantage, instead of metallurgical joining.
6   Explain why plastics adhesives have become very important in engineering.

Chapter 13
Presswork

13.1. Press tools are used to cut and to cold-form thin metal that is usually supplied in the form of sheet or strip. Pressings are more usually made from low-carbon steel, 70/30 brass, aluminium alloys, and copper.

13.2 Presswork operations

Presswork operations can be divided into cutting operations and forming operations.

13.2.1 Cutting operations.

The basic cutting operations are *piercing*, *blanking*, and *cropping*. Piercing (fig. 13.1) implies the cutting of holes within the outside contour of the finished workpiece: the 'punching' (the name given to the metal that is removed) is the scrap, and the metal left is the workpiece. Several holes may be pierced simultaneously.

Blanking (fig. 13.2) implies that the outside contour is produced by removing metal from the stock; the 'punching' is therefore the work-

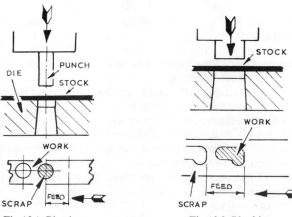

Fig 13.1 Piercing   Fig 13.2 Blanking

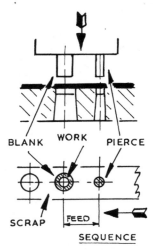

Fig 13.3 Combined piercing and blanking

piece. Several blanks may be produced simultaneously, to speed up production. These two basic operations can be combined ('piercing-and-blanking'), as shown in fig. 13.3, so that a pierced-and-blanked workpiece is produced at each stroke of the machine. Figure 13.3 illustrates a die-set for this operation; in the example, a washer is produced at each stroke. The piercing tool produces the hole, the stock is fed to bring the hole so produced under the blanking tool, and the washer is blanked at the next stroke: from then on, one completed washer is produced at every stroke. If the circumstances are suitable, two blanking tools and two piercing tools can be used, so that two workpieces are produced at each stroke of the press.

Cropping implies the simple cutting to length of strip, and uses a simple blade-like tool.

13.2.2 Forming operations. In these operations, no cutting is involved, but the material may have been previously pierced and/or blanked. The basic features of die-sets for bending and forming operations are the forming punch and the forming block.

Figure 13.4 illustrates *simple bending*. The included angle of the punch and block is usually smaller than that to be produced, to allow for spring-back; the amount depends upon the angle being produced, and the properties of the material—in the case of a low-carbon steel, an angle of 87° would be used to produce an angle of 90°.

Cup-like shapes are produced by *deep drawing* (see fig. 10.12). The basic features of a deep drawing set are the punch and the die. It may be necessary to draw very deep cups in stages, with an annealing stage

Fig 13.4 Simple bending

between each drawing stage, in order to remove the work-hardening caused by the drawing. The final stage is often an 'ironing' operation, in which the space between the punch and the die is less than the thickness of the stock before that stage.

Embossing (see fig. 10.16) involves the pressing of sheet metal between dies, so that the metal is locally bent and stretched with very little change in its thickness. Embossing produces a component of which one side is the negative of the other.

Coining (see fig. 10.17) differs from embossing and other presswork operations, in that slightly thicker workpiece material is used, and the material is caused to flow and to fill the die cavity by local indentation and extrusion: the part so produced has sides that are not 'related'. A second part can be held in a cup-shaped part by *crimping*, in which the sides of the cup are pinched or squeezed to hold the second part.

13.3 Presses

Presses can be operated by hand or foot, or by power. Power presses are usually equipped with a guard, to ensure that the operator's hands are away from the space between the ram and the table when it is in operation; alternatively, the press may be designed so that the operator must operate a control point with each hand before it will operate. Power presses are classified according to the ram action.

13.3.1 Single-acting presses.
These presses have one ram or slide, operated by crank, eccentric, toggle, or screw. The crank, eccentric, and toggle presses may be set to disengage at the top of the stroke, or to run continuously. Intermittent operation is used for 'second operation' work, where the workpieces must be positioned by hand. In the interests of safety, continuous operation must be used only with an automatic feed.

13.3.2 Double-acting presses.
These presses have two rams or slides, and are used when it is necessary to use a separate holder and punch arrangement. When a large pressing is produced, the outer slide carries

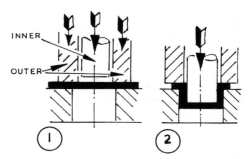

Fig 13.5 Double-acting press

the blank holder, and is set in advance of the inner slide, which carries the punch (fig. 13.5). The holder presses the sheet against the face of the die before the former pushes the sheet into the die. The outer slide is stationary when the punch is operating upon the material.

13.3.3 Triple-acting presses. Presses of this type are similar to the double-acting presses, but they have a third slide, so that the material can be pushed up into a recess in the bottom of the punch, as in fig. 13.6.

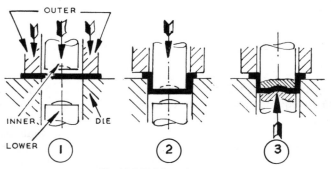

Fig 13.6 Triple-acting press

13.3.4 Press capacity. Presses are further classified according to their capacity, which includes the stroke, the bed size and the minimum distance between ram and table, the press speed, and the force that it can exert.

13.4 Feeding
The feeding of strip material for blanking, piercing, etc., may be by hand, or by friction drive between rollers operating in conjunction with the slides. Second-operation work, such as the cupping of blanked

material, may be by hand, or automatic, by hopper, etc. Work that is produced by pressing into blind dies must be removed by an ejector which may be part of the press itself, or be part of the die-set.

13.5 Die-sets

The two parts of a die-set may be separate, and positioned by the setter on the machine ram and table. Smaller die-sets are more usually produced using standard die-sets marketed by the makers of 'unit tooling parts'; the use of these sets produces a saving of tool-room and press-tool setters' time. These standard die-sets consist of two main parts (*a*) the top plate, and (*b*) the bolster and guide pillars; fig. 13.7 shows a typical die-set. Die-sets are available in a range of configurations. The top plate and the bolster can be made either of cast iron or of steel; the guide pillars are made of steel. The top plate is located relative to the bolster by the two pillars, so that alignment can be made easily.

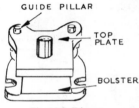

Fig 13.7 Die-set

13.5.1 Press-tool set for simple blanking (fig. 13.8). A simple blanking set consists of a *punch* and *die*, which act together to shear the workpiece; a *bolster*, to hold the die; a *guide*, to ensure that the stock is located; a *stop*, to position the stock, using the last hole to be blanked; and a *stripper*, to remove the stock from the punch during the return stroke. In the example shown, the operator positions the stock against the stop, which he can see through the sighting 'window' on the stripper plate, which is a combined stripper plate and guide. The punch and die are made from an alloy steel.

13.5.2 Follow-on pierce-and-blank press-tool set (fig. 13.9). The principle of the pierce-and-blank operation is described in section 13.2.1. In the illustration (fig. 13.9), the end of the punch is at an angle to the direction of punching; this inclination is called *shear*. The application of shear will cause the force to build up gradually; the maximum force will be less than that required when a flat-ended punch is used, because the shearing action will be gradual. Shear may be applied either to the punch or to the die.

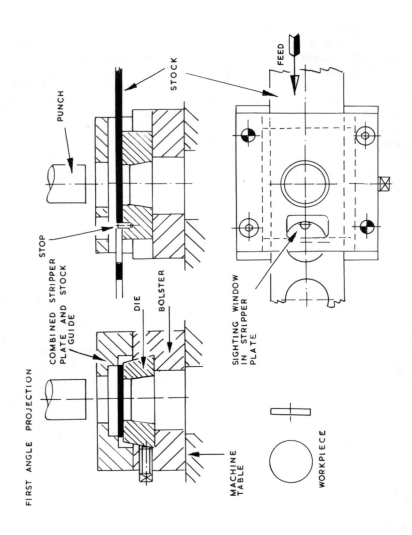

Fig 13.8 Press-tool set for simple blanking

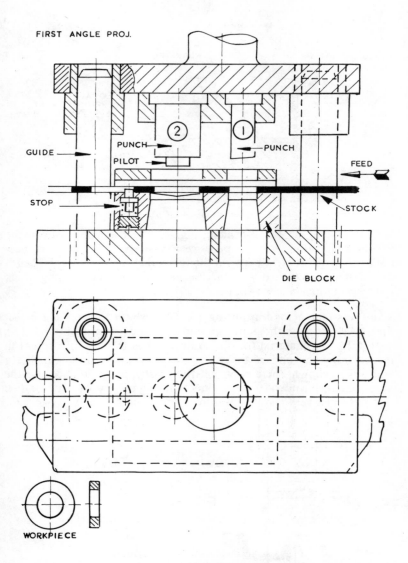

FIRST ANGLE PROJ.

GUIDE

PUNCH

PILOT

STOP

PUNCH

FEED

STOCK

DIE BLOCK

WORKPIECE

Fig 13.9 Follow-on pierce-and-blank press-tool set

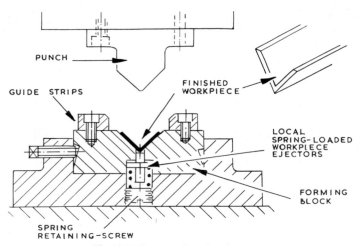

PUNCH

GUIDE STRIPS

FINISHED
WORKPIECE

LOCAL
SPRING-LOADED
WORKPIECE
EJECTORS

FORMING
BLOCK

SPRING
RETAINING-SCREW

Fig 13.10 Press-tool set for V-bending

13.5.3 Press-tool set for V-bending (fig. 13.10). The set shown in fig. 13.10 is for bending strip to produce a V-shape; it is therefore necessary to locate the strip between the two guide strips before the bending is done. The finished workpiece is ejected from the forming block by the spring-loaded pins shown.

13.5.4 Press-tool set for drawing (fig. 13.11). The basic features of a die-set to produce a cup are the punch and drawing die (to control the metal), location for the material (in this example, it is located in a recess in the face of the die), and means of stripping the cup from the punch. (In the example shown, there is no need for a stripper plate, because the finished cup is stripped from the punch during the return stroke, when it springs open very slightly, and fouls the shoulder on the bolster.)

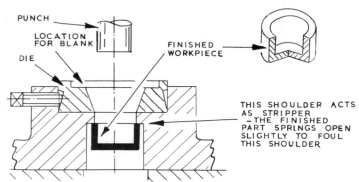

PUNCH

LOCATION
FOR BLANK

DIE

FINISHED
WORKPIECE

THIS SHOULDER ACTS
AS STRIPPER
– THE FINISHED
PART SPRINGS OPEN
SLIGHTLY TO FOUL
THIS SHOULDER

Fig 13.11 Press-tool set for drawing

Summary

1   Press tools are used to cut and to cold-form thin metal.
2   Presswork can be classified as (*a*) cutting operations, and (*b*) forming operations.
3   The basic cutting operations are piercing (where the 'punching' is the scrap), blanking (where the 'punching' is the workpiece), and cropping (cutting to length).
4   The basic forming operations are bending, deep-drawing, embossing, coining, and crimping.
5   Presses are classified according to ram action (single-acting, double-acting, or triple-acting) and capacity.
6   A press-tool set consists of a punch and die, or a punch and a forming block. It may also include a guide and a stop, and either a stripper or an ejector.
7   Strip metal may be fed by hand or by friction drive. 'Second operation' work may be fed by hand or by hopper.
8   The tools may be positioned separately on the ram and table, or be attached to die sets.

Questions

Set A

1   Make a sketch of a simple press-tool lay-out for producing a small shallow cup in 70/30 brass.
2   What is meant by the work-hardening of a metal? Briefly outline the difficulties which work-hardening introduces into press-tool work.
3   Make a sketch of a simple press-tool set to produce a 90° angle V-strip, 900 mm long × 30 mm wide before bending.

Set B (questions requiring further study)

4   Sketch a typical tensile-test curve, and indicate which parts of the curve are related to presswork.
5   Examine the methods used to position strip during presswork, and discuss the special features of each.
6   Investigate 'shear', as applied to press tools, and explain how its amount is determined.

Chapter 14
Plastics in Engineering

14.1 Plastics materials

A plastics material may be defined as an organic material which, at some time in its history, is capable of flow, and which, upon the application of adequate heat and pressure, can be caused to flow and take up a desired shape, which will be retained after the heat and pressure are withdrawn. (An organic material is one that is composed wholly, or mainly, of carbon compounds.) These materials consist of long molecular chains, which produce many of the properties associated with plastics. It is convenient to classify plastics into (a) thermosoftening (or thermoplastic) materials, and (b) thermosetting (or thermohardening) materials.

14.1.1 Thermosoftening materials. These materials can be softened and resoftened indefinitely by the application of heat and pressure, as long as the heat does not cause damage. They consist of a basic unit (or units) called a *monomer*, which is a substance that is capable of joining up with other monomers to form chains of great length, to produce a *polymer*. In the case of *co-polymers*, there may be two or three different monomers in each chain; these may be distributed along the chain at random, or be in blocks of a similar kind. The following diagram represents the structure of a thermosoftening plastics material:

$$-M-M-M-M-M-M-M-M-M-M-M-$$
$$-M-M-M-M-M-M-M-M-M-M-M-$$
$$-M-M-M-M-M-M-M-M-M-M-M-$$

In the diagram, M represents the actual repeating unit, sometimes called the *mer*; in actual materials, the chains will be tangled.

When a thermosoftening material is heated, the chains move apart; and, under pressure, slide past each other, to take up new positions which are retained after the heat and pressure is removed.

Plastics materials of this type are of varying rigidity, depending upon the structure of the basic material (called the *binder*) and the other materials that are present. These other materials include a large quantity of *filler* (to produce the strength), small amounts of colouring matter, and a *plasticiser*—a softening agent, to act as an internal lubricant to allow the chains to move more freely.

Thermoplastic plastics materials reach the manipulator in the form of sheets, films (thin sheets), rods, tubes, and moulding materials. They can be formed or shaped with very little force, at temperatures slightly above that of boiling water; they can be joined by using a suitable solvent, or, in some cases, by the application of heat and suitable pressure.

These materials do not melt, but flow at a suitable temperature and pressure. They are particularly suitable for injection moulding and extrusion, behave like glass when blown, and can be formed into bottle- and dome-like shapes by pressure and vacuum techniques.

14.1.2 Thermosetting materials. These materials undergo a chemical change when they are subjected to heat and pressure, after which they cannot be changed by further application of heat and pressure.

The following diagram represents the structure of a thermosetting plastics material:

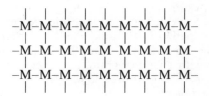

These materials are partly changed during their production, and reach the manipulator in a thermoplastic condition. As the result of further heating and pressure, the three-dimensional cross-links are developed, so that definite distances are maintained between the chains, and they are prevented from sliding past each other. Thermosetting plastics materials are therefore rigid, and are insoluble, because it is virtually impossible for a solvent to enter between the chains, to disperse them. In actual materials, the chains are tangled as well as cross-linked. The heating process that develops the cross-linking is sometimes called *curing*.

Thermosetting plastics materials reach the manipulator as moulding powders, resins that are cast, or used in a lay-up process, or as paper or cloth that has been impregnated with resin.

In addition to the basic material, a *filler*; *colouring matter*; a *plasti-*

ciser; a *hardening agent*, to produce the cross-linking; and an *accelerator*, to speed up the action of the hardening agent, are included in these materials.

14.1.3 Raw materials. The raw materials used in the production of plastics materials can be classified as (*a*) animal or vegetable, (*b*) coal, and (*c*) oil.

The vegetable and animal materials are cellulose and casein. Cellulose is the main constituent in the cell walls of all vegetable matter, though only a few sources are suitable for conversion into plastics; casein is the main protein in cow's milk, and is now used in the production of buttons.

Coal is distilled to produce coal gas, ammonia, coal-tar, and a residue of coke: all of these can be used to produce plastics materials.

Crude petroleum can be made to produce methane, ethylene, propylene, butylenes, aromatic hydrocarbons, and naphthenates, all of which are used in the production of various plastics materials.

14.2 Some typical thermosoftening plastics materials

14.2.1 Cellulose plastics. These materials are produced by modifying the cellulose chains that occur naturally. Nitrocellulose and cellulose acetate are two typical plastics of this type.

Celluloid is an example of nitrocellulose. It is a good material for fabricating, tends to be discoloured by prolonged exposure, but it can be coloured. It is extremely inflammable. It is often made into laminated blocks, which are sliced into sheets, and used for the production of knife handles with an ivory grain, and spectacle frames with tortoiseshell markings; it is also used for cycle pumps and mud-guards, umbrella and shaving-brush handles, printed price tickets, etc.

Cellulose acetate in sheet form is used in the optical trade, and for lampshades and similar decorative applications. Cellulose acetate is also used for textiles (Tricel, for example).

14.2.2 Vinyl plastics. The wide range of plastics in this group are called

'vinyl' plastics because chains include
$$\begin{array}{c} \text{H} \quad \text{H} \\ |\quad\quad| \\ \text{C}=\text{C} \\ | \\ \text{H} \end{array}$$
which is known as vinyl.

The general shape of a polyvinyl chain is

The shape of *polythene* is

$$-\overset{\displaystyle H}{\underset{\displaystyle H}{C}}-\overset{\displaystyle H}{\underset{\displaystyle H}{C}}-\overset{\displaystyle H}{\underset{\displaystyle H}{C}}-\overset{\displaystyle H}{\underset{\displaystyle H}{C}}-\overset{\displaystyle H}{\underset{\displaystyle H}{C}}-\overset{\displaystyle H}{\underset{\displaystyle H}{C}}-\overset{\displaystyle H}{\underset{\displaystyle H}{C}}-\overset{\displaystyle H}{\underset{\displaystyle H}{C}}-$$

in which the X is hydrogen (H).

The shape of *polyvinyl chloride* (PVC) is

$$-\overset{\displaystyle H}{\underset{\displaystyle H}{C}}-\overset{\displaystyle H}{\underset{\displaystyle Cl}{C}}-\overset{\displaystyle H}{\underset{\displaystyle H}{C}}-\overset{\displaystyle H}{\underset{\displaystyle Cl}{C}}-\overset{\displaystyle H}{\underset{\displaystyle H}{C}}-\overset{\displaystyle H}{\underset{\displaystyle Cl}{C}}-\overset{\displaystyle H}{\underset{\displaystyle H}{C}}-\overset{\displaystyle H}{\underset{\displaystyle Cl}{C}}-$$

in which the X is chlorine (Cl).

The shape of *polystyrene* is

$$-\overset{\displaystyle H}{\underset{\displaystyle H}{C}}-\overset{\displaystyle H}{\underset{\displaystyle C_6H_5}{C}}\quad\overset{\displaystyle H}{\underset{\displaystyle H}{C}}-\overset{\displaystyle H}{\underset{\displaystyle C_6H_5}{C}}\quad\overset{\displaystyle H}{\underset{\displaystyle H}{C}}-\overset{\displaystyle H}{\underset{\displaystyle C_6H_5}{C}}-$$

in which the X is phenyl (C_6H_5), so that the monomer is styrene of the form

$$\overset{\displaystyle H}{\underset{\displaystyle H}{C}}=\overset{\displaystyle H}{\underset{\displaystyle C_6H_5}{C}}$$

These chains are produced by *polymerisation*, which involves the 'opening out' of the double bond of the monomers, so that they all join up to form the long chains.

For example, ethylene monomers can be joined by polymerisation to form polythene:

$$\overset{\displaystyle H}{\underset{\displaystyle H}{C}}=\overset{\displaystyle H}{\underset{\displaystyle H}{C}}\longrightarrow -\overset{\displaystyle H}{\underset{\displaystyle H}{C}}-\overset{\displaystyle H}{\underset{\displaystyle H}{C}}-\overset{\displaystyle H}{\underset{\displaystyle H}{C}}-\overset{\displaystyle H}{\underset{\displaystyle H}{C}}-\overset{\displaystyle H}{\underset{\displaystyle H}{C}}-\overset{\displaystyle H}{\underset{\displaystyle H}{C}}-$$

Polythene. This is available as low-density polythene, high-density polythene, and high-molecular-weight polythene. Low-density polythene is used for thin-walled flexible tubing, piping-cable insulation, thin extruded films, and blown forms such as bottles. The high-density polythene has a higher softening-point, and is stronger and more rigid; it is used where hot liquids and steam must be resisted. Typical applications of high-density polythene are test tubes and similar laboratory ware, bowls and jugs, valves and taps for petrol and paraffin containers, shockproof housings for power tools and appliances, and lighting fittings. The high-molecular-weight polythene is tough and hard, and has high electrical resistance; it is used in papermaking gears, which are lubricated with oil and water emulsion.

Ethylene co-polymers. A typical example of this group is polypropylene. It is very light, and has a higher heat-resistance than is usual for plastics, and is used for chairs, cisterns, pipe-fittings, and hospital ware.

Polystyrene. Polystyrene flows easily at about 180°C, and so is very suitable for injection moulding. It is used for model construction kits, toys, display items, and strip lighting diffusers. (In the latter application, it is used in the clear form as an alternative to perspex, because, although not as optically brilliant as perspex, it is easier to make, and is therefore cheaper.) Toughened polystyrene is used for dustpans, radio grills, refrigerator parts, and shoe heels. ABS (acrylonitrile-butadiene-styrene) is an important high impact polystyrene that is being used for car dash-panels and fittings, gear-box covers, and —electroplated—for radiator grills.

Polyvinyl chloride (PVC). This plastics material is available in a range of grades, controlled by the method of manufacture, and by the addition of ingredients such as plasticisers, lubricants, etc. It can be extruded into bottle-like shapes, and rolled into thin sheets, which can be embossed to produce leather substitute. It is used for such widely ranging applications as insulation for electrical wiring, window curtain material, motor-car lining and upholstery, flooring material, toys, pipes, and gutterings.

Polymethyl methacrylate. This is available as sheets (perspex) and moulding powder (diakon). It has good light transmission, good weather-resistance, and is fairly tough. It is used as a substitute for glass, where the latter cannot be used. In sheet form, it is used for machine guards, windshields, and display fittings, and is moulded into brush handles, hair-dryer casings, telephone cases, and radio dials and panels.

Fluorine plastics. These are similar to polythene, but contain fluorine in place of hydrogen. They are non-inflammable, and have a high softening-point. Polytetrafluoroethylene (PTFE) has a good resistance to chemical or solvent action, and has a very low frictional resistance. It is used for acid-plant gaskets, ignition-cable sheathing, bearings, and cathode-ray tube holders.

14.2.3 Condensation polymers, including polyesters. Condensation polymerisation implies that a chain is produced by 'dovetailing' dissimilar molecules by means of a chemical change, which usually eliminates a third product that is not part of the final product. These plastics are thermosoftening if cross-links are not developed, and thermohardening if cross-links are developed.

Polyamides (the 'nylon' materials). These are so named because the polymer consists of short carbon chains that are linked by amide groups. (Amide groups contain nitrogen, hydrogen, carbon, and oxygen.) The various 'nylons' are designated by numbers that indicate the number of carbon atoms in the 'starting materials'. Nylon is used in monofilament form for brushes; and as mouldings for gears, self-locking nuts, door mechanisms, fuel-tank caps and floats, and bearings. *Polyesters* (N.B. acid + alcohol → ester + water). Polyethylene terephthalate, Terylene, can be treated during its manufacture to produce a tough material that can be extruded as film, or treated to make it very strong, and suitable for use in capacitors, printed circuits, magnetic recording tape, and typewriter ribbons.

14.3 Some typical thermosetting plastics materials

14.3.1 Phenolic plastics. These are produced from phenol and formaldehyde, in the presence of an acid, if the product is to be suitable as a moulding powder that develops cross-links when combined with a hardener. When produced from phenol and formaldehyde in the presence of an alkaline catalyst, the product is a resin that easily cures without a hardener when finally heated. By variation of procedure and of filler material, a range of phenolic plastics can be produced. Typical applications are distributor caps, electric plugs, and door handles.

14.3.2 Aminoplastics ('amino'—from ammonia—refers to the chemical nature of these plastics). Urea formaldehyde is used in the production of thin-walled articles such as cups and tumblers, and for tough electrical fittings. Melamine formaldehyde is harder and stronger, and is used for the moulding of plates and dishes.

14.3.3 Polyurethanes (these contain the 'urethane link'). Materials in this group are used as foam for seats and arm rests, and as a hard, tough, and high chemical-resistance coating material that can be pigmented.

14.3.4 Epoxy resins. In these materials, an ether with an 'epoxy' ending, that can be used at a later stage to produce the linking, is produced. These resins are used in laminating, and in glass-reinforced plastics.

14.3.5 Laminates. In the high-pressure laminates, the sheets are fibrous or porous materials, and are bonded into a solid mass by using an impregnating resin. The resin is applied in liquid form, and the cross-linking is obtained by heating. Phenol formaldehyde, urea formaldehyde, and melamine formaldehyde are the usual resins. The first of these is dark, and used mainly for industrial laminates, but the latter two are clear, and used to laminate and cover decorative material.

Low-pressure laminates are produced by 'laying up' the reinforcing materials with liquid polyester or epoxy resins, and then subjecting the assembly to low pressures: this process is usually applied to glass fibre reinforcement.

14.4 Manipulation methods
The manipulation methods can be classified into (*a*) moulding, (*b*) forming and pressing, (*c*) casting, and (*d*) laminating.

14.4.1 Moulding methods. In these methods, the material is in the form of powder or granules, and is subjected to heating and pressure. *Compression-moulding* (fig. 14.1) is the most common method used for the shaping of thermosetting plastics, but it is also applied to thermo-

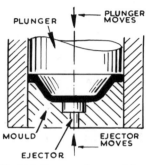

Fig 14.1 Compression-moulding

plastic materials when the parts to be produced are too large for them to be made by injection moulding. The equipment consists of a press with two heated platens carrying the punch and die units. Figure 14.1 illustrates a positive mould; the thickness of a moulding produced by this type of mould depends upon the quantity of moulding powder placed in it. Other compression-moulding methods include the flash mould, in which the two parts of the mould close to produce a fixed cavity thickness, with the excess material being squeezed out through a flash gutter, leaving a fin that must be removed (this is similar to forging, using forging dies). *Injection-moulding* (fig. 14.2) is similar to

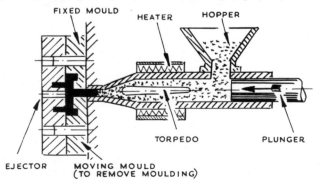

Fig 14.2 Injection-moulding

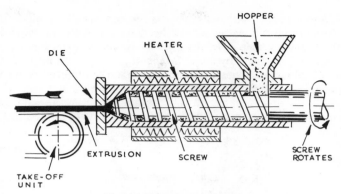

Fig 14.3 Extrusion-moulding

pressure die-casting. The moulding powder is introduced into the injection chamber, where it is forced by plunger into the heating zone, and into the closed mould. When the mould has been filled, the material is rapidly cooled, the mould is opened, and the moulding ejected. This process is used for the production of construction kits. *Extrusion-moulding* (fig. 14.3) is used to produce continuous lengths of material. In this process, the material is continuously fed through the die, by means of a rotating screw.

14.4.2 Forming and pressing. These processes are applied to plastics that have already been made into sheet form. The sheets are subjected to heat and pressure, to produce container-like shapes. There are many variations of the basic methods described here. Figure 14.4 illustrates *simple pressing*, in which the heated sheet is clamped into position over

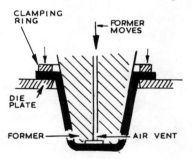

Fig 14.4 Simple pressing

the die plate, and then pressed into shape by the former. In this method, the inside shape will be the more accurate. Figure 14.5 illustrates *vacuum-forming*, in which the sheet is clamped to the mould, and sucked in to produce the shape. Compressed air is used to eject the finished moulding, and to accelerate the cooling. This method produces mouldings whose outside is the more accurate, but causes thinning, and is unsuitable if the thickness must be uniform. Part-spherical forms can be produced by *blow-forming* (fig. 14.6), without the aid of a mould. If other forms are required, the material can be blown into a mould (fig. 14.7), but this method tends to cause local thinning.

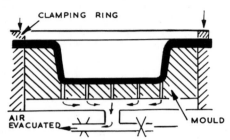

Fig 14.5 Vacuum-forming

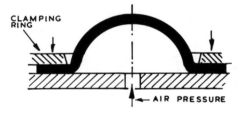

Fig 14.6 Blow-forming without mould

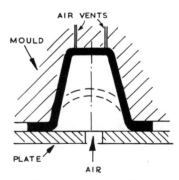

Fig 14.7 Blow-forming with mould

14.4.3 Casting. Suitable plastics materials can be cast using similar techniques to those used for metals. The moulds can be of lead, rubber, or PVC. Casting can be used to produce film, by spreading the molten material on to a polished rotating drum or band, and removing when solid, using take-off rolls. The speed of cooling, and the stretching action of the take-off rolls can be varied to produce a range of properties.

14.4.4 Laminating. In high-pressure laminating, paper or woven fabric is impregnated with a thermosetting plastics material (called the resin), dried, and then several of these impregnated sheets are heated under pressure, to form the laminate. This method can be applied to the manufacture of tubes, by winding the material on to a mandrel, while heat and pressure are applied by rollers. The tube is 'cured' by further heating, before removal from the mandrel.

In the low-pressure technique, the laminate is built up, layer by layer, on to a former of wood, plaster, or plastics. The reinforcement is glass fibre woven into sheets, using textile techniques. Each layer is impregnated with resin, applied by brush, and the resin is allowed to become tacky before the next layer is applied. When the lay-up is completed, the assembly is cured before removal from the former. The weave of the reinforcement is important, because it controls the strength and the 'directional' properties of the laminate.

14.5 Joining and machining

Suitable plastics materials can be joined using a solvent or cement. Joining can also be done by welding, using a filler rod, or by heat and pressure. The latter process is similar to the seam-welding of metals.

Plastics materials can be machined using conventional methods, but it must be realised that most plastics materials have a relatively low softening-point, and so cutting conditions must be studied carefully. Plastics are often brittle, and so shock-loading and vibrations must be prevented. Special attention must be paid to the removal of swarf, because many of these plastics produce a powdery swarf that hinders cutting action, and may even cause tool breakage.

Summary

1 A plastics material is organic, and capable of flow under suitable conditions at some time in its history.
2 Plastics materials are classified as (*a*) thermosoftening (or thermo-plastic) plastics, and (*b*) thermohardening (or thermosetting) plastics. The former can be resoftened indefinitely by the application of heat.
3 In addition to the basic materials, a plastics material may include a filler and a plasticiser, and, in the case of thermohardening plastics, a hardener also.
4 Typical thermosoftening plastics materials are cellulose plastics, vinyl plastics, condensation plastics, and polyesters.

5   Typical thermohardening plastics materials are phenolic plastics, aminoplastics, polyurethane, epoxy resins, and laminates.
6   Manipulation methods are classified as moulding, forming and pressing, casting, and laminating.
7   Certain plastics materials can be joined by using a solvent or a cement, or by welding.
8   Plastics materials can be machined using conventional methods, but care must be taken to avoid overheating, and damage due to shock-loading or vibration.

Questions

Set A
1   What are the implications of the grouping of plastics materials into two main groups?
2   Examine a number of articles made in plastics, and indicate the type of plastics used, and the reason for their use.
3   Continue the examination of the above articles, to determine the method used in their manufacture.

Set B (questions requiring further study)
4   List a number of parts now made in plastics materials, which were originally made from metal. Discuss the possible reasons for the change of material.
5   Prepare a study on designing in plastics materials.

Chapter 15
Metal-cutting Tools and Machine Tools

15.1 Rake and clearance angles

Figure 15.1 represents the cross-section through a simple metal-cutting tool (the direction of cutting is relative, and is obtained either by moving the tool to the left, or the workpiece to the right). The *rake angle* controls the chip formation, and is in turn governed by the mechanical properties of the material being cut. The force F acting upon the tool is reduced by increasing the rake angle, as shown in fig. 15.2. The tool, however, is weakened by increasing the rake angle, and so each increase ceases to be effective when the weakening exceeds the benefit gained by reducing the force acting upon the tool. In general, a small rake angle is used to cut brittle materials, and a large rake angle to cut ductile materials, as shown in table 15.1.

Table 15.1

Material being cut	Hard brass, bronze, and cast Iron	High-carbon steel, medium cast iron, brass and bronze	Medium-carbon steel, soft cast iron, brass and bronze	Low-carbon steel	Aluminium, and light alloys
rake	0°	8°	15°	25°	40°

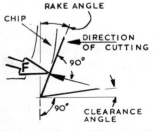

Fig 15.1 Cutting tool characteristics

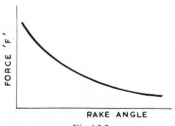

Fig 15.2

The rake shown in fig. 15.1 is positive, but in some cases it may be negative, as shown in fig. 15.3, to direct the force towards a thicker section of the tool. The *clearance angle* is introduced to prevent the tool from rubbing on the surface already cut. Its magnitude depends

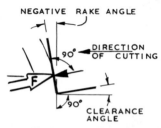

Fig 15.3 Negative rake

upon the shape of the surface being cut, but it is kept as small as possible to avoid weakening the tool.

15.2 Chip formation

Research workers have classified chip formation into *tear* and *shear*. Tear (fig. 15.4) involves compression of the workpiece material adjacent to the tool face, so that a crack runs ahead of the cutting tool, and towards the body of the workpiece. The chip is highly deformed, and the workpiece material is relatively undeformed. Cutting takes place intermittently, and there is no movement of the workpiece material over the tool face.

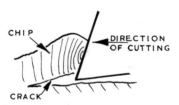

Fig 15.4 Chip formation by tear

15.2.1 In the formation of the chip by shear, there is a general movement of the chip over the tool face. Chip formation by shear may be continuous or be discontinuous. In continuous chip formation, the pressure of the workpiece builds up until the material fails by slip along the line SS (fig. 15.5); in practice, the inside of the chip displays the 'steps' produced by the intermittent slip, but the outside of the chip is burnished smooth by the action of the chip rubbing upon the tool face. Continuous chip formation is associated with ductile workpiece materials, and cutting tools with a large rake angle.

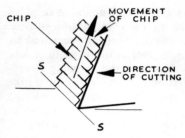

Fig 15.5 Continuous chip
formation by shear

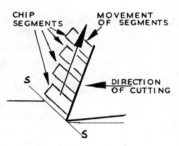

Fig 15.6 Discontinuous chip
formation by shear

15.2.2. In discontinuous chip formation, the pressure builds up but produces complete shear, so that the chip is in the form of segments, as in fig. 15.6. Discontinuous chip formation is associated with brittle workpiece material, and cutting tools with a small rake angle.

15.2.3 The formation of built-up edge (fig. 15.7). Built-up edge is associated with continuous chip formation; it is produced by the underside of the chip becoming elongated, and, as a result of the combination of high temperature and pressure, some of the chip material becoming welded to the tool face. As cutting continues, the material

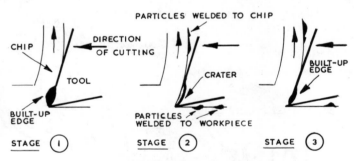

Fig 15.7 Formation of built-up edge

piles up on the tool face, forming a dome over which the chip flows as it leaves the parent material. The chip movement and pressure cause the dome to become work-hardened, so that particles of it break away, and become welded to the chip and to the body of the workpiece. As the dome breaks down, some of the tool material breaks away as well, causing a crater to be produced on the tool face. After the breakdown of the dome, the built-up edge forms again.

The formation of the built-up edge, and its breakdown, take place very rapidly. The built-up edge is caused by the combination of heat and pressure—its formation can therefore be delayed or prevented by making the tool face smooth, by using a tool material with a low coefficient of friction with the workpiece material, and by using an efficient cutting fluid. The pressure can be reduced by having a large rake angle, and the tendency of welding to occur can be eliminated by making the cutting tool from a material that is non-metallic. The actual solution used in a specific case will depend upon the prevailing conditions.

15.3 The connection between cutting conditions and tool shape

It has already been stated that the magnitude of the rake angle depends mainly upon the mechanical properties of the workpiece material, and that of the clearance angle depends upon the tool and workpiece geometry. The location of the rake and clearance angles depends upon the tool and workpiece geometry and the direction of the tool feed. The 'development' of tool shape from a simple wedge will be considered using the following examples.

15.3.1. Figure 15.8 illustrates cutting applied to the turning of a flange which is narrower than the tool. The feed is radial, and a simple wedge tool, with a rake angle and a clearance angle, is adequate. If it is

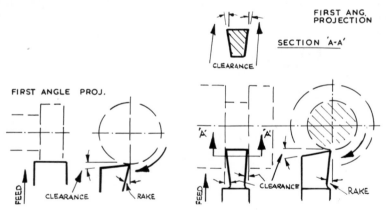

Fig 15.8 Turning with a simple wedge tool   Fig 15.9 Tool for turning a groove

required to produce a groove (or to part-off), it is necessary to introduce additional body clearance angles, to prevent the tool from rubbing the sides of the groove (fig. 15.9).

15.3.2. Sometimes the feed is as shown in fig. 15.10, which illustrates a planing tool. In this example, the cutting tool reciprocates relative to the workpiece—it cuts when moving in one direction, and returns before cutting again, so that the surface is cut by a number of passes. Before each pass, the tool is fed as shown, so that the material is removed in strips; the distance W is the feed per stroke. The cutting edge extends from J to L, but only the portion JK is engaged (the distance JK depends upon the depth of cut D).

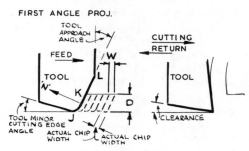

Fig 15.10 Planing tool

The principal cutting edge is, therefore, not at the nose, but to one side of it, this side depending on the direction of the feed, which means that the tool must be 'handed' accordingly. The *tool approach angle* controls the actual width of the chip (for a specific feed), and also the direction of the force N. It is also necessary to include a body clearance angle (called the *tool minor cutting edge angle*) to prevent the tool from rubbing on the surface. These angles are shown in fig. 15.10.

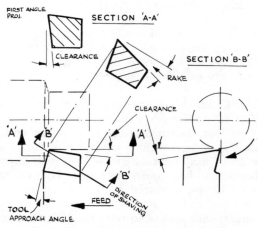

Fig 15.11 Tool for turning a long cylinder

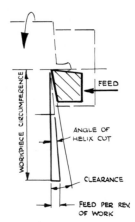

Fig 15.12 Clearance related to feed

15.3.3. When a long portion is turned using a lathe, it is necessary to employ a feed parallel to the axis (fig. 15.11). Examination of the plan view in fig. 15.11 will indicate that this operation is similar to planing, except that the feed action is continuous, and the chip is removed in the form of a helix. It is therefore necessary to ensure that the cutting clearance is large enough to prevent the tool from rubbing on the face of the 'step' produced during the turning operation. This clearance is related to the feed per revolution of the workpiece (see fig. 15.12). For example, when a bar of 50 mm is turned with a feed of 2·5 mm per revolution, the tangent of the helix angle will be $2·5/50\pi = 0·0157$, and so the minimum clearance angle will be $1°$. In practice, a clearance angle of between $4°$ and $6°$ is commonly employed.

15.3.4 Single point cutting tool angles. The nomenclature for single-point cutting-tool angles is laid down in BS 1296; this specification is based upon the rake angle normal to the cutting edge. Figure 15.13 shows the main features of BS 1296.

15.3.5. Spade drills and twist drills are closely related to the simple wedge tool. Figure 15.14 shows a spade drill. This type of drill can be made either from bar, flattened at the end and ground to shape, or from flat plate that is located and secured to a bar. The spade drill shown in fig. 15.14 includes rake angles, but many spade drills are completely flat, and so have zero rake angles. If this diagram is compared with fig. 15.12, it will be seen that the spade drill is similar to the single-point tool used to turn a cylinder, except that the spade drill has two cutting edges, and is used to produce an internal cylinder. The spade drill shown is ground to a point, so that each cutting edge has

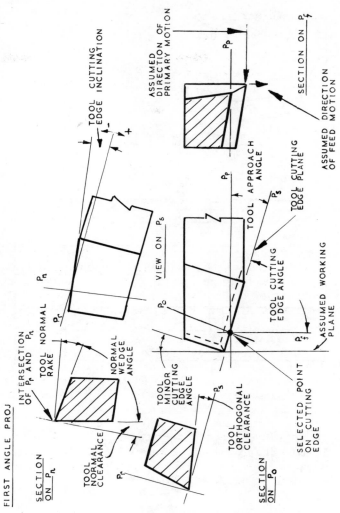

Fig 15.13 Single-point cutting tool angles

an approach angle. A general-purpose spade drill would have an approach angle of about 17°, but one for producing or finishing a flat-bottomed hole would not have an approach angle. The spade drill can be made with a back taper, so that a body clearance is produced, to prevent it from rubbing on the wall of the hole it has produced (this body clearance would be similar to the plan trail angle of a single-point tool).

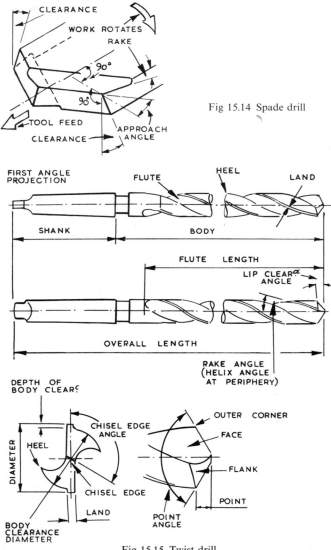

Fig 15.14 Spade drill

Fig 15.15 Twist drill

   The geometry of a twist drill is easier to understand if it is regarded as basically a flat spade drill twisted about its axis to form a helix; the helix angle produces the rake angle. The twist drill is more complicated because it is machined from a cylindrical bar (fig. 15.15); the reader will understand the geometry of the twist drill more readily if he examines a large twist drill at this stage. The end of a twist drill is pointed, to produce an approach angle; the point angle is usually 118°, but it may be between 90° and 140° if the drill is designed for a special operation. The point of a drill cannot be part of a cone, because the flanks would rub on the bottom of the hole being produced; and so the flanks are ground back to an angle of about 10°, to produce cutting clearances. The body of the drill must be shaped to prevent it from rubbing on the side of the hole; its diameter is therefore reduced, leaving a 'land'. It is also given a small back taper towards the shank. The helix angle is usually between about 22° and 27°, but may be between 10° and 45° for special work. The drill nomenclature shown in fig 15.15 is based on BS 328, Part 1.

15.3.6. Milling cutters can be broadly classified as end-cutting and peripheral-cutting. The shell end mill shown in fig. 15.16 is a typical end-cutting cutter. Each tooth acts like the simple metal-cutting tool shown in fig. 15.1, and must have cutting and body clearances. The

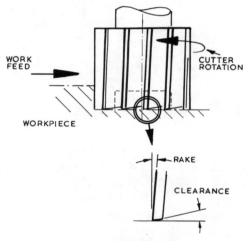

Fig 15.16 Shell end mill

teeth may be parallel to the axis of the cutter (zero rake), or be inclined, to produce a positive or negative rake angle, as required to suit the material being cut, or the cutting-tool material. Figure 15.17 shows a peripheral-cutting cutter. Again, the teeth must have cutting clearances, and the teeth may be radial (zero rake), or be inclined, to produce positive or negative rake. While the cutter is rotating about its own axis, the workpiece is fed towards it, so that, when each chip is removed, the surface produced is of trochoid form. This means that a larger clearance angle is required to prevent the heel of the tooth from rubbing on the surface; the clearance is usually in stages, as shown in fig. 15.17, so that adequate clearance is combined with tool strength. When a peripheral-cutting cutter is to cut a groove,

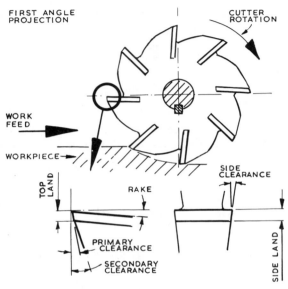

Fig 15.17 Peripheral-cutting cutter

the sides of each tooth must be ground back to produce body clearance, otherwise the teeth will rub on the sides of the groove already cut.

15.4 Investigations into metal cutting

A considerable amount of research work has been done on metal cutting, to study the formation of chips, the forces acting upon the tool, the best shape cutter for a specific job, the economics of tool life, etc. The forces acting upon a tool tip are measured by a tool dynamometer, to which the tool is secured. For example, the forces acting upon a lathe tool can be resolved as shown in fig. 15.18. The tangential force is usually the largest, and depends upon the tool cutting angles and the cutting conditions; the back force and the feed force depend upon the tool plan shape and the cutting conditions. The power consumed during cutting depends upon the tangential force, and so one of the objects of investigations is to reduce the tangential force without excessively weakening the tool (see also section 15.1).

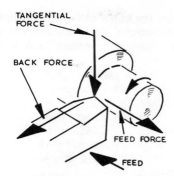

Fig 15.18 Forces acting on a lathe tool

The tool life (between regrinds) is also investigated. This depends upon cutting speed, the tool material, the workpiece material, and the finish required, as shown in the following expression:

$$VT^n = C$$

where V is the cutting speed, T is the tool life, C is a constant, and n depends upon the finish, workpiece material, and tool material (n is usually between $\frac{1}{5}$ and $\frac{1}{12}$).

The above expression gives an estimate of the tool life. It is usually necessary to consider the most economical compromise between the speed of metal removal, and the cost of removing and regrinding the tool, and resetting the machine to continue production. The most economical life for a tool cutting edge may thus be as low as thirty minutes, or as high as 300 minutes actual cutting time.

15.5 Cutting fluids
It has already been stated (section 15.2) that cutting involves pressure on the tool face, and chip movement across the tool face. This causes tool overheating, and results in tool wear, which in turn limits the cutting speed that can be used.

15.5.1. The primary functions of a cutting fluid are to lubricate the chip and tool, and to keep the tool cool by dissipating the heat. This results in a longer tool life, with greater metal removal rate, reduced power consumption, and better surface finish. The cutting fluid should also cool the chip and the workpiece, and carry the chips away from the cutting zone.

15.5.2. The lubrication function is best done by an oil-base solution, usually with the addition of sulphur in some form. The specific heat of this type of fluid is rather low, but there is little possibility of the chip adhering to the tool face.

The cooling function demands a fluid with a high specific heat; and a water-base fluid is indicated. Such solutions are prepared by adding certain soaps to water, to form the familiar milky liquid.

15.5.3. The choice of fluid depends upon the material, and the type of machining to be done. The water-base solutions are cheaper, but, whichever is chosen, the following properties are important.

(a) The fluid must not be injurious to the operator, and should not be offensive by smelling unpleasantly or marking clothing.

(b) It must 'keep' well, and must not make a chemical attack on the work, the machine tool, or the container in which it is kept.

15.5.4. The following are brief notes on the different engineering materials, and the cutting fluids employed on them. Cast iron is turned, bored, milled, and planed in the dry condition, as the graphite which it contains acts as a lubricant, and also breaks up the chips. Tapping and reaming of cast iron require a mineral oil. Mild steel is generally machined with a water-base solution, except that in some cases an oil-base solution is preferred for finish turning, to give a better surface. Machine tapping and reaming, and deep boring operations are best done with oil. Hand tapping is done with lard oil. Alloy steels, particularly the harder grades, usually require oil-base fluids for all normal machining work, and lard oil for hand tapping and reaming; rape oil is used for machine broaching. Brasses and bronzes require water-base solutions. Aluminium may be machined dry: if a water-base solution is used, care must be taken in selecting a suitable fluid, as aluminium is readily attacked by alkaline solutions.

Most metals are ground with water in which a little carbonate of soda has been dissolved.

In all cases, a good flow of coolant is advisable, providing that it does not spoil the operator's view of the work. Occasional drops of water falling on a heated tool can easily cause it to crack. This is particularly important with the carbide-tipped tools (see later in this chapter), and, unless a really good coolant flow can be arranged, dry cutting is best with these tools.

15.5.5. The problem of lubrication can be reduced by the inclusion of lead or manganese sulphide in the metal to be cut; a typical application is free-cutting steel, for bars to be machined by capstan or automatic lathes.

15.6 Cutting-tool materials
It has been implied that the rate of metal removal is limited by the tool material. Research indicates that, although the rate of metal removal can be increased by increasing the depth of cut and the feed rate, the

most promising approach is to attempt to increase the cutting speed, because the force required to perform the cutting does not increase as a result. The solution is not easy, because the tool face becomes hotter when the cutting speed is increased, and so tends to become softer and weaker. Developments in cutting-tool materials have been directed towards the retention of hardness and strength at elevated temperatures; this property is known as *red hardness*. Other properties required of a cutting-tool material are low coefficient of friction, resistance to built-up edge, toughness, and good compressive strength. Not all of these properties are present in one material, and the choice of material depends to a large extent upon the conditions expected during cutting, and the characteristics of the machine tool to be used.

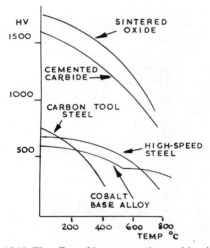

Fig 15.19 The effect of heat on cutting-tool hardness

Cutting-tool materials can be classified as (*a*) ferrous materials, (*b*) non-ferrous materials, and (*c*) non-metallic materials. Figure 15.19 shows the effect of heat upon the hardness of the principal cutting-tool materials, and it will be seen that the material can have either a fairly low hardness, retained at fairly high temperature, or a very high hardness which is lost easily, but which leaves the material still very hard.

15.6.1 Ferrous materials. *Plain carbon steels*, with about 0·7% carbon, hardened and tempered, are still in use for some cutting tools, such as large taps and dies, chisels and scrapers, and prototype form tools. These are unsuitable for cutting at high speeds, because they soften at temperatures over about 250°C.

High-speed steels contain between 14% and 22% tungsten (according to duty), and about 4% chromium. Five per cent cobalt is included if the workpiece material has high abrasive characteristics. They retain their hardness at temperatures up to about 660°C, and they must be hardened by quenching from about 1250°C to obtain full hardness. To reduce the costs, high-speed steel tools may be in the form of an 'end', butt-welded to a plain-carbon steel shank, or be in the form of a 'bit' attached to a holder.

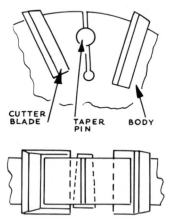

CUTTER
BLADE   TAPER   BODY
             PIN

Fig 15.20 Inserted cutter blades

15.6.2 Non-ferrous materials. *Cobalt-base alloys* contain about 33% chromium, 20% tungsten, 3% carbon and cobalt (remainder), and are extremely brittle: they cannot be forged, and are used as cast, no heat-treatment being necessary to develop hardness. These materials are used extensively as blades, inserted into a cast-iron milling-cutter body (fig. 15.20), or as a tip, applied to a carbon steel shank.

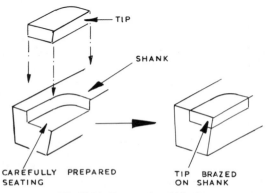

TIP

SHANK

CAREFULLY   PREPARED   TIP   BRAZED
SEATING   ON   SHANK

Fig 15.21 Cemented carbide tip

Cemented carbide tool material consists of a mixture of tungsten carbide and cobalt particles, sintered to produce tips that are clamped or brazed to a carbon steel shank (fig. 15.21), or applied as inserted blades. Owing to their brittleness, cemented carbide materials cannot be used for complete tools, and the tool-holding, and work-holding devices, as well as the machine tool, must be rigid and vibration free.

15.6.3 Non-metallic materials. *Sintered oxides* consist of at least 85% aluminium oxide, with other oxides, carbides, or nitrides to give additional strength. These materials have a high red-hardness, and are chemically inert, so that the formation of built-up edge is minimised. They can cut at high speeds, but demand even greater rigidity and freedom from vibration than do cemented carbides. They are used in the form of tips that are brazed, bonded, or clamped to a shank.

Diamond is used to finish, turn, and bore non-ferrous metals, producing an excellent surface finish. Very high speeds and fine feeds are used; the diamond tool is brazed to a holder which is in turn held in a suitable tool-holder. Special machine tools are used, with bearings and drive designed to give minimum vibration.

15.6.4. The actual cutting speed depends upon the nature of the workpiece material, the workpiece shape, the condition of the machine tool, and the cutting-tool material. The following table gives the relative cutting speeds for three types of cutting-tool material when used in the centre lathe upon three common engineering materials.

Type of tool	Grey cast iron	Mild steel	Soft tool steel
plain high-carbon steel	20–40	20–40	10–20
high-speed steel	60–120	40–120	20–40
carbide-tipped tool	200–350	300–600	50–100

15.7 Storage and distribution of tools

The machine-shop tool-store should always have an adequate stock of sharpened tools of all the standard shapes. Any special tools should be prepared in the tool-room, before the job for which they are required is put on the machines. This preparation is automatic in a well-organised workshop; in other shops it is done haphazardly, with considerable waste of time and temper.

The grinding of all tools must be done in the tool-room, by a specially trained worker; any other course is fatal to fast and accurate production. Two conditions are essential if this method is to succeed:

(*a*) There must be no off-hand grinding machines in the shop, and the management must be adamant against the specious arguments for their introduction.

(*b*) There must always be a sharpened tool ready to be exchanged for the blunted tool sent back by the machine operator. The tool-grinder must have an efficient deputy. If both the tool-grinder and the deputy are absent, the tool-room foreman must grind the tools himself. A minor but important point in tool exchange is to suppress firmly the self-appointed critics in the tool-room who pass remarks about damaged tools. If a particular worker is using too many tools, the shop foreman should investigate quietly and tactfully, and try to improve the position by logical discussion.

15.8 Tool grinding

The grinding of single-point tools is usually divided into two operations. The first operation is to grind the forged tool to the shape required, including the particular angles required, as previously mentioned using a fairly coarse grinding wheel, to obtain a fast rate of metal removal using—say a 30H. A keen cutting edge is then obtained with a finer wheel—say a 60J (see fig. 22.9).

Immediately the cutting edge is dulled, the tool should be withdrawn from service, and reground. If a tool is kept in use after the edge is dull, the cutting force will rise rapidly, the work surface will be rough, and, due to overheating, the cutting edge may crumble away entirely. If the tool is allowed to reach this state, a good deal of grinding will be required to restore the correct shape, and a large amount of valuable material will have to be ground away. On the other hand, if the tool is reground at the right time, the sharpening operation can be done quickly, and with little loss of material.

The working face of the grinding wheel should not be allowed to develop a wavy surface, as this will prevent the correct shaping of tools. A diamond in a special holder is passed across the wheel face to true it up immediately any hollow places develop. A good operator will not use the centre of the wheel face all the time, but will try to use as much of the width as possible, thus avoiding rapid wear of the wheel at one place.

Tool grinding is usually done dry. Driblets of water falling on a hot tool are liable to cause fine surface cracks, particularly near the cutting edge, which is likely to be the hottest place during grinding operations. Surface cracks near the cutting edge will cause rapid crumbling when the tool is put to work. Dry grinding sets up considerable heat, and consequently special grinding wheels are required; these have cool cutting qualities. In all cases the grinding must be done with a light pressure, and, if the tool shows signs of 'blueing', grinding should be stopped for a short time.

Wet grinding of tools is sometimes practised, but a deluge of water is required, consequently the progress of the work cannot be watched by the operator.

Safety precautions are very important in grinding. The tool-rest should fit as closely as possible to the wheel surface, to prevent any possibility of the work becoming wedged between the wheel and the rest. This wedging action is highly dangerous, and may cause a serious injury to the operator's hands, or may lead to a burst wheel. In dry grinding, a dust-removal system is essential, and a transparent shield over the front of the wheel is a safeguard against sparks which may fly out and burn the operator or his clothing.

15.9 Movements of cutter and workpiece
In the foregoing sections, the emphasis is mainly upon the cutter geo-metry and materials, but in section 15.3 reference is made to the cutter/workpiece relationship. In this section, this relationship is con-sidered in more detail.

15.9.1 Figure 15.22 illustrates a reciprocating tool producing a V-shaped groove. In this example, the cutter or workpiece reciprocates to provide the cutting motion, and the depth of cut (feed) is introduced at the start of each cutting stroke. The shape of the groove depends en-tirely upon the tool shape, although the depth of the groove depends upon the depth to which the tool is fed.

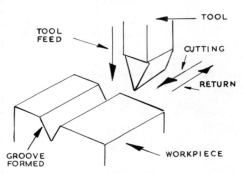

Fig 15.22 Forming using a reciprocating tool

Figure 15.23 illustrates the equivalent to this, when a V-shaped tool is used to cut a groove in a cylindrical bar. In this example, the work-piece rotation provides continuous cutting motion, and the tool is fed radially. Again, the shape of the groove depends upon the shape of the tool. These two examples are typical *forming* operations, and forming can be defined as shape-production in which the shape is a negative of the tool shape. This method is used extensively for small work on capstan and automatic lathes, etc., but cannot be used for forms in-volving a long cutting edge, because of tool chatter, although a long

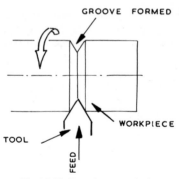

Fig 15.23 Forming on a lathe

form may be produced by a group of cutters placed side by side, providing this produces the form-accuracy required.

Form relief. A form tool requires front clearance, like other tools, and the front face of the tool must therefore have the profile inclined at the clearance angle. This is known as *form relief*. The tool is sharpened on the tool breast only, as shown in fig. 15.24.

There are various methods of producing the form-relieved profile, but the following is commonly employed. A flat plate-gauge is made by hand filing to the reverse of the *tool nose*. From this gauge, a mild-steel crushing roller is made in the centre lathe: the diameter of this roller is not important, but the profile is carefully made to fit the gauge exactly. The crushing roller is now used to make a reversed profile on a grinding wheel. To do this, the wheel is roughed out by diamond dressing, and then revolved slowly, in contact with the crushing roller, which revolves in unison with it, and is gradually forced into the wheel surface.

The form tool is machined fairly closely to the shape, and then hardened, and is mounted in a vice on the grinding-machine table. The

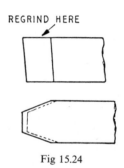

Fig 15.24

tool is inclined at the desired relief or clearance angle, and the front
face is ground to shape by the wheel. The process is shown in fig. 15.25.
If a number of form tools of identical pattern are required, the grind-

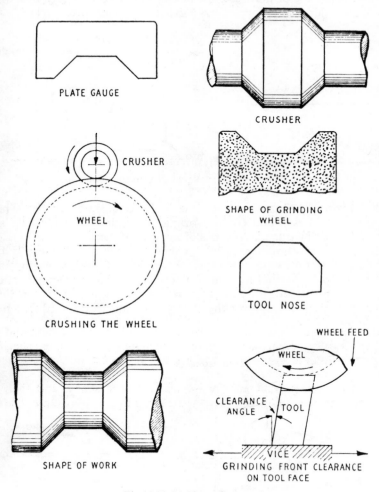

PLATE GAUGE

CRUSHER

CRUSHER

WHEEL

SHAPE OF GRINDING
WHEEL

CRUSHING THE WHEEL

TOOL NOSE

WHEEL FEED

WHEEL

CLEARANCE
ANGLE   TOOL

SHAPE OF WORK

VICE

GRINDING FRONT CLEARANCE
ON TOOL FACE

Fig 15.25 Making a form tool

ing wheel is shaped by the mild-steel crushing roller, and is then used
to grind a hardened steel roller, which will serve to recrush the wheel
many times.

It was emphasised that the original flat gauge is made to the shape
of the tool nose. Note that the profile depth is represented by the

distance L in fig. 15.26. This distance is measured at right angles to the front of the tool. The form depth produced on the work is, of course, represented by the distance M. Widths will not be affected. In making the flat gauge, the distance L must be calculated from the distance M, the relationship being $L = M \cos \theta$, where θ = clearance angle.

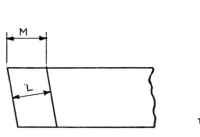

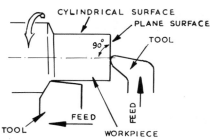

Fig 15.26   Fig 15.27 Generating on a lathe

15.9.2. Figure 15.27 illustrates a lathe tool producing a cylinder. The cutting motion is produced by workpiece rotation, and the feed is continuous and parallel to the axis of rotation. If the feed is at an angle to the axis of rotation (fig. 15.28), a cone is produced. If the feed is at right angles to the axis, a plane surface is produced. In these examples, the direction of the tool movement controls the shape produced, and the shape of the tool produces the correct cutting action. When the machine movements control the shape, it is said to be produced by *generating*.

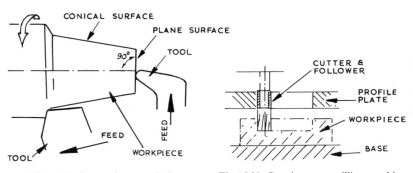

Fig 15.28 Generating on a lathe   Fig 15.29 Copying on a milling machine

15.9.3. If the shape is too complicated to employ simple machine movements, and too large to employ forming, the tool is made to follow a path determined by a model, a template, or a cam. Figure 15.29 shows this applied to milling. When the shape is determined by some device other than the tool or the machine movements, it is said to be produced by *copying*.

15.9.4. Forming is often combined with generating copying. For example, a screw thread can be regarded as a helical groove of V-form. Figure 15.30 illustrates the production of a screw thread; it will be seen that the thread groove is *formed*, and the helical path of the groove is *generated*.

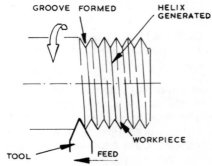

Fig 15.30 Screw-thread production (forming and generating combined)

15.10 The requirements of a machine tool

It has been shown that the correct production of a shape requires not only a correctly shaped cutting tool, but also the correct position and movement of the tool and the workpiece. The latter are obtained by the machine tool, the main requirements of which can be summarised as follows:

(*a*) to position the workpiece relative to the cutting tool,
(*b*) to secure the workpiece,
(*c*) to position the cutting tool,
(*d*) to secure the cutting tool,
(*e*) to provide the required workpiece and tool movement, and control of that movement,
(*f*) to provide a suitable range of cutting speeds and feeds,
(*g*) to incorporate means of lubricating itself, and a system for the circulation and filtering of the cutting fluid.

The machine must be designed so that the controls are within easy reach of the operator, without hazarding his safety.

15.10.1 Speed progressions. Cutting speeds and feeds have already been mentioned. In the majority of machine tools, various materials have to be machined, and in certain cases either the workpiece or the tool diameter may vary. Consider the case of a centre lathe of 300-mm swing (the term 'swing' is discussed in section 18.1). If medium-carbon steel is being machined at 25m/min, and the workpiece diameter is 300 mm, the speed of the lathe spindle is determined as follows:

$$\text{cutting speed} = \text{circumference} \times N \qquad \text{where } N = \text{revs/min}$$

i.e. $$25 = \frac{300\pi}{1000} \times N$$

from which $$N = \frac{250}{3\pi} = 26\cdot5 \text{ revs/minute}$$

On the other hand, if the lathe is required to turn a 25-mm diameter brass bar at 60 m/min, then the lathe spindle must revolve at

$$60 \times 1000/25\pi = 765 \text{ revs/min.}$$

These two cases are somewhat extreme, since they would not usually both occur on one lathe in a well-arranged workshop, they do, however, illustrate the problem involved in arranging the spindle speeds.

The work in large workshops is always 'routed' to suitable machines, but nevertheless almost all machine tools require a number of different speeds. The general-purpose lathe in the small workshop or tool-room requires the widest possible speed range; the limiting feature is gearbox design.

Returning to the 300-mm-swing lathe already mentioned, suppose the maximum and minimum speeds are 500 revs/min and 20 revs/min. The minimum cutting speed for 300-mm diameter work will be $300\pi/1000 \times 20 = 18\cdot8$ m/min. The maximum cutting speed for 30-mm diameter work will be $30\pi/1000 \times 500 = 47\cdot1$ m/min. There will be a number of intermediate speeds, and the lay-out of these speeds is of great importance.

Suppose there are to be eleven speeds in all, then one method of arranging them would be in *arithmetic progression*. With this method, the same addition is made between each speed, and the eleven speeds would be as follows:

Speed number	1	2	3	4	5	6	7	8	9	10	11
Revs/min	20	68	116	164	212	260	308	356	404	452	500

The addition made in each case is therefore 48 (revs/min), and the formula can be deduced as follows:

Let $$N_1 = \text{first speed}$$
$$N_n = \text{last speed}$$
$$n = \text{number of speeds}$$

Then the speed addition $(a) = \dfrac{N_n - N_1}{n - 1}$

$$\text{In the case quoted } a = \frac{500 - 20}{10} = 48$$

If the cutting speed is assumed to be 18 m/min, the workpiece diameter for which each spindle speed is best suited is as follows:

Speed number	1	2	3	4	5	6	7	8	9	10	11
Revs/min of spindle	20	68	116	164	212	260	308	356	404	452	500
Workpiece dia., in mm	288	84·5	49·5	35	27	22	18·6	16·1	14·2	12·7	11·5

This arrangement is unsuitable because the speeds are not evenly distributed over the range.

The usual method is to arrange machine-tool speeds in *geometric progression*. This involves multiplying each speed by a constant to obtain the next higher speed. Using the same symbols as before, and letting r = multiplier,

$$N_1 \times r = N_2, N_2 \times r = N_3, \text{ and so on.}$$

There will thus be one less multiplication than the number of speeds in the range, and the general formulae are as follows:

$$(1) \quad N_n = N_1 r^{(n-1)}$$

$$(2) \quad r = \sqrt[(n-1)]{\frac{N_n}{N_1}}$$

These may be rewritten:

$$(3) \quad \log N_n = \log N_1 + (n-1) \log r$$

$$(4) \quad \log r = \frac{\log N_n - \log N_1}{(n-1)}$$

For the speed range 20 to 500 revs/min, with eleven speeds, the formulae may be applied as follows:

$$(1) \quad 500 = 20 \, r^{10}$$

$$(2) \quad r = \sqrt[10]{\frac{500}{20}}$$

$$= 1·38$$

That is, r is the tenth root of 25.

The spindle speeds so obtained and the workpiece diameter for which each speed would give a cutting speed of 18 m/min is as follows:

Speed number	1	2	3	4	5	6	7	8	9	10	11
Revs/min of spindle	20	27·6	38·2	52·6	72·6	100	138·3	191	264	365	500
Workpiece dia, in mm	288	207	150	109	79	57·2	41·5	30	21·7	15·7	11·5

This arrangement is much better because the speeds are more evenly distributed over the range

The actual speeds chosen will depend on the particular machine tool and its function. Thus a small pillar drill which takes drills from 1·5 mm to 10 mm diameter will have a higher set of speeds than a large radial drill with a maximum drill size of 60 mm diameter. Again, a shaping machine may have four speeds in all, to accommodate different materials and tools used; while a general-purpose lathe, with its versatile range of performance, may have twelve, or even sixteen, speeds.

Summary

1 The basic angles of a metal-cutting tool are (a) the rake angle (which is governed by the mechanical properties of the metal being cut, and (b) the clearance angle (which depends mainly upon the workpiece geometry).

2 During cutting, the chip may be formed by tear or by shear. The chip formed by shear may be continuous or discontinuous, depending mainly upon the characteristics of the workpiece material. Continuous chip formation may cause a built-up edge to be formed.

3 The shape of the cutting tool depends not only upon the mechanical properties of the workpiece material but also upon the shape to be produced, and the tool and workpiece movements that are used to produce that shape.

4 Cutting fluids are used to lubricate the chip and tool, to dissipate heat, and to flush away the swarf.

5 The rate of cutting is usually limited by the heat that is generated; new cutting-tool materials have been developed, mainly with a view to overcoming the effect of heat. Cutting-tool materials can be classified as (a) ferrous materials, (b) non-ferrous materials, and (c) non-metallic materials.

6 A shape can be produced either by forming or by generating, or the two in combination. If the tool is controlled by some device other than the machine movements, the process is said to be copying.

7 The machine tool must have means of locating and holding the tool and the workpiece. The speed of workpiece and tool must be suitable for a wide range of materials and workpiece sizes.

Questions

Set A

1 Discuss the considerations which determine the most economic life for the cutting edge of various tools.

2 A boring tool with a depth of section of 25 mm is boring a 125-mm-diameter hole. Calculate the minimum front clearance. Suggest a means whereby this front clearance angle may be reduced.

3 A planer tool is cutting with a depth of 5 mm and a feed per stroke of 0·25 mm. The chip of metal presses on the tool with a pressure of 800 MN/m^2. What is the force on the tool?

4 Briefly describe two methods of generating a flat surface. Would you consider the lathe parting-off tool to be a form tool? Give reasons for your answer.

5 Complete the following table for not less than five machine tools: the centre lathe is given as an example:

Machine tool	Operation	Cutting motion	Feed motion	Motion to adjust cutting depth
centre lathe	generating cylinder	work revolves	tool moves in straight line	tool moves in straight line

6 Describe the process of hardening a high-speed steel tool. Explain why a special furnace is required for this process.

7 The following are all centre lathe operations: generating a cylinder, generating a cone, generating two parallel flat surfaces, producing a round hole, producing an internal thread, forming annular grooves on a cylinder. Take each operation in turn, suggest another machine tool, and briefly describe how the operation would be performed on this machine tool.

8 Show whether the following speeds are in a geometric progression: 10·5, 11·27, 12·11, 13, 13·96, 15, 16·22, 17·42, 18·71
   rev/min. If necessary, correct the speeds to give a true geometric
   progression.
9 Calculate a suitable speed range for a drilling machine for HSS
   twist drills from 10 mm to 25 mm in diameter.
10 Lay out a speed range with twelve speeds for a centre lathe, starting at 14 revs/min. The highest speed is to give a cutting speed of
   0·6 m/s on a bar 25 mm in diameter.
11 A geometric progression is to have eight speeds, beginning with
   18 revs/min, and extending to 90·2 revs/min. Calculate the common ratio, and the remaining six speeds.
12 Suggest one machine-tool part which could be made from each of
   the following: cast iron, medium-carbon steel, nickel-chrome steel,
   phosphor-bronze, mild-steel sheet.

Set B (questions requiring further study)
13 Discuss the various methods used in the machine-shop to produce
   flat surfaces. Divide the methods into generating processes and
   forming processes.
14 Write an account of the methods of manufacture of metallic carbide tips for cutting tools.
15 Discuss the influence of top rake on lathe form-tools, and explain
   how the V-thread form-tool is modified if top rake is used.

Chapter 16
Marking-out and Location of Work

16.1 Methods of marking out

When a casting or forging is received for machining, it will be larger than the finished size by an amount known as the *machining allowance*; furthermore, holes too small or too intricate for forging or founding may be required. The article is therefore *marked out*. This is done by scribing lines to indicate the position and extent of the necessary machining.

To carry out this work, certain datum planes are required. The common datum is the surface plate or 'marking-out table' which is described in Chapter 17. A number of instruments and fixtures are used for marking, measuring, or holding the work. The try-square is used to set up machined surfaces at right angles to the surface plate, and also to serve as a guide for a hardened steel scriber with which lines are marked. A scribing block (fig. 16.1) or a height gauge is used to scribe lines which will be parallel to the surface plate, and the hooked end of its scriber is used to check relative heights from the surface plate. Scribing compasses of several sizes are required, and also hermaphrodite compasses or 'jennies'. These latter are shown in fig. 16.2. The centre punch (fig. 16.3) is used to make the light punch-marks which define important lines and their intersections.

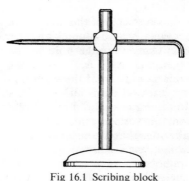

Fig 16.1 Scribing block

Fig 16.2 Hermaphrodite compasses ('jennies')

Fig 16.3 Centre punch

Two common fixtures are the angle plate, which holds work at right angles to the surface plate, and the V-blocks which are used in pairs to hold cylindrical work, so that its axis is parallel to the surface plate.

For rough castings and forgings, it is usual to chalk the surfaces, to give a background for the scribed lines; but for smooth machined work the surfaces are rubbed with Prussian blue, or with copper sulphate solution. This latter solution leaves a thin coating of copper on the work. For the finest marking out it is best to clean the work, wipe on a little oil, and polish with a clean rag. A hard scriber will then make fine smooth lines on most machined surfaces except hard steel. Non-ferrous metals usually scribe quite readily. It has been mentioned that lines for machining are ruled, but another important function of marking out is to 'try up' the casting or forging to see that it is machined to the best advantage. For this reason, the work is laid out from the part drawing, the centre lines being scribed and centre punched, and the machining lines measured from these centre lines.

Consider the casting shown in fig. 16.4. The two square end faces are to be machined, and the rough cored hole must be bored so that its centre is 125 mm from each face, and its axis is parallel to the two faces. There is intended to be a 3-mm machining allowance on each face, and 6-mm on the diameter of the hole. If the machinist recklessly machines both faces equally, and obtains an overall length of 250 mm, he may discover later that the rough hole has been cast out of centre, and cannot then be bored to give the 125-mm dimensions. A preliminary marking out would reveal the eccentricity of the hole, which could then be allowed for by distributing the machining to suit.

The method of marking out would be as follows. Place the casting on one end-face on the surface plate. With the hooked end of the scribing block, make sure that the top face is reasonably parallel with the surface plate: some packing or wedging from the plate may be required. In the centre hole, knock in a wooden 'false centre' at each side. With the 'jennies', find the centre of the cored hole, and mark it at each

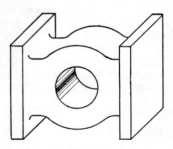 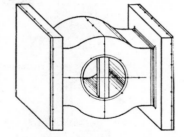

Fig 16.4 Casting   Fig 16.5 Casting marked-out for machining

side on the false centres. With the pointed end of the finger of the scribing block, make sure that the centre at each side is the same height from the plate; if this is not so, then adjust the centres a little, or tilt the casting slightly, or make both adjustments, depending on what will best suit the final machining.

When the final setting has been decided, firmly mark the centre line at each side with the scribing block, and centre-punch it. Lower the scribing-block point 125 mm, and scribe the machining mark all round the edge of the lower square face, and centre-punch it. Raise the scribing-block point 250 mm, scribe round the edge of the upper square face, and centre-punch it. Mark the circle for boring the centre hole. The completely marked-out casting is shown in fig. 16.5.

The use of V-blocks is illustrated in the marking out of a keyway in a shaft. The shaft is placed in V-blocks which are known to be a pair. The height of the shaft from the plate can be tried at each end by the scribing-block hooked end. If the shaft has no centre marks in the ends, these can be made with the jennies, or four lines can be scribed with the scribing block, the shaft being turned through 90° after each line is scribed. The alternative methods are shown in fig. 16.6.

Fig 16.6 Marking a shaft centre

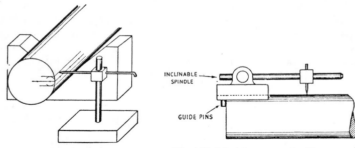

Fig 16.7 Marking out a keyway   Fig 16.8 Marking out end of keyway

From the centre, a centre line is now drawn to the edge, and continued along the shaft. Small dividers are set to half the keyway width, and two part circles are scribed. These part circles are now used to set the scribing block, and the upper and lower edges of the keyway are marked. The shaft is now as shown in fig. 16.7. The try-square is used to mark the depth of the keyway. If the shaft is short, it may be stood on end, so that the inner end of the keyway may be scribed with the scribing block; otherwise, a special type of scribing block, with guide-pins and an inclinable spindle, may be used, as shown in fig. 16.8 The base is V-shaped, to rest on the shaft.

It is often advisable to machine some faces of a casting before marking out other important dimensions. The machined faces, which must be chosen carefully, and machined with due regard to the final dimensions, are then used as datum faces.

The bracket shown in fig. 16.9 has two important dimensions: the 200-mm length, and the 100-mm rise from the base to the two holes. It is also important that the two holes should be coaxial. The base and

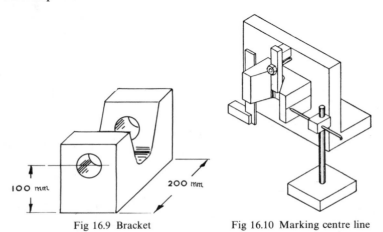

Fig 16.9 Bracket   Fig 16.10 Marking centre line

the two flat ends are carefully machined, and the casting is placed on a surface plate. The horizontal centre line for the two holes is marked with the scribing block, but the vertical centre line is rather more difficult. The bracket is mounted on an angle plate, and set with the end faces vertical, this setting being done with a try-square (fig. 16.10). The centre lines can then be drawn with the scribing block.

16.2 Accuracy of marking out

Ordinary marking out is done with a rule, and the limitations of the rule are mentioned in section 23.4.1. Several other factors tend to lower the accuracy still further: the width of a scribed line may be anything from 0·075 mm to 0·250 mm, the accuracy of punched inter-sections is often not very good, and cumulative errors arise. Over short lengths on flat surfaces, an accuracy of 0·250 mm can be maintained, but with angled surfaces, and lengths of 0·5 m, the maximum accuracy may be no better than 1 mm.

When a high degree of accuracy is required, methods other than plain marking out become essential. Certain of these methods will be described later.

16.3 Coordinates

Two systems or coordinate measurement are used in engineering; *polar coordinates* are distances measured along radial lines from a common centre. The three holes shown in fig. 16.11 are dimensioned in polar coordinates.

It is obvious that the accuracy with which the holes are positioned is dependent on correct setting out of the angles given, and of the distances from the common centre: as the distance from the centre increases, slight angular errors will cause greater displacement of the holes.

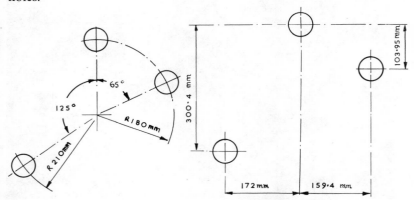

Fig 16.11 Polar coordinates   Fig 16.12 Rectangular coordinates

The possibility of error is lessened by the use of *rectangular coordinates*; the three holes shown in fig. 16.12 are set out by this method. The holes are now dimensioned relative to two centre lines at right angles to each other. In practice it is often possible to use flat-machined surfaces in preference to centre lines, and in such cases the measuring instruments used can be end standards instead of line standards (see section 23.3.3), thus simplifying the measurement. A further advantage is that the linear distances between hole centres can be calculated simply, and checked readily.

Fig 16.13 Jig-boring-machine   *Newall Engineering Co. Ltd*

The *jig-boring machine* (fig. 16.13) is used for the precise setting out and machining of holes (most jig-boring machines can be used for precision drilling, boring, grinding, tapping, and milling). The high degree of accuracy demands precise setting, and precise machining. The latter is ensured by having a heavy column to carry the boring head, and a rigid base to carry the workpiece. The boring spindle is carried in special bearings, to prevent deflection.

The positioning of the table requires special attention, because, if an ordinary leadscrew were to be used, the accumulation of errors would cause errors of an unacceptably high magnitude at the end of the table traverse (this problem is discussed in conjunction with the micrometer, in section 23.4.4).

If a leadscrew is used to position the table, a corrector system must be used; but the following alternative methods are now favoured.

(*a*) Optical setting. In this method, an accurately engraved metal scale is fitted to the stationary scale, and a datum line is engraved on the moving scale. The setting is viewed with the aid of a magnification system attached to the moving member.

(*b*) Digital read-out display. In this method, a diffraction-grating system produces a read-out display that gives the setting.

(*c*) Setting using rollers (fig. 16.14). This system uses a number of 25-mm rollers which are located on the bed of the machine. A micrometer unit is positioned on the bed to the nearest 25 mm by locating it over the appropriate roller. Finer setting is obtained by adjustment of the micrometer. The table is then advanced, so

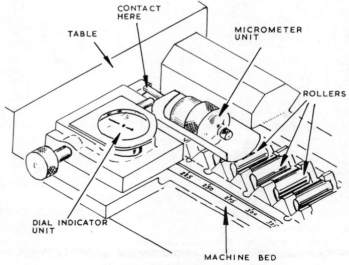

Fig 16.14 Setting using rollers

that it makes contact with the micrometer spindle. Variation in 'feel' is eliminated by making this contact through a dial indicator system, in which the needle indicates variation of feel. The table position is adjusted so that the needle is at zero every time. The dial indicator is discussed in section 23.5.1.

These machines are relatively expensive, but they provide a rapid way of setting out holes to an accuracy of 0·0025 mm. In large toolrooms they are indispensable. In addition, where the number of components required is relatively small, but accuracy is essential, the jig-boring machine is often used as a production machine, thereby eliminating the need for complicated and costly jigs.

In many small tool-rooms, the setting out of holes to close limits is still carried out by means of toolmaker's buttons. This method is fairly accurate, but very slow compared with the jig-boring machine; it is also much more dependent on individual skill.

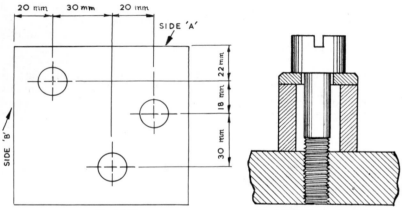

Fig 16.15   Fig 16.16 Toolmaker's button

Suppose three holes each 15 mm in diameter are to be bored in a plate to the dimensions shown in fig. 16.15. The sides A and B of the plate, and the top surface, will require to be machined flat and truly at right angles to each other. Three 6-mm tapped holes are marked out, drilled, and tapped, using a rule and any drilling machine. The toolmaker's button is a hollow cylinder carefully ground on the circumference and the ends. Three buttons are mounted as shown in fig. 16.15, each one being lightly secured by its setscrew. Each button must now be set concentric with the desired position of the 15-mm hole. The movements are made by lightly tapping the buttons with a piece of wood—an operation which requires a good sense of touch, and considerable patience. The measurement of the actual position is done

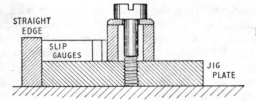

Fig 16.17 Setting a button

by various means, according to circumstance; but the commonest in-struments are slip-gauges, vernier height-gauge, or micrometer. An example is shown in fig. 16.17. Here the button is being set by slip-gauges from a straight-edge at the edge of the work, allowance being made, of course, for half the button diameter. In similar circumstances the tool-fitter might prefer to stand the jig plate on its edge on a sur-face plate, and then use the vernier height-gauge.

When all the buttons have been correctly positioned, and the hold-ing screws firmly secured, the plate is ready for machining. If the plate is of reasonable size, it is mounted on a centre lathe, and fixed with one button on the lathe centre line—i.e. when the plate revolves in the lathe, the button runs truly. The method of checking is illustrated in fig. 23.17. This is an assurance that the proposed hole is concentric with the lathe centre line. The button is removed, and a 15-mm-diameter hole is bored. Each button in turn is brought on the lathe centre line, removed, and the corresponding hole drilled.

The reader will remember that the original tapped hole for the button-setting screw was marked out by rule, and will not be con-centric with the final hole. Therefore, in boring the hole, the following

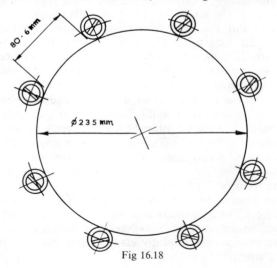

Fig 16.18

procedure is adopted: the original threaded hole is opened out with a short drill to, say, 12-mm diameter, this drill following the tapped hole to some extent. A small boring tool is now used to open out the hole, and with a number of light cuts the final hole is brought to the desired centre.

A common tool-room problem is the boring of holes equally spaced out round a circle. This may be done on the jig-boring machine if a circular dividing table is available, but the disc-and-button method is also practised.

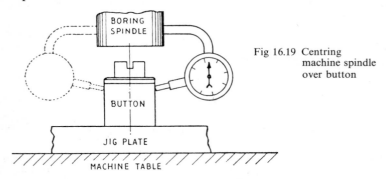

Fig 16.19 Centring machine spindle over button

For example, let us say that eight holes are to be bored very accurately at 45° to each other on a 250-mm-diameter pitch circle. Eight buttons, each 15 mm in diameter, are available. A mild steel disc 235 mm in diameter and about 15 mm thick is turned on a lathe. This is placed on the work, which has already been marked out by rule and compasses, and has eight small tapping holes. The disc and buttons are arranged as shown in fig. 16.18. The polar distances of 125 mm are thus fixed automatically, by keeping the buttons in contact with the disc. The chordal distance of 80·6 mm is set by slip-gauges. In some cases, the centre of the eight holes must be very accurately placed; if so, the disc must have a central hole, and it is then set by slip-gauges or other instruments, and secured to the work in the same way as a button.

In cases where the work is too large to be manoeuvred on a lathe, it may be placed on a vertical milling machine, or even a good radial drilling machine, and each button brought directly under the boring spindle, as shown in fig. 16.19. The dial indicator should give the same reading throughout a revolution of the boring spindle.

16.4 Jigs and fixtures
It has already been stated that the workpiece must be located relative to the cutting tool, and be secured in that position. After the workpiece has been marked out, it is still necessary to position it with respect to the machine movements, and to clamp it in that position before machining is started.

When several identical workpieces are to be produced, the need to mark out each part is eliminated by the use of jigs and fixtures, but if a casting or forging is involved, a trial workpiece is marked out, to ensure that the workpiece can be produced from it, and to ensure that ribs, cores, etc., have not become misplaced.

Jigs and fixtures are alike in that they both incorporate devices to ensure that the workpiece is correctly located and clamped, but they differ in that jigs incorporate means of tool guiding during the actual cutting operation, and fixtures do not. In practice, the only cutting tools that can be guided while actually cutting are drills, reamers, and similar cutters; and so jigs are associated with drilling operations, and fixtures with all other operations. Fixtures may incorporate means of setting the cutting tools relative to the location system.

The advantages of jigs and fixtures can be summarised as follows:

    (*a*) marking out and other measuring and setting-out methods are eliminated;

    (*b*) unskilled workers may proceed confidently and quickly in the knowledge that the workpiece can be positioned correctly, and the tools guided or set;

    (*c*) the assembly of parts is facilitated, since all components will be identical within small limits, and 'trying' and filing of work is eliminated;

    (*d*) the parts will be interchangeable, and, if the product is sold over a wide area, the problem of spare parts will be simplified.

Bolt holes often have 1·5-mm or even 3·0-mm clearance for the bolt, and the reader may doubt the necessity of making precision jigs for such work. It must be remembered that the jigs, once made, will be used on many components, and the extra cost of an accurately made jig is spread over a large output. Furthermore, it is surprising how small errors accumulate in a mechanism during its assembly. When a clearance is specified, it is better to ensure its observance, rather than to allow careless marking out and machining to encroach upon it.

16.4.1 The location of workpiece. Figure 16.20 represents a body that is completely free in space; in this condition it has *six degrees of freedom*. Consider these freedoms with respect to the three mutually perpendicular axes XX, YY, and ZZ. The body can move along any of these axes; it therefore has three freedoms of *translation*. It can also rotate about any of the three axes; it therefore has three freedoms of *rotation*. The total number of freedoms is six. When work is located, as many of these freedoms as possible must be eliminated, to ensure that the operation is performed with the required accuracy. Accuracy is ensured by machining suitable location features as early as possible, and using them for all location, unless other considerations mean that other location features must be used. Should that be necessary, the new lo-

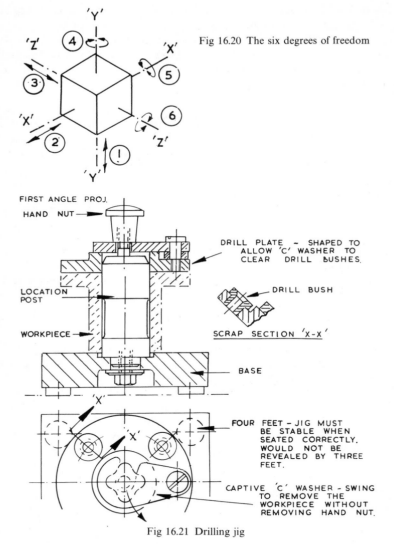

Fig 16.20 The six degrees of freedom

Fig 16.21 Drilling jig

cation features must be machined as a result of location from the former location features. The planning of the operation sequence is discussed in Chapter 27.

16.4.2 The clamping of the workpiece. The clamping system must be such that the workpiece is held against the cutting forces, and the clamping forces must not be so great as to cause the workpiece to become distorted or damaged. The workpiece must be supported beneath the point of clamping, to ensure that the forces are taken by the main frame of the jig or fixture, and on to the machine table and bed. When jigs and fixtures are designed, the clamping system is designed to ensure that the correct clamping force is applied, and that the clamps can be operated quickly—but with safety.

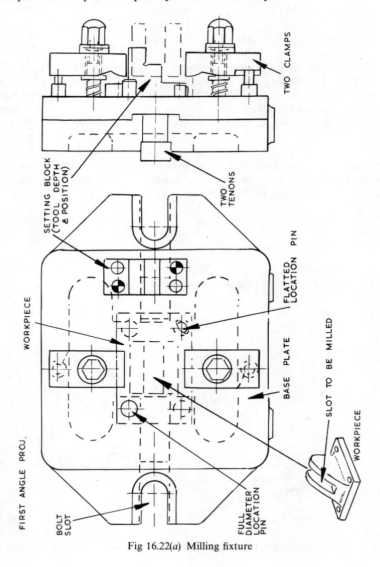

Fig 16.22(a) Milling fixture

16.4.3 Typical drill jig. Figure 16.21 illustrates a drilling jig for drilling four holes in the flange of a workpiece that has been completed except for the four holes. The workpiece has an accurately machined bore, and is located from the bore and the end face, from a cylindrical post. There is no need to control the rotational position about the axis of the bore, because, up to the time when the holes are drilled, it is symmetrical about that axis. The four bushes used to control the drill are held in the drill plate, which, with the hand nut, is used to clamp the workpiece against the base of the fixture.

16.4.4 Typical milling fixture. Figure 16.22(*a*) illustrates a simple milling fixture for milling the slot in the otherwise completed workpiece shown. The workpiece is located from two of the four holes in its base, and from the underside of the base. The workpiece is clamped in position, and the cutter is located against the setting block, which provides setting for cutter position and depth of cut. The fixture must be positioned relative to the machine table; this is done by engaging the two tenons at the bottom of the fixture in the slots in the machine table. The fixture is secured to the machine table with T-bolts, also engaging in the slots in the table (fig. 16.22(*b*)).

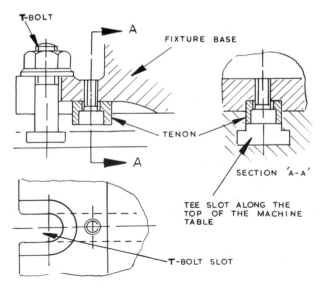

Fig 16.22(*b*) The location and clamping of a milling fixture

Summary

1   Small-quantity production involves marking out to produce guide-lines for machining. Marking out is also done upon trial castings and forgings, to check that there is enough metal allowed for 'cleaning up'.
2   Holes and similar features may be positioned either by polar coordinates or by rectangular coordinates.
3   Precise setting out and machining of holes are carried out using a jig-boring machine; but, with skill, good results can be obtained by using toolmaker's buttons.
4   If the quantity permits, workpieces are located and clamped in jigs or fixtures, instead of marking out each workpiece. Jigs and fixtures incorporate means of locating and clamping the workpiece. Jigs also include means of guiding the tool during the cutting, and fixtures include means of setting the tool before cutting.

Questions

Set A

1   A round bar, 100 mm in diameter, is to have octagonal flats machined on one end. The distance across each pair of flats is to be 65 mm. Describe a method of marking out the bar for machining, and a method of checking the finished bar.
2   A 125-mm-bore T-pipe, 400 mm long and 200 mm from the centre to each face, has been machined on the flanges. It is to be checked to ensure that the three faces are square to each other, and is then to be marked out. Describe these operations in detail.

Set B (questions requiring further study)

3   Describe, with the aid of sketches, the use of fixed bushes and slip-bushes in jig work.
4   Explain why a jig-boring machine does not use the leadscrew as means of setting in the same way as other machine tools.
5   Under what circumstances would a jig be used instead of marking out and machining?

Chapter 17
Plane Surfaces

17.1 Introduction to plane surfaces

Sir Joseph Whitworth pointed out that the plane surface was the basis of most of the precision work in engineering, and the industry owes him a great debt for the original work he did in about the year 1840 in instituting a proper system for making accurate plane surfaces. Most machine tools have a series of plane surfaces disposed at certain fixed angles to each other, and these surfaces are the datum planes from which the shape of the machined article is determined. Engineering measurement is largely based on *end standards of length*, which for the moment may be described as measures depending on the distance apart of two parallel plane surfaces.

The engineer's *surface plate* is made in many sizes, the most useful being those of rectangular shape and varying in size from 100 mm × 100 mm to 1·8 m × 1·2 m. The small plates have two handles, while the large plates are mounted on stands, and are usually called *surface tables*.

The accuracy of the flat surface is denoted by the maximum deviation from the 'mean true plane'; this term is illustrated in fig. 17.1. British Standard 817 states the maximum deviation for various sizes of plate, and for several grades of accuracy. For example, in the best quality of plate (Grade A), the greatest permissible deviation is 0·018 mm on a plate 1·8 m × 1·2 m. Another important point is the number and distribution of 'high spots', which must be numerous, and evenly spaced.

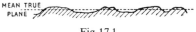

Fig 17.1

Plane surfaces may be originated as follows. Three plates, A, B, and C, of equal size, are made in good close-grained cast iron; they are rough machined, and are then allowed to 'age' for some months, to allow any internal strains to work out. After ageing, some warping will probably have occurred. This is removed by planing up on a good planing machine, only light cuts being used. The three plates are now 'bedded up' by hand scraping, the following order being used throughout: A is bedded to B, then A to C, and finally B to C.

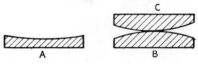

Fig 17.2

The principle involved in this procedure is illustrated by fig. 17.2. B and C may both be convex, but on being brought together this defect will be shown up, and partially corrected by scraping. Each in turn will now show up the concavity of A.

After a number of repetitions, the surfaces will become flat within the desired limits.

The process of 'bedding' may now be described briefly. One of the surfaces is very thinly coated with red lead and oil, or Prussian blue marking compound. Two surfaces are now rubbed together; the coated surface will be rubbed clean at its high spots, while the clean plate will be marked at the high spots. Both plates are now scraped with a flat scraper at the high spots, and the rubbing is repeated. The high spots will thus be gradually distributed over the whole of both plates, until the two surfaces correspond very closely.

The ordinary flat scraper is shown in fig. 17.3. Flat scrapers are often made from large flat files; these are ground up to remove the serrations, and are then forged to shape at the end, and hardened and tempered. The cutting edge is ground slightly convex, to a large radius, so that the corners do not dig in to the work. A scraper requires frequent honing on an oilstone, as a sharp cutting edge is essential.

Surface plates are also finished by grinding on a precision grinding machine, or by hand lapping on a lapping plate.

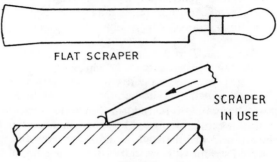

FLAT SCRAPER

SCRAPER IN USE

Fig 17.3

Lapping plates are usually made from soft cast iron. They should be as flat as possible, but not necessarily as flat as the surface plate. Uusually a series of V-grooves is machined across the lapping face, as shown in fig. 17.4. The pitch of the grooves is about 10 mm. The

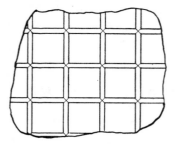

Fig 17.4 Surface of lapping-plate

surface of the plate is smeared with fine abrasive dust mixed with oil, and the surface plate is rubbed on the lap. Providing the high spots on the lap are well distributed, the surface produced will be much more accurate than that of the lap.

Hardened steel *toolmaker's flats* are ground and lapped to an accuracy of 0·0003 mm over the whole surface. They are usually circular, and about 200 mm in diameter.

17.2 Straight-edges

The straight-edge may be regarded as a long, narrow surface plate; three straight-edges may be originated in the same manner as three ordinary surface plates. Straight-edges up to 1·5 m long may be of plain, rectangular section. The longer the straight-edge, the greater must be the depth, to prevent 'sagging' when in use. Straight-edges longer than 1·5 m are usually made in cast iron and of 'bow-back' design, as shown in fig. 17.5. Straight-edges are used principally to

Fig 17.5 Long 'bow-back' straight edge

check flat surfaces, to align a number of articles, or to rule accurate straight lines. When a surface is to be checked, contact may be determined in several ways. When convenient, the most searching test is to have a source of white light behind the straight-edge; a gap of 0·0025 mm can be readily discerned in this way. Other methods used include the smearing of the straight edge with Prussian blue, or the introduction of thin slips of paper or metal between the two surfaces. The slips should be held equally tightly by the weight of the straight-edge.

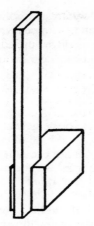

Fig 17.6 Try-square

17.3 The try-square

The try-square consists of two straight-edges firmly fixed at right angles to each other; the two edges of each straight-edge must be parallel to each other. Figure 17.6 shows a typical try-square, and fig. 17.7 shows three applications. In C it is desired to rule a line at right angles to a surface.

Cylindrical squares are also made, and are sometimes used as a mas-

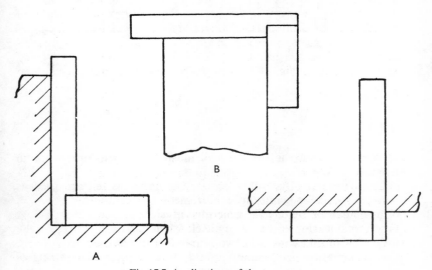

Fig 17.7 Applications of the try-square

ter square for checking try-squares. A hollow steel cylinder is ground carefully on the diameter, and is lapped up on the ends, so that these are at right angles to the axis of the cylinder.

The important point about the cylindrical square is that it gives line contact with a flat surface.

17.3.1 Generation of try-squares. Try-squares may be generated in sets of three, in a similar manner to the generation of flat surfaces. Figure 17.8 illustrates the principle. The base of each square is bedded to the surface plate. Squares A and B are brought together. In the figure, each of these squares is obtuse-angled, so the upper part of the blades will bed together, and this is the point at which metal is removed. However, each in turn is also bedded with square C, which is shown acute angled and will lead to metal being removed from the lower part of each blade. Regular interchange will produce three correct squares. The insides of the squares are then corrected by comparison with the outside of any of the squares, as shown.

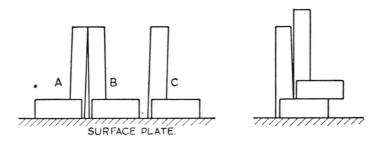

SURFACE PLATE.

Fig 17.8 Generation of try-squares

Summary

1 The plane surface is the basis of most of the precision work in engineering.
2 The engineer's surface plate and the toolmaker's flat are used as datum planes for precision measurement.
3 Plane surfaces are usually generated in sets of three.
4 The straight-edge is used as a check for flatness.
5 The try-square is basically two planes at right angles.
6 Try-squares are, like plane surfaces, usually generated in sets of three.

Questions

Set A
1 To what extent is the plane surface the datum for engineering?
2 Explain why toolmaker's flats are generated in sets of three.

Set B (questions requiring further study)
3 Describe how the accuracy of a straight-edge can be determined using a set of slip gauges and a surface plate.
4 Describe how the accuracy of a try-square can be determined using an angle plate, a parallel bar and nut and bolt, a surface plate, and slip gauges.

Chapter 18
Lathes

18.1 Main features of a centre lathe

A simple lathe is basically a machine for rotating a workpiece while a cutting tool is moved relative to it. Figures 15.23, 15.27, and 15.28 showed how these basic movements are combined to produce a range of shapes. Holes can be drilled, reamed, and tapped by holding the cutter in the tailstock.

Figure 18.1 shows a typical centre lathe; the centre lathe is the basic lathe used in tool rooms and similar general machine shops.

The dimensions which decide the suitability of a lathe for a particular job are:

(a) the maximum distance between the headstock and tailstock centres, usually termed the *length between centres*;

(b) the largest diameter of work which will revolve without fouling the bed, termed the *swing over bed*;

(c) the largest diameter of work which will revolve without fouling the tool carriage, usually referred to as the *swing over carriage*;

(d) the diameter of the hole through the lathe spindle, important when bar-material is to be turned.

Fig 18.1 Centre lathe   *Dean, Smith & Grace Ltd*

A cast-iron bed forms the base of the machine. The carriage, carrying the tool post, moves along the top of the bed, guided by the slides, which must be accurately produced. The bed is usually of box section, for best stiffness, and suitable holes are cast in the horizontal ribs, to allow the swarf to escape. The top surface of the lathe bed takes the weight of the headstock, tailstock, and carriage, but the guiding surfaces are the narrow surfaces indicated by G in fig. 18.2.

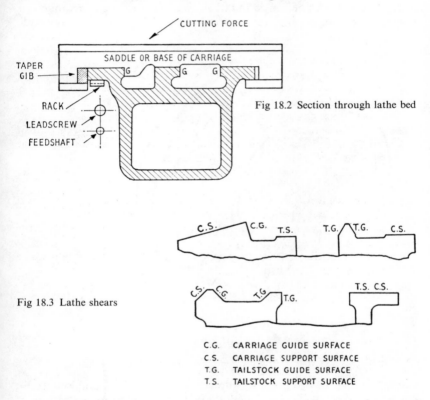

Fig 18.2 Section through lathe bed

Fig 18.3 Lathe shears

C.G.	CARRIAGE GUIDE SURFACE
C.S.	CARRIAGE SUPPORT SURFACE
T.G.	TAILSTOCK GUIDE SURFACE
T.S.	TAILSTOCK SUPPORT SURFACE

The guiding surfaces must not be too far apart, as widely separated guide surfaces tend to cause *cross-wind*, a jamming effect, similar to that associated with sash-type windows. Figure 18.3 shows some alternative arrangements of guides (or shears).

The headstock is securely bolted to one end of the lathe bed, with its centre-line parallel to the bed guideways, in both horizontal and vertical planes. The driving motor may be built into the headstock, or, alternatively, a constant-speed pulley may be used to take the power input. The headstock contains a gearbox, so that the spindle speed can be set to suit the cutting conditions. The design of the lathe spindle and its bearings is of the utmost importance, as the thrust of the cutting tool will tend to deflect the spindle. The spindle, which is made of high-tensile steel, suitably hardened and tempered, is mounted on two bearings placed at opposite ends of the headstock casting. These bearings have the minimum running clearance, and may be phosphor bronze bushes, accurately finished in the bore by honing, or may be heavy ball or roller bearings. In either case, one bearing is arranged to take the thrust of cutting, and to prevent the spindle from moving end-

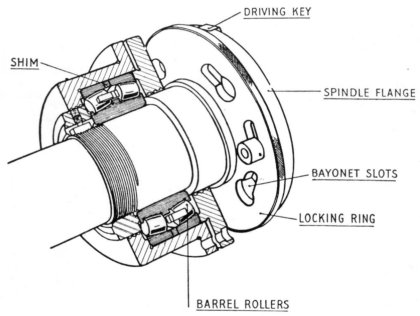

Fig 18.4 Lathe spindle with pre-loaded bearings (*John Lang & Sons Ltd*)

ways; the other bearing usually allows the spindle to expand longitudinally as a result of the heat generated during the cutting operation.

The use of pre-loaded bearings should be noted. A lathe spindle may run in a certain position when unloaded, but the application of a cutting force to the work is liable to move it over if there is any 'play' in the bearings. In the pre-loaded roller bearings, there is no 'play'. Instead, the rollers are always pressed against the inner track by a fixed force or pre-load.

Figure 18.4 shows a patented design of front bearing for a lathe spindle. The double row of barrel rollers runs on a solid double inner track and a split double outer track. The two halves of the outer track are separated by a shim, the thickness of which is carefully set. Thus, when the bearing is assembled, the two outer tracks are pressed together, and the required pre-load pressure is placed on the rollers.

It may also be noted that, due to the shape of the rollers and tracks, the bearing has self-aligning properties, and will take end thrust in both directions.

The overhang of the spindle nose is kept to a minimum, to guard against bending. Figure 18.5 shows a typical spindle nose. The spindle is hollow, to allow long bars to be passed through. The live centre revolves with the spindle; when it is not required, it may be removed from its taper socket. The various face plates and chucks are all made to be secured to the flange by bolts or studs, and positioned by the taper spigot. The flange in fig. 18.4 is a quick-release type. The chucks have four studs which can pass through the flange and locking-ring with the nuts in place. When the chuck has been pushed in place, the locking-ring is rotated slightly, to bring the narrow end of the slots under the nuts, which are then tightened by about half a turn. This design has the tapered spigot already mentioned, and also a fitted driving key, which takes all driving strain off the studs.

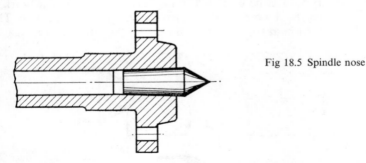

Fig 18.5 Spindle nose

At the bottom of the headstock, a further small gearbox is provided. This transmits the power for driving the feed-shaft and the leadscrew. These two are devices for moving the lathe carriage. The feed-shaft is used for most turning operations, but when the carriage motion must be synchronised with the rotation of the lathe spindle, the leadscrew is used. This matter will be discussed more fully under screw-cutting operations.

When turning, the carriage is driven by the feedshaft, which rotates a pinion mounted in a casting at the front of the carriage (called the carriage apron). This pinion engages with a rack along the front of the bed, so that it pulls itself and the carriage along the bed. When screw-cutting, a more direct relationship between spindle rotation and carriage movement is necessary; the carriage movement is obtained by engaging a split nut over the leadscrew, which rotates in relation to the spindle rotation.

The carriage supports and guides the cross slide so that it moves at right angles to the guides on the bed; this relationship is necessary when a face is required at right angles to the axis of a cylinder (see fig. 15.27). The tool-post is mounted on an auxiliary slide mounted, in turn, on the top of the cross slide. This slide is called the *compound slide rest*, and can be swivelled to any angle, and used manually for turning short tapers, and other operations. Both the cross slide and compound slide rest have large hand wheels with finely graduated dials for precision tool-setting.

The tailstock is used to carry the centre, which supports the outer end of the workpiece; it can be moved along the bed to suit various work-lengths, and be locked in any position. The work is usually supported by a centre, located in the tailstock spindle; but a cutting tool, such as a drill, can be placed there instead, and fed into the work by the tailstock hand-feed, while the cutting motion is obtained by workpiece rotation. The tailstock casting is usually in two sections, so that its spindle axis can be offset for taper-turning between centres (section 18.9.1).

18.2 Types of lathe work

A common type of lathe work is turning *between centres*. The work is drilled at each end, by means of a centre drill, as shown in fig. 18.6. The cylindrical portion at the bottom ensures that the lathe centre engages

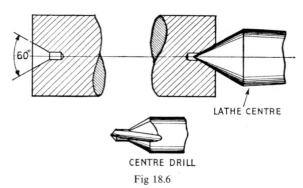

LATHE CENTRE

CENTRE DRILL

Fig 18.6

only the cone shaped part, and clears at the point. It will be realised that a bar properly held between centres cannot move in any way, except to rotate about its own axis, consequently the conical surfaces are the datum faces from which all diameters are produced. For this reason, the centre holes should be drilled very carefully, and for precision work, such as gauges, the centres should be machine ground, or lapped out with a conical lap and fine grinding paste. The conical surfaces are very small, and are not easy to lubricate. If the work is heavy, adequate support must be given to prevent wearing of the surface at the tailstock end (the headstock centre revolves with the work). The tailstock centre must be adjusted with care: too heavy pressure prevents lubrication, and too light a pressure will allow the work to 'jump' when the cut is taken. A freely revolving centre (or 'live' centre) is useful for high-speed turning.

The chief advantage of working between centres is that the work can be removed from the machine and replaced, and will still revolve about the same axis. Similarly, if a part is turned in a lathe, and subsequently ground in a cylindrical grinder, the same datum faces are used throughout. The student may be puzzled to decide whether the six-point principle is applicable to centred work. It may be pointed out that a circle is determined if three points on its circumference are located.

In order to drive the work, a carrier 'dog' is fastened to one end, and the finger of the dog is driven by a catchplate mounted on the spindle nose (fig. 18.7). One serious disadvantage of this method of driving is that the work cannot be machined where the dog fits, and at some stage of the machining process the shaft has to be turned end for end in the lathe.

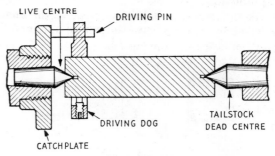

Fig 18.7 Working between centres

It is not possible, of course, to turn irregular-shaped pieces between centres, nor is it possible to bore a hole through the work. However, the use of centred *mandrels* opens up a wide field of application for work between centres.

A mandrel is a piece of round bar which has been centred at each end, and has then been machined and ground to run truly on the centres. It has a taper of about 0·6 mm per metre length, so that work with a central hole can be pressed on to a suitable part of the mandrel.

If the mandrel is to be used only once, mild steel will be a cheap and suitable material, but most shops have a set of standard mandrels made from medium-carbon steel. These are hardened and tempered, and ground up to a good finish; the centres may be lapped or ground out after hardening. In order to protect the centres of permanent mandrels, a recess is usually arranged, and the end of the mandrel is made

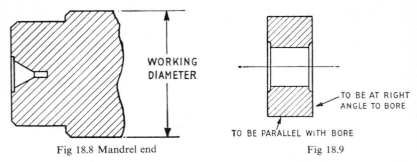

Fig 18.8 Mandrel end   Fig 18.9

smaller in diameter, so that burrs on the end will not prevent the mounting of work. A mandrel end is shown in fig. 18.8.

Figure 18.9 illustrates a simple but typical application of mandrel turning. It is important that the hole in the component should be concentric with the outside diameter, and square with the flat faces. The part may be turned up roughly in a chuck, and the hole drilled as near central as possible. The hole is finished, bored, or reamered, and the part is mounted on a suitable mandrel. The circumference and the flat faces of the work are then lightly skimmed to the final size.

Mandrels are made with various fittings, and a mandrel with a collar and screw-thread is shown in fig. 18.10.

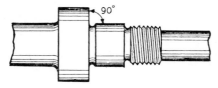

Fig 18.10 Collared mandrel

18.3 Chucks

Round, square, and hexagonal bar of short length is often machined in a suitable chuck. The three-jaw *self-centring chuck* has a *scroll* mechanism, so that the jaws move in or out at the same time when the chuck key is turned. If the work is symmetrical to the jaws, it is automatically centred by the chuck, and no adjustment is necessary. Where the stock is bright-drawn bar, the three-jaw chuck provides a very quick method of gripping it; the majority of work in capstan lathes is done in this type of chuck.

The four-jaw *independent chuck* has the jaws carried in slots. Each jaw can be adjusted separately, by its own screw. Forgings or castings of slightly irregular shape can be gripped by suitable setting of each jaw. Chucks may be used for long work, instead of the dog-and-catchplate method, and work is gripped by the chuck at one end, and the other end rotates on the tailstock centre, as shown in fig. 18.11.

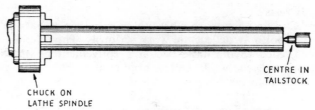

CHUCK ON
LATHE SPINDLE

CENTRE IN
TAILSTOCK

Fig 18.11

With this method, the work is more rigidly supported, but the location principle of two centres is destroyed.

Two methods of holding work by 'false pieces' often occur in chuck work. A short piece of bar may be gripped firmly in a chuck, and turned to a suitable diameter: thin section rings, which are difficult to grip, owing to their fragility, may be pressed gently on to the bar, and lightly machined on their ends or outer circumference. If the bore of such rings requires machining, then 'a 'stack' may be suitably bored out, and the rings gently pressed inside the stack (see fig. 18.12). With either of these methods, the 'false piece' must not be disturbed until all the rings have been completed, as the original machining of the piece provides the datum.

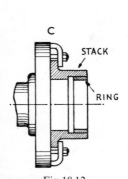

C

STACK

RING

Fig 18.12

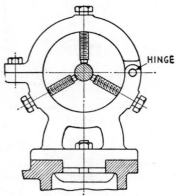

HINGE

Fig 18.13 Fixed steady

18.4 Face-plates

These are plates adapted for mounting on the spindle nose. A number of slots is provided so that irregularly shaped castings or forgings can be clamped to the face-plate by bolts and straps. Brackets or angle plates can be mounted to aid in holding the work. The face-plate may be likened to a revolving surface plate, the surface being at right angles to the lathe axis. Providing the surface is in good condition, it forms an excellent datum for accurate setting of the work.

18.5 Steady rests

These are used for long work where there is a danger that the cutting force of the tool may deflect the work seriously. The *fixed steady* (fig. 18.13) is fastened to the lathe bed at a convenient point, the three fingers supporting the work. Unless bright round bar is being used, it is necessary first to machine a short length of bar, on which to set the bearing pads of the steady fingers. The *travelling steady* is arranged to be bolted to the carriage, and it thus supports the work immediately behind the tool throughout the traverse. Steadies must be set carefully, so that they are not marking the work, but are tight enough to prevent 'whipping'. The travelling steady is set on the diameter of the turned work, as it follows the tool (see fig. 18.14).

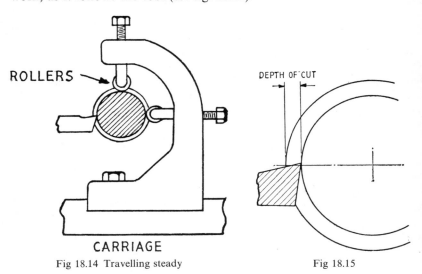

ROLLERS

DEPTH OF CUT

CARRIAGE

Fig 18.14 Travelling steady   Fig 18.15

18.6 Setting of tools

This important operation is often done in a negligent manner, and much unsatisfactory work can be traced to this cause. Figure 18.15 shows a turning tool set in position for plain bar turning. It is advisable to set the cutting edge on the centre line of the job, but the top rake prevents this if the cut is reasonably deep; consequently, it is usual to set the tool point slightly above the centre, and thus none of the cutting edge is below the centre. This precaution is taken to ensure that the tool does not 'dig in'.

In taper turning, it is essential to set the cutting edge on the centre line, otherwise a truly conical shape cannot be generated. The point is illustrated in fig. 18.16, in exaggerated form. At the large end of the work, the low setting of the tool will cause it to turn a slightly larger diameter, but at the small end of the work the effect will be much more pronounced. The deviation depends on the cosines of the angles α and β. Now, the relationship between the sides of a right-angle triangle is dependent on the squares of the lengths of the sides, and consequently the cosine of an angle does not vary according to a straight-line law. Therefore the shape generated does not have a straight side. In fact, if the tool is set below the centre line, a concave surface is produced. Incidentally, this illustrates the point that in generation the shape of the generated surface depends on the paths of the tool and work, not only on the shape of the tool, or on the path of the tool.

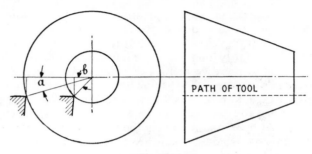

PATH OF TOOL

Fig 18.16

The commonest cause of 'chattered' work is excessive overhang of the cutting tool. The tool vibrates as a pendulum, and alternately is forced down, and then springs back, due to its elasticity. The minimum possible overhang from the tool-post should be used, and the top slide of a compound rest should not be wound out to the limit, but instead should be kept well over the cross slide.

Finally, when the tool is set, the turner should check up to make sure that in making the cut no part of the set-up will foul the tool.

18.7 Speeds, feeds, and depths of cut
The theoretical considerations have been briefly reviewed in Chapter 15, but a number of factors must be considered in the turning of any job. The following points have decisive influence.

18.7.1 The type of work.
When a rigid article, such as a large-diameter plain bar, is being rough turned, there is little danger of deflection, and surface finish is unimportant; consequently, deep cuts at the maximum speed and feed are employed. The only limits are the rigidity and power input of the lathe, and the desired life of the tool edge.

On the other hand, slender work is usually turned with light cuts, but the rate of metal removal may be improved by the use of very high cutting speeds. With some components of a fragile nature, the permissible gripping pressure is very low, and consequently light cuts and low speeds may be essential.

18.7.2 Type of material being machined, and type of material used for the tool. These two factors have already been discussed in Chapter 15.

18.7.3 Surface finish required. There is a general tendency to use light cuts and high speeds with fine feeds, to obtain a good surface finish. Not only is the surface smooth in these circumstances, but also the metal immediately under the surface is less disturbed.

18.7.4 Type of operation. Some operations need to be done at low speeds, to suit the operator, or the type of tool. Screw-cutting, tapping, and reaming are examples of this. Form tools are expensive, and are expected to have a fairly long life; when they are in use, feed and speed may be reduced to preserve them. For single-point tools, the period between regrinds may be as low as one hour's cutting time, but certain operations are exceptions to this. In the precision boring of large cylinders, for example, any appreciable tool wear in the finishing cut would lead to a tapered bore, and removing the tool for regrinding part way through a traverse would be fatal. Such considerations reduce the depth of cut and rate of feed, and, in the case of steel cutting tools (as opposed to carbide-tipped tools), the cutting speed also. Another example is in the complicated set-ups in automatic lathes, or capstan and turret lathes. It is better to try to arrange a reasonably long run before stopping to regrind tools. The setter will often reduce the speed or feed of a particular operation if he finds that the tool is blunting much more quickly than any other. He prefers to send all the wearing tools for regrinding at one time, rather than have continued short stoppages.

18.7.5 Use of a cutting fluid. This generally allows a considerable increase in the cutting speed.

18.7.6 Type of lathe. A certain minimum amount of work must be done to remove a certain volume of metal in a lathe; therefore the maximum power input to the lathe must be considered. The rigidity of the lathe is also an important factor; it is well known that many old lathes are quite unsuitable for modern carbide-cutting tools, as they were designed before such tools were envisaged. They lack the necessary rigidity, power input, and high-speed range.

   With a good selection of carbide-tipped tools of various grades and a range of shapes, metal may be removed at a remarkable speed in a modern lathe. There is little point in giving a long list of various speeds, feeds, and cutting depths for all the different materials, but the following are a few examples typical of modern practice:

Material	Speed m/s	Depth of cut mm	Feed mm/rev
cast iron (130 HB)	1·0	6	0·35
mild steel	1·8	9	0·25
60/40 brass	2·5	9	0·25
aluminium	3·5	19	0·35

18.8 Lathe operations

It is outside the scope of this book to describe how various components are machined, but certain operations call for special mention.

18.8.1 Ending up. When a piece of bar has been sawn off and centred, a very common operation is that of machining to correct length, or 'ending up'. This involves working close to the dead centre. A half centre will enable better work to be done, and a tool with a sharp nose angle is required. The operation is shown in fig. 18.17.

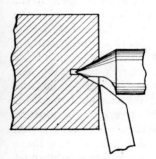
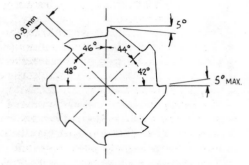

Fig 18.17 Ending up   Fig 18.18 Section of reamer

18.8.2 Drilling, reaming, and boring. For holes of moderate size, drilling is usually employed; if a smooth finish is required, the hole is drilled slightly under size, and is then reamed. A section through a reamer is shown in fig. 18.18. A portion of the reamer immediately behind the cutting edge is ground to give 'front clearance' of 5°. This surface is called the 'land', and the 5° angle is termed 'primary clearance'. Behind the land, the tool is cut away more sharply, to leave room for chips of metal. This is termed 'secondary clearance'. The 'top rake' never exceeds 5°, and is often zero—i.e. the tool breast is radial. The odd distribution of the cutting edges round the circumference lessens the possibility of 'chatter' marks in the hole, due to harmonic vibration. The flutes of the reamer are usually spirally disposed, being given a left-hand inclination. This is equivalent to giving a negative 'side-rake' to the cutting edge, and prevents the reamer screwing into the work.

Reamers are operated at a slow speed, and the amount of metal removed is usually only 0·2 to 0·7 mm. Generally, the work is held in a chuck or on a face-plate; the drill, and later the reamer, are held in the tailstock socket, and fed forward by the tailstock hand-wheel. For long work, a fixed steady is used to support the work close up to the drill. Further notes on reamers and reaming will be found in Chapter 19.

Flat plates, and some types of bracket, can be drilled more readily if they are fastened to the slide rest, or held up against the tailstock. The drill is then put in the lathe spindle socket, and feed is applied to the work by means of the carriage or tailstock hand-wheel. Figure 18.19 shows a 'drilling pad' fixed in a lathe tailstock.

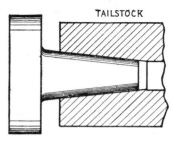

TAILSTOCK

Fig 18.19 Drilling pad

One disadvantage of drilling and reaming is the tendency of drills to 'wander' away from the desired centre line; the reamer will automatically follow the same path. This may be counteracted to some extent by first drilling a small 'pilot' hole, and then following with a larger drill; but, for accurate work, a boring tool or boring bar is more satisfactory. If two or more concentric bores have to be produced, a piloted boring bar or counterbore should always be used. (Counterbores are described in Chapter 19.)

18.9 Taper turning and boring

18.9.1 Setting over the tailstock. This is limited to turning between centres, and is suitable only for slight tapers. A typical example is the turning of mandrels. The tailstock is thrown out of line with the headstock, and is locked in the new position; the set-up is shown in fig. 18.20. Consider a bar 300 mm in length, and 0·2 mm smaller in diameter at one end than the other. If the lathe tailstock is 0·1 mm *farther away* from the front shear than the headstock, the work will be machined 0·2 mm larger in diameter at the tailstock end. This is due to the fact that the cutting tool traverses a path parallel to the front shear. Several points must be noted. The amount of taper is determined by the movement of the tailstock from the central position: if bars of different

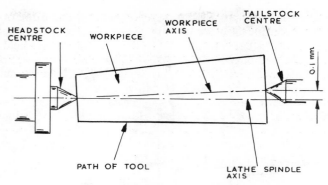

Fig 18.20 Taper turning by setting over the tailstock

lengths are to be turned to the same taper, the set-over must be calculated each time—in fact, if the bars are all of one length, they must all be centred to the same depth if the tapers are to be identical. The tailstock centre cannot align itself properly with the centre hole in the bar; this is shown in exaggerated form in fig. 18.21. Sometimes centres with ball ends are used to overcome this difficulty, but they are somewhat fragile.

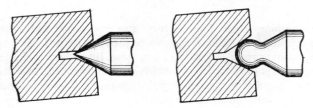

Fig 18.21

18.9.2 The taper-turning attachment. This is shown in fig. 18.22. Under ordinary turning conditions, the infeed of the tool is determined by the cross-slide screw, but when using the taper-turning attachment, the slide-rest is freed from this screw, and its movement is controlled by the slide on the attachment. The attachment can be pre-set to the required angle, and locked in position, thus allowing an exact taper to be produced on any number of components. Furthermore, internal and external tapers which match each other can be produced if the attachment is left undisturbed.

18.9.3 Setting the compound slide-rest. This method is used for turning short tapers. The top slide can be swivelled to any angle, the setting being made using the graduated base, which is usually marked in degrees. With this method, the automatic feed cannot be used, and the tool feed is by hand. Only short tapers can be turned, as the movement of top slide is limited, but, within these limitations, this is the quickest and simplest method of taper turning.

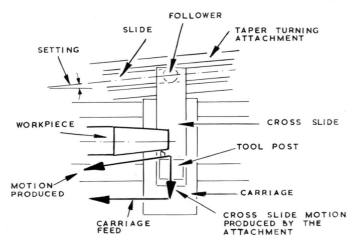

Fig 18.22 Taper-turning attachment

18.9.4 Combining feeds. This method can be used if the lathe is specially geared so that the carriage can be moved along the bed while the cross slide moves in or out at the same time. By changing the gears, the relative amounts of these two motions can be adjusted, thus producing the required tapered path of the tool. This method allows a taper to be turned for the full length of the bed.

18.10 Screw-cutting

With the introduction of capstan lathes equipped with self-opening die-heads, and more recently with the advent of thread-milling and thread-rolling machines, screw-cutting using a lathe has become less common, but is still an important operation. The lead accuracy of the thread so produced depends upon the truth of the leadscrew, but the accuracy of the form depends upon the skill of the operator, and the use of a correct chasing tool for finishing the thread.

18.10.1. In order to obtain a particular thread, it is necessary to rotate the work, and at the same time to traverse the cutting tool parallel to the axis of the work. The speed of the traverse must bear a constant relationship to the speed of workpiece rotation. If the lathe spindle and the leadscrew are positively connected by gear-wheels, this connection will be produced. Consider a lathe fitted with a leadscrew which has a lead of 5 mm; if the work and the leadscrew are geared 1 : 1, then the thread so generated will have a lead of 5 mm. If the leadscrew is made to rotate once while the work revolves twice, then the movement of the cutting tool will be 2·5 mm per revolution of the work, and so the thread so generated will be of 2·5 mm lead.

A positive-geared connection between the work and leadscrew is therefore required, with facilities for changing the gear ratio. In the more expensive lathes, this is produced by a gearbox, but on many lathes it is necessary to set up a train of gears to connect the lathe spindle and the leadscrew. Change-wheels are usually supplied in sets; a full set usually consists of wheels of from 20 teeth to 120 teeth, in steps of 5 teeth.

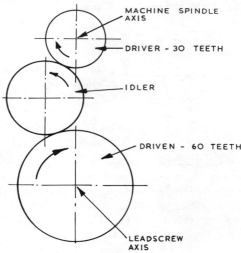

Fig 18.23 Simple gear train

Consider again the production of a screw-thread of 2·5 mm lead, using a lathe with 5-mm lead leadscrew: a gear-wheel of 30 teeth is placed on the lathe spindle, and one of 60 teeth on the leadscrew. The spindle and leadscrew axes are fixed, and so in order to accommodate a wide range of gears that can mesh, an adjustable quadrant and stud is included in the casing, so that intermediate gears can be fitted to effect the link-up. Figure 18.23 illustrates the gear arrangement for this example. The 'idler' gear in the simple train shown does not alter the gear ratio produced, but it does ensure that the rotation of the lead-screw will be in the same direction as that of the lathe spindle.

This *simple train* is determined as follows:

$$\frac{\text{number of teeth in driver gear}}{\text{number of teeth in driven gear}} = \frac{\text{lead to be cut}}{\text{lead of leadscrew}} = \frac{2·5 \text{ mm}}{5 \text{ mm}} = \frac{30}{60}$$

18.10.2. Now consider the production of a screw-thread of 2·6 mm lead, using the lathe with a 5-mm lead leadscrew.

$$\frac{\text{number of teeth in driver gear(s)}}{\text{number of teeth in driven gear(s)}} = \frac{\text{lead to be cut}}{\text{lead of leadscrew}} = \frac{2·6 \text{ mm}}{5 \text{ mm}} = \frac{26}{50}$$

This ratio cannot be obtained using a simple train, but can be split up using a *compound train*:

$$\frac{26}{50} = \frac{130}{250} = \frac{65}{50} \times \frac{2}{5} = \frac{65}{50} \times \frac{30}{75}$$

These gears are arranged as shown in fig. 18.24.

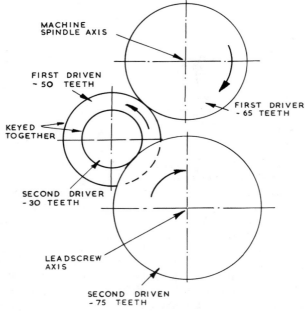

Fig 18.24 Compound gear train

The work to be screwed is turned to the top diameter of the thread, and a 'landing groove' is machined, as shown in fig. 18.25. This groove gives the necessary clearance for withdrawing the tool at the end of the thread. Figure 18.25 also shows the thread profile gauge which is used to check the shape of the tool nose, and to ensure that the axis of the tool is at right angles to the axis of the work.

If the tool were fed straight into the work, it would cut at both sides, and the two converging chips would crowd together, causing tearing of the work surface, and probably breaking the tool. To prevent this, the

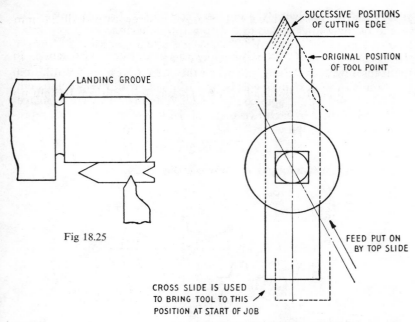

Fig 18.25

Fig 18.26 Feed for screw-cutting

cross slide is used for disengaging the tool, but the cut is put on by the top slide. The method is illustrated in fig. 18.26. The tool is left slightly loose in the post, and the cross-slide hand-wheel is brought to zero. The tool nose is now made just to touch the work, and the tool is firmly secured in the tool-post. Therefore, with the cross-slide hand-wheel at zero, the tip of the tool will always be at the top diameter of the thread. The carriage is now wound to the right, so that the tool just clears the free end of the work. The lathe is started, and the leadscrew nut is engaged; the tool moves to the left and makes a fine spiral mark on the work. When the landing groove is reached, the leadscrew nut is disengaged, and the cross-slide is wound out to clear the tool from the work. The carriage is returned to the starting point, and the cross slide reset to zero. A small cut is now put on by the top-slide hand-wheel, and the process is repeated. By this method only one side of the tool will be cutting (see fig. 18.26). Twelve or more cuts may be applied before the thread attains full depth.

18.10.3. When the lever is pressed to engage the leadscrew nut, the screw will usually have to turn slightly before the nut slips into place. This does not matter if the lead of the leadscrew is a multiple of the lead being cut, but in all other cases the nut may not engage at the right point for following the partially cut thread. For example, if the thread being cut has a lead of 2 mm, and the machine leadscrew has a lead of 5 mm, the work will turn two and a half turns for one turn of the leadscrew. Thus the nut, which can engage at every revolution of the leadscrew, may be engaged when the work is in a 'half revolution' position, so the next pass will be out of phase with the previous cut, and the thread will be spoiled (fig. 18.27). Actually, the correct engagement occurs once in each two turns of the leadscrew, since this represents five turns of the work.

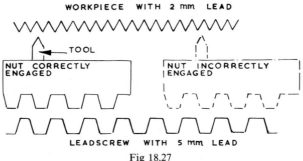

WORKPIECE WITH 2 mm LEAD

Fig 18.27

There are several methods of preventing this occurrence. When short threads are cut, the work can be rotated backwards by hand, with the tool retracted a little, and the leadscrew engaged. Another method is to set a stop to fix the carriage position at the start of screw-cutting, and to mark the angular position of the chuck relative to the headstock, and the leadscrew relative to its bearing, and to start each pass only when all these three conditions are reproduced.

A chasing dial is fitted to most modern lathes. This is a graduated dial on the top of the carriage, connected by a short shaft to a worm-wheel which engages with the leadscrew, and so indicates the leadscrew rotation. The dial has eight or sixteen marks, according to the number of teeth on the worm-wheel, and there is a fixed mark on the carriage. Thus, when the dial moves one graduation, it indicates that the leadscrew has turned once. In the case of cutting the 2-mm lead, the leadscrew nut could be engaged at every other mark (say, at the even numbers), as this means every other turn of the leadscrew, and thus every fifth turn of the work. Again, if a lead of 4 mm is being cut with the 5-mm lead-screw, the work will make one and a quarter turns for one turn of the leadscrew, and the nut can be engaged at every fourth mark—that is, at every fourth revolution of the leadscrew, and every fifth turn of the work.

18.10.4. A screw-thread is often completed by a chasing tool (fig. 18.28), and it will be realised that this is is a particular type of form tool. It may be applied by hand, and steadied by a guide-bar placed in the tool-post. The thread is picked up by the chaser, which is then pressed firmly into the thread, and quickly withdrawn when the landing groove is reached. The chasing operation is continued until a screw-thread gauge will screw firmly on to the work. Alternatively, the chaser may be mounted in the tool-post, and the thread completed with the aid of the leadscrew. Internal threaded work is produced in a similar manner.

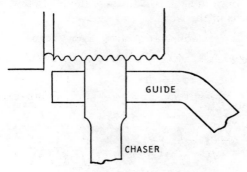

Fig 18.28 Thread chasing

18.11 Capstan and turret lathes

These lathes are used for large-scale production, but are sometimes used when several tools are to be set up and retained for the machining of more than one workpiece. Figure 18.29 illustrates a typical capstan lathe. The most obvious difference between a capstan lathe and a centre lathe is that the tailstock is replaced with a turret with six facings, giving six tool-mounting stations. This turret is used for mounting tools such as drills, reamers, dies, and turning tools used for axial cutting. The turret is indexed into position by clockwise rotation of the 'star' wheel at the front of the turret, and can be hand-fed by rotating the star wheel in an anti-clockwise direction. The turret can be fed automatically if required. Movement of the turret is controlled by stops, the stop for each station being indexed into position when the turret is indexed. Additional tool stations are available on the carriage, as in the case of the centre lathe; a four-way tool-box is available at the front, and a single tool-post at the rear (the tool at this station is mounted upside-down, so that the direction of workpiece rotation does not have to be changed). The tools mounted on the carriage are used for cutting in a radial direction, and for such operations as groove-cutting, form-cutting, and parting off. Capstan lathes are used mainly for bar work; a collet system is incorporated to grip the bar, and a feeding device advances the bar when the collet is opened. The larger capstan lathes are also used for chuck- and fixture-held workpieces.

Fig 18.29 Capstan lathe   *Alfred Herbert Ltd*

The turret lathe can be regarded as a large capstan lathe, used for chuck- and fixture-held workpieces.

18.12 Lathe alignments

If a lathe is to generate a true cylinder with square ends, the work must revolve about a straight-line axis, and the tool must traverse either of two straight lines, as required; one line must be parallel to the work axis, and the other must be at right angles to it. With a new lathe, these conditions should apply within 0·02 mm per metre length when a cut is being made. Over a period of time, certain defects appear, as a result of wear, and it should be added that very few lathes escape damage due to careless workmanship. One essential point must be grasped before considering the checking of machine tools or the work produced by them. It has been mentioned previously (in Chapters 16 and 17) that a satisfactory datum is required before accurate measurements of any sort can be made. In checking machine tools, this must always be kept in mind, otherwise the work becomes meaningless. Suppose a bar has been machined between centres in the lathe. The accuracy of the bar, considered as a cylinder, will depend on the lathe. It might be suspected that the bar is varying in diameter along its length, and this could be determined by a suitable micrometer. It would be quite useless to mount an indicator dial-gauge in the tool-post, and traverse this along the length of the work, since the inaccuracy in the work may be due to the fact that the tool is not traversing a straight path—i.e. the shear of the lathe is not a straight edge, in which case the dial-gauge would merely traverse the same path as the tool. If, however, the dial-gauge is guided by a known straight edge, then the datum has been provided, and the shape of the work is then being compared to the shape of the straight edge. Another method is to mount a known true cylinder in the lathe; the dial-gauge may then be guided by the lathe shear, which will be compared to a straight line on the surface of the cylinder. There are many possible lathe defects, and only the more common ones can be mentioned here.

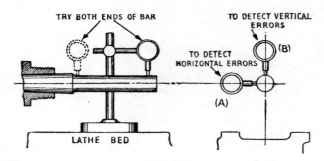

Fig 18.30

18.12.1 Headstock defects. The headstock centre line must be parallel with the bed in both horizontal and vertical planes, otherwise the lathe will not face the work at right angles, nor turn a parallel cylinder. It will be realised that, since the facing tool only cuts to the centre, faced surfaces will be either concave or convex, according to the inclination of the headstock: the defect can therefore be detected by placing a straight-edge on faced work, and the micrometer on cylindrical work. A horizontal inclination of the headstock will be much more serious than a vertical in-inclination; either defect can be measured by the set-up shown in fig. 18.30.

The taper hole in the spindle nose may be damaged, usually by burrs being formed at the mouth of the hole. If a round bar is ground parallel, and one end is tapered to suit the spindle nose, this can be inserted and tried with a dial-indicator (see section 23.5.1) through one revolution (fig. 18.31). One result of a damaged hole in the spindle nose is that the live centre used with work between centres revolves eccentrically, i.e. the point describes a small orbit (see fig. 18.32). In consequence, the work centre also moves in the same way, and com-

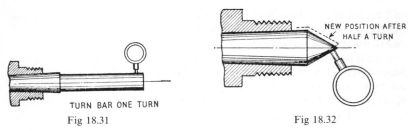

TURN BAR ONE TURN
Fig 18.31   Fig 18.32

NEW POSITION AFTER
HALF A TURN

ponents turned between centres may show a particular diameter to be eccentric if it is near the headstock end of the work. This defect is rather puzzling to anyone encountering it for the first time. It can be detected with a dial-indicator as shown. The socket should be trimmed up if possible; but, if this cannot be done, the live centre should be ground to a true cone with a tool-post grinder, while the lathe spindle revolves slowly. After doing this, the centre must not be removed from the socket.

It is interesting to note that the work on a cylindrical grinder is arranged to revolve between two dead centres, thus eliminating the possibility of the live centre revolving in an orbit. This is done by driving the catch-plate round a stationary centre.

A much more serious defect is the permanent bending of the end of the lathe spindle. Fortunately this is rare, and can occur only as the result of a serious accident, or the grossest misuse. There is no remedy save fitting a new spindle.

Wear in the spindle bearings causes taper work, usually accompanied by chatter marks. There may be means of taking up the wear; if not, new bearings should be fitted. Chucks and face-plates may not fit the spindle nose squarely, particularly when the threads become worn. The result is taper bores and diameters, and end faces which are not flat. This out-of-squareness is generally due to burrs on the mating faces, or to dirt being trapped. In either case the remedy is obvious.

18.12.2 Misalignment of the tailstock. This may occur unwittingly as the result of turning a slow taper, and omitting to realign the tailstock. The tailstock may be fitted with a taper dowel pin, to register the central position.

18.12.3 Wear of the guideways. This occurs inevitably in all lathes. Generally, the wear is more pronounced at the headstock end, as much of the work will be short, and the carriage is frequently traversing this part of the bed. If a parallel ground bar with a tapered end is placed in the spindle nose, and a dial-indicator is mounted on the tool-post, irregularities of the front shear will be shown up. The horizontal check is most important (position A in fig. 18.30), but the vertical position B should also be checked. The result of this wear will be that the work will reveal the same defects as the front shear. The remedy is to plane up the shear, and either to bed it to a straight-edge, or to grind it parallel with the lathe centre line.

Chattered and uneven work is often caused by play in the guide-ways. This play should be taken up by means of the taper gibs or fitting slips provided for this purpose (fig. 18.2). Besides the main longitudinal slides, the cross slide should also be corrected, otherwise flat faces cannot be produced.

18.12.4 *Capstan and turret lathes* are checked in a similar manner, with additional checks for turret accuracy.

18.13 Care of Lathes
The following remarks apply to most other machine tools, as well as lathes.

The accuracy of the machine depends on the guiding surfaces. These must be protected from damage at all times. There is a tendency today to fit shields or covers for the guideways; this is an excellent idea. Spare tools should be kept in racks, never on the machine bed, where they may be bumped on the bed, or may even become jammed between moving parts; it is for such eventualities that the slipping clutch is fitted. The machine should be oiled regularly, and all swarf should be removed as soon as possible.

Periodically, the machine should be taken out of service, checked, and corrected. This is work for a skilled machine-tool fitter who knows what to examine, and how to rectify any defects. The machine should never be taxed beyond its capacity; this entails systematic distribution of the work in the machine-shop, and clear instructions to the operators. The most important point is the proper training of young workers, and the fostering of an intelligent pride in the work done, and in the machine which helps to do it.

18.14 Safety in the machine-shop
As most apprentices spend at least some portion of their time on the centre lathe, the following points on safety in the machine-shop may be appropriate at the end of this chapter.

Shop safety is largely a matter for the foreman and his deputies, but senior workmen should be encouraged to help in this very important matter. Unsuitable clothing should be discouraged—loose flapping coats or sleeves which are wide or too long cause accidents. The careless worker should be shown logically to what end his conduct will lead. The foolhardy should be treated with ignominy. Horseplay in the machine-shop is tempting fate; it must be stopped immediately, and any workman who stops it must be backed up uncompromisingly by the management.

Guards and other safety devices must be kept in repair, and never removed by the ordinary worker. Electric wiring deteriorates in time; whenever the insulation becomes frayed, or the wire kinked, it should be renewed. The modern practice of using low-voltage lighting on machine tools is an excellent idea. Tools such as spanners, wrenches, and tommy-bars should fit snugly; if they do not, they should be renovated or scrapped.

Factory inspectors are people with special knowledge of industrial hazards. Frank discussion places the wisdom at the service of the management; irritation over their activities is illogical, and usually futile.

Summary

1 A lathe is used principally to produce cylindrical surfaces and plane surfaces at right angles to the axis of rotation; other features such as tapers and helices are also produced using a lathe.
2 A cast iron bed forms the base of the machine, and serves as a guide for the saddle and tailstock.
3 The workpiece may be held between centres, in a chuck, or from a face-plate.
4 The speeds, feeds, and depths of cut depend upon the type of work, the workpiece material, the finish required, and the lathe being used.
5 The principal operations performed are ending up, drilling, reaming and boring, taper turning, and screw-cutting.
6 Production work is usually done using capstan and turret lathes.
7 Lathe alignment tests include check upon the spindle, the tailstock, and the guideways.

Questions

Set A
1 Discuss the factors which influence the depth of cut used in various lathe operations.
2 What parts of a lathe take the thrust of cutting (*a*) in turning bars with a knife-tool, (*b*) in surfacing the end of a cylinder?
3 A lathe is turning all work to a slight but irregular taper at one end. Suggest possible causes for this defect, and explain how it may be rectified.
4 A casting gripped in a lathe chuck is bored out 75 mm in diameter to a depth of 50 mm. It is found that the hole is 0·05 mm bigger diameter at the bottom than at the top. What is wrong with the lathe, and how can it be corrected?
5 An annular groove in a shaft is 10 mm deep, 18 mm wide at the top, and 12 mm wide at the bottom. It is turned in a lathe with a

form-tool which has no top-rake, and 6° front clearance angle. Calculate the dimensions of the tool nose, measured at right angles to the clearance face, and sketch the tool.

6 A lathe tool is cutting a bar 100 mm in diameter revolving at a speed of 110 revs/min. The depth of cut is 5 mm, and the feed is 0·040 mm per revolution. Calculate (*a*) the cutting speed in m/s, (*b*) the volume of metal removed in mm^3/min.

7 Explain the function of the leadscrew of a centre lathe. Could a lathe leadscrew be used to graduate a rule? Outline the principle involved, and state the conditions which must be maintained to ensure accurate graduation.

8 Calculate suitable change-wheels for cutting the following threads: 3·5 mm lead, 7·5 mm lead. The lathe used has a 5-mm lead leadscrew, and change wheels of 20T to 120T, in steps of 5T.

9 It is not usual to have power-feed to the top slide of a lathe. Why is this so? What is the purpose of arranging the top slide with a swivelling motion? Can the top slide be used to turn cylindrical work?

10 A mandrel 400 mm long is to be turned in a lathe to a taper of 0·80 mm per metre on the diameter. Calculate a suitable set-over for the tailstock. If several mandrels were required, what precautions would be required to ensure that all had the same taper?

11 Sketch a simple component suitable for manufacture between centres in a lathe, and describe its manufacture.

12 Cast-iron rings, 150 mm in diameter, 25 mm wide, and 120 mm bore, have been turned in a centre lathe. It is desired to reduce the width slightly. With the aid of sketches, show how this could be done.

13 A bar, 40 mm + 0·05 mm in diameter and 450 mm long, is to be turned from 45-mm diameter black bar, and a hole, 12 mm in diameter and 50 mm deep, is to be drilled up one end of it. Describe these processes as performed on a centre lathe.

14 A right-angled plate with faces 300 mm square is to have a 100-mm-diameter hole bored in the centre of one face. Explain, with sketches, how this operation could be carried out on a centre lathe.

Set B (questions requiring further study)

15 Contrast the following operations as performed on an ordinary lathe and on a vertical boring mill: (*a*) facing up the flanges of a short pipe of large diameter, (*b*) boring a hole approximately 600-mm diameter with a taper of 10° included angle in a casting 750 mm in diameter and 1200 mm long.

16 Make a sketch showing the bearings and mounting of a lathe spindle.

17 Describe a suitable method of determining (*a*) that a lathe bed 12 metres long is level throughout its length, (*b*) that the headstock and tailstock centres are coaxial.

18 Discuss the various causes of 'chattered' work in the centre lathe, and suggest suitable remedies.

19 Make a sketch of a boring tool for use on long bores, such as gunbarrels, and explain the working principle.

Chapter 19
Drilling Machines

19.1. Drilling machines are used to machine holes and associated features; they are therefore used for drilling, reaming, counterboring, countersinking, spotfacing, and tapping. These operations, and the cutters, are discussed in section 19.3.

19.2 Types of drilling machines

19.2.1 Portable drilling machines. These machines are used for small holes in large or awkwardly shaped workpieces; they are a more robust version of the 'handyman's' power drill. Portable drilling machines are power-operated, but the feed action is by pushing. They are sometimes mounted on a stand to convert them into sensitive drilling machines.

19.2.2 Sensitive drilling machines. These are the smallest of the fixed machines, and are used for small-diameter work. No power feed is provided, but the drill head is counterbalanced, and fed through a hand lever system. This arrangement allows the operator to feel the force acting on the drill; hence the term 'sensitive'. The spindle speeds are high, to suit the small-diameter drills.

19.2.3 Column drilling machines. Machines in this group are used for larger-diameter holes, and allow the drill to be fed either by hand or by power. In the model shown in fig. 19.1, the table can be given precise movement by a leadscrew and graduated sleeve system. The size of work that can be accommodated is limited by the distance between the spindle and the column, but these machines are rigid, and ideal for production work. Figure 19.2 shows a six-spindle column machine, which is basically six machines sharing a common table. It allows a large number of drills, etc., to be set, and the workpiece, in its jig, is stationed under each spindle in turn. A multi-spindle machine is used for production work involving a large number of holes in one facing; this system uses several spindles in a special head, so that all spindles are driven from a common shaft. The drills are not controlled by a bush plate as in other production systems (see fig. 16.21), but the rela-

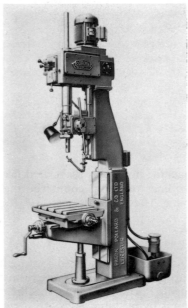
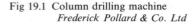

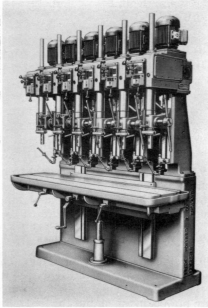

Fig 19.1 Column drilling machine
Frederick Pollard & Co. Ltd

Fig 19.2 Six-spindle column drilling
machine
Frederick Pollard & Co. Ltd

tive positions of the drills are controlled by a plate which forms part of the drill head. The workpiece must be located relative to the drill head, but the relative depths of drilling are controlled by spindle settings.

19.2.4 Radial-arm drilling machines. The column-type machines are inconvenient for large workpieces, or when a large number of holes is to be drilled, because the workpiece must be positioned under the spindle, and secured before each hole is drilled. For work of this nature, a radial-arm machine (fig. 19.3) is often more convenient to use, although less rigid than the column-type machine. The radial-arm machine consists of a massive pillar, which supports a strong and rigid L-shaped arm. This arm can be moved up and down the pillar, and be swung about the pillar axis; it can be locked in the required position. The arm carries the drill head, which can be positioned as required along the arm, and locked in position. The drill head includes a vertical feed slide. The illustration shows a bed-type machine, in which the workpiece is clamped to the bed, or to a block which is itself clamped to the bed. Radial-arm machines are also produced with a table that can be raised or lowered as required.

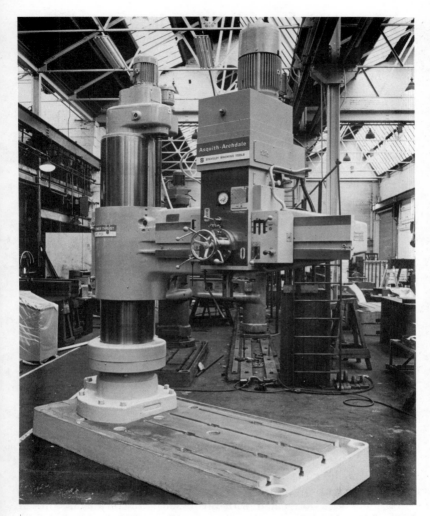

Fig 19.3 Radial-arm drilling machine   *Staveley Machine Tools*

19.3 Operations and cutters

19.3.1 Drilling. Figure 15.15 showed the principal features of a twist drill, and there are special problems associated with the operation it performs. The cutting edges are usually working at the bottom of a blind hole, and consequently it is difficult to get the swarf away from the work; this becomes worse as the hole is deepened. The other problem is caused by the drill cutting at its end—the drill will be cutting at a faster rate at the outside than at the inside end of the cutting edge. The drilling speeds usually quoted are for the outside end of the edge. The following are typical speeds for standard high-speed drills:

cast iron	0·4–0·6 m/s
mild steel	0·3–0·5 m/s
60/40 brass	0·8–1·0 m/s
medium carbon steels	0·2–0·3 m/s

The actual path traversed by the cutting edge of the drill is helical, because of the feed motion; the lead of the two helices (one for each edge of a standard two-flute drill) being equal to the feed per revolution of the drill. It follows, therefore, that the helix angle will be small for the outer edge, and will increase rapidly near the drill point. Thus the feed per revolution should be increased with increasing drill size if a reasonable chip thickness is to be maintained. The following are typical feed rates for various drill sizes for 'hard' and for 'soft' materials: grey cast iron, steel with less than 0·3% carbon, brass, bronze, and aluminium alloys are typical 'soft' materials; steels with more than 0·3% carbon, and all alloy steels are typical 'hard' materials.

Drill diameter (mm)	'Hard' materials feed mm/rev	'Soft' materials feed mm/rev
1·5	0·05	0·05
3·0	0·05	0·07
6·0	0·07	0·10
9·0	0·10	0·15
12·0	0·12	0·20
19·0	0·18	0·30
25·0	0·22	0·35

19.3.2 Reaming. The hole produced by a twist drill has a rather rough surface, and is not usually a true cylinder. When smooth, accurate holes are required, they are drilled slightly below the finished size, and then opened out with a reamer, which is passed through at a low speed, and often lubricated with oil. Fixed reamers are used for a particular size of hole, but slight variations in the hole diameter can be made in the workshop by selecting reamers that are slightly different from their nominal size. Figure 18.18 shows a section through a fixed reamer. Figure 19.4 illustrates the principle of the adjustable reamer; it shows six blades that are located in tapered slots, and clamped in position by two nuts. If the right-hand nut is slackened, and the left-hand nut tightened, the blades will move to the right, and the diameter will be increased. Helical teeth give a better cutting action than straight teeth (the helix is usually left-hand for a right-hand rotating reamer, to prevent the reamer from 'digging in') Adjustable reamers

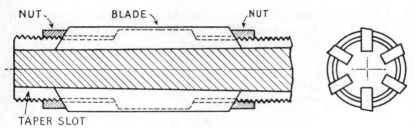

Fig 19.4 Principle of the adjustable reamer

are often made with special blades with a number of cutting edges, to produce the effect of a helical reamer.

19.3.3 Counterboring. Two-diameter holes, such as that shown in fig. 19.5, are often required to take screw and bolt heads; the larger diameter is called a counterbore. A counterbore may be made by a cutter-bar and loose cutter, as shown in fig. 19.6. The lower end of the bar is a close-running fit in the small hole, and is termed a pilot, since it guides the cutter. A counterboring cutter can be made from an existing drill, or be made specially, as shown in fig. 19.7.

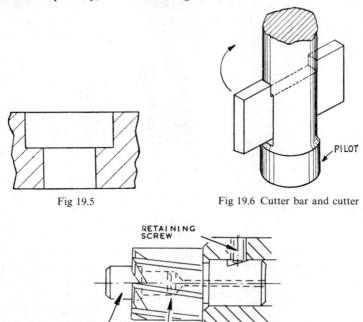

Fig 19.5

Fig 19.6 Cutter bar and cutter

Fig 19.7 Counterboring cutter

19.3.4 Spotfacing. A spotface is a shallow counterbore, to produce a locally machined face on an otherwise rough casting or forging. It is usually produced using a counterboring cutter.

19.3.5 Countersinking. A countersink is a large chamfer applied to a hole so that a countersink screw can be accepted. Figure 19.8 shows a typical cutter used for countersinking.

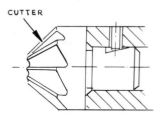

Fig 19.8 Countersinking cutter

19.3.6 Tapping. A screw-thread can be cut in a hole of suitable diameter by tapping. Figure 19.9 illustrates the principal features of a typical tap, which is basically a screw with a number of flutes cut along its length, to produce cutting edges. It is necessary to introduce form relief, to prevent the tap from rubbing on the hole being tapped. The tap shown in fig. 19.9 is used for hand tapping, but other taps are designed for machine tapping.

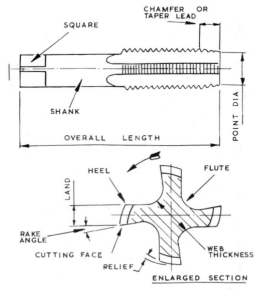

Fig 19.9 Tap

19.4 Location of workpieces

Small-quantity production is usually done with the workpiece clamped to the machine table or bed; a setter is often employed to locate and clamp the workpiece ready for the operator to carry out the machining. The limitation associated with the ordinary column and radial arm machines is that holes can only be drilled vertically; angular holes must therefore be drilled with the workpiece set at the required angle. In large shops, at least one machine is provided with a tilting table; for smaller work, two angle plates may be bolted together by one bolt through their vertical faces, as shown in fig. 19.10, and the upper plate can be tilted as required. V-blocks are also in common use on the drilling machine table.

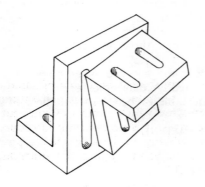

Fig 19.10

Large-quantity production is carried out using a drilling jig (see fig. 16.21), so that the workpiece, drills, and reamers are located without the need for marking out and setting. The setter would, in this case, prepare the machine and the tools, and set the depth-control devices.

19.5 Drilling-machine alignments

The radial-arm machine is dealt with in the following notes, but column machines are dealt with in a very similar manner.

As the table or bed is the location for the workpiece, it is used as the datum for the alignment checks. The level and flatness of the table or bed are checked in both directions, using a spirit level (fig. 19.11).

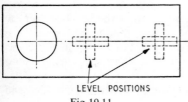

LEVEL POSITIONS
Fig 19.11

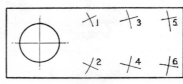

Fig 19.12

The next step is to check the radial-arm relative to the table. This is done by attaching the dial-indicator (see section 23.5.1) to a spindle which, in turn, is located in the drill head. The radial arm is placed in the mid-position on the pillar, and the vertical adjustment is locked; the drill-head spindle motion is locked in a convenient position. The effect of rotation of the arm about the pillar is checked with the drill head close to the pillar, in the mid position, and at the end of the arm; this indicates the 'sag' of the arm, caused by the weight of the drill head. Figure 19.12 illustrates this test: the first position of the drill head gives readings 1 and 2; the second position gives readings 3 and 4; and the third gives readings 5 and 6. It must be emphasised that, although the dial-indicator is attached to the drill head, and touches the table, it is the radial arm, not the table, that is being checked. The variations in table flatness indicated by the levelling and flatness checks are used in conjunction with these readings to give the actual error caused by the arm.

The accuracy of the spindle is now checked. A test mandrel is placed in the spindle bore, and rotated. A dial-indicator is mounted on a stand placed on the machine table or bed, and the effect of spindle

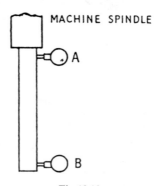

Fig 19.13

rotation is checked. Figure 19.13 illustrates this check, and it will be seen that two checks are made, at position A and position B. This check indicates whether the spindle bore rotates concentrically with and parallel to the drill-head centre line.

The squareness of the spindle relative to the table or bed is now checked by placing a dial-indicator mounting spindle in the machine spindle, and rotating it, as shown in fig. 19.14. Variations in the levelling and flatness of the table are taken into account when calculating the actual errors.

The test illustrated in fig. 19.15 is used to determine whether the spindle feed is square with the table.

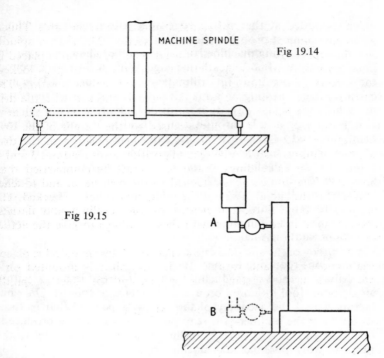

MACHINE SPINDLE

Fig 19.14

Fig 19.15

A

B

Summary

1 Drilling machines are used for drilling, reaming, counterboring, spotfacing, and tapping: these are all operations dealing with holes and associated features.
2 Drilling machines can be classified as (a) portable drilling machines, (b) sensitive drilling machines, (c) column drilling machines, and (d) radial-arm drilling machines.
3 The workpiece may be clamped to the machine table, held in a vice, or, in the case of large-quantity production, located and clamped in a jig.
4 When drilling machine alignment tests are carried out, the table or bed is used as a datum or support for the dial-indicator, and its accuracy is determined first. Checks are then made to determine the accuracy of the spindle rotation, and of the guideways.

Questions

Set A

1 Calculate a suitable speed in revs/min for a 25-mm-diameter HSS drill working in mild steel. If such a drill, when working on a steel

block, is dulled at the cutting edge after a few minutes drilling, what are the most probable causes?

2 A radial-arm drilling machine has a loose table. The table is put in position with swarf underneath one edge. What will be the effect on the following operations: (*a*) drilling and counterboring a hole in a casting which is resting on a machined face on the table, (*b*) reaming a hole which has already been drilled squarely to a machined face, (*c*) drilling a hole through a shaft held in V-blocks, the hole being intended to pass through the axis of the shaft?

3 In spotfacing a surface with a loose cutter fixed in a cutter bar, upon what does the flatness of the surface depend? Suggest suitable speeds in revs/min for the following operations: (*a*) spotfacing grey cast iron to a diameter of 75 mm with a high-carbon steel cutter, (*b*) drilling 12-mm-diameter holes to a depth of 150 mm in mild steel with a HSS drill. Give reasons for your answers, and mention any special precautions that should be taken.

Set B (questions requiring further study)

4 Describe a method of producing a rough V-thread in a hole with a single-point tool mounted on a drilling-machine spindle. On what factors would the accuracy of the thread depend? What features would limit the number of thread pitches that could be produced?

5 Compare the various types of drilling machine with respect to the range of work possible, and machine rigidity.

Chapter 20
Shaping, Slotting, and Planing Machines

20.1. These machines are similar to each other in that the cutter (or cutters) reciprocates relative to the workpiece, cutting in *one* direction, then returning before the feed is applied and the next cut taken. This was illustrated in fig. 15.10, which shows that the material is removed in the form of a number of strips.

It is obvious that the return stroke is a non-cutting stroke, and so it is usual to have a system whereby the return speed is greater than the cutting speed, in order to minimise the non-productive time. The reciprocating action also means that the tool or machine table is accelerating at the start of the cutting stroke, and retarding at the end of the stroke; in certain cases this results in a considerable variation in the cutting speed throughout the stroke.

During the return stroke, the cutter passes over the surface just machined, so a mechanism is introduced to ensure that the cutter does not damage the surface.

Shaping, slotting, and planing machines are basic reciprocating machines; but special machines, such as certain gear-cutting machines, are also of this type.

20.2 The shaping machine
The machining of small rectangular components, particularly in moderate quantities, is often done on the shaping machine. This handy little machine occupies little floor space, and is easily set up, much of the work being held in a table vice. Single-point tools are commonly used; these are cheap to buy and are easily reground: this is in contrast to the milling machine, which uses expensive cutters, which are not easy to regrind, and require a special tool-grinding machine. In the small workshop and tool-room, the shaping machine is invaluable, but for large-scale production the milling machine is usually preferred. (The tool-room is the workshop where jigs, fixtures, and tools are made.) Figure 20.1 illustrates a typical shaping machine. The cutting tool is mounted on the end of a ram, which reciprocates to give the cutting motion, while the work-table is moved to produce the feed motion. The tool slide is moved to adjust the depth of cut.

Fig 20.1 Shaping machine   *Butler Ltd*

The body casing contains the driving arrangements for the various movements, and also carries two slides. The top slide carries the ram, and a saddle is mounted on the front slide. This saddle can be raised and lowered by means of a screw-jack, and has a pair of horizontal slides on which the work-table is moved by the feed motion. The outer end of the table is supported by a slide mounted on a bracket, thus improving the rigidity. On some machines, the table can be tilted, and a circular setting scale is provided. This facilitates the machining of angular faces.

The top slides are V-shaped, and the base of the ram has slides to suit (fig. 20.1). The front end of the ram has a short slide carrying the tool-box, which is moved on the slide by the handle at the top when the cut depth is adjusted. A short vertical feed motion can thus be imparted for machining out a square corner. The tool-box and slide can be

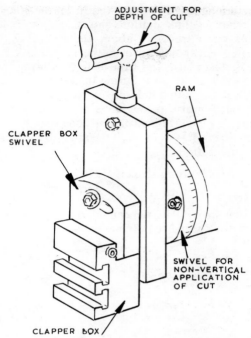

Fig 20.2 Shaping machine tool-box and slide

swivelled on the ram, and set by the circular scale (fig. 20.2). By this means the tool can be fed down a short, angular surface. The tool-box is fixed to a swivel-pin near its top inner surface, thus allowing it to swing forward on the return stroke, and so clear the work surface. This mechanism is termed a *clapper box*, and will be seen in fig. 20.2; its action is shown in fig. 20.3. The feed motion is imparted to the tool at the start of each cutting stroke, and a little over-run is therefore required.

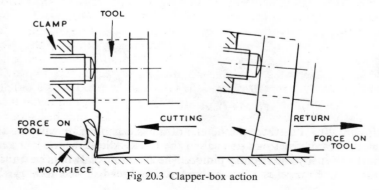

Fig 20.3 Clapper-box action

20.2.1 Quick-return action. The quick return on the idle stroke is provided by a mechanical link motion, shown diagrammatically in fig.
20.4. The crank-pin P revolves about the centre O with uniform
angular velocity; it engages in a slot in the slotted link FR, which has
its fulcrum at F. The pin moves from P to P_1 during the forward or
cutting stroke, and from P_1 to P during the return stroke. During this
cycle, the end R of the slotted link moves from R to R_1 and back to R.
It will be seen that P moves through a smaller angle during the return
stroke than during the cutting stroke, so that the return stroke takes
place in a shorter time. For example, if the arc P to P_1 is associated with
210°, then the time ratio is

$$\frac{\text{cutting stroke}}{\text{return stroke}} = \frac{210}{150} = \frac{7}{5}$$

The length of the stroke RR_1 depends upon the radius OP, which is
adjusted to suit the cutting requirements.

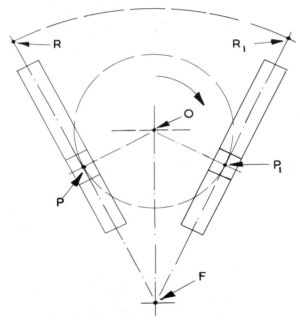

Fig 20.4 Quick-return link motion

Figure 20.5 illustrates the details of the mechanism. It will be seen
that the crank pin P is attached to the stroke wheel, which is a gear
wheel driven by the driving pinion. The position of P relative to the
centre of this wheel is adjusted by a screw-thread device, to vary the

stroke. The position of the ram relative to the centre of the stroke wheel axis is adjustable as shown, to alter the 'position' of the stroke. Reference to fig. 20.4 will show that the end of the slotted link moves through an arc. In order to convert this to a linear movement, the fulcrum has a trunnion bearing, so that the end of the slotted link can move in the bearing to adjust the position of R to suit. An alternative to this is to incorporate a link member between the end of the slotted link and the link that is attached to the ram.

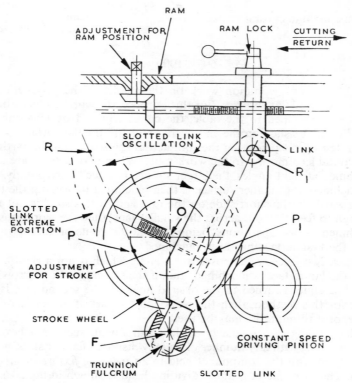

Fig 20.5 Quick-return mechanism

In giving the particulars of a commercial shaping machine, the makers usually state the maximum and minimum number of cycles per minute, and the number of speeds available. The number of cycles is, of course, equal to the number of revolutions per minute of the stroke-wheel.

In shaping-machine calculations the *average cutting speed* is sometimes mentioned. This is the length of the cutting stroke, divided by the time required to make one such stroke.

For example, a shaper working on a 450 mm stroke makes thirty cycles per minute. The ratio

$$\frac{\text{cutting time}}{\text{return time}} = \frac{7}{5}$$

What is the average cutting speed?

Time for one cycle $= \dfrac{1}{30}$ minutes

Time for one cutting stroke $= \dfrac{7}{12} \times \dfrac{1}{30} = \dfrac{7}{360}$ minutes

Average cutting speed $= \dfrac{450 \times 360}{60 \times 1000 \times 7} \simeq 0\cdot39$ m/s

20.2.2. The most common work on the shaper is the production of moderate-sized flat surfaces. For this purpose, the work is placed in the vice, or is clamped to the table; the cut is adjusted by lowering the tool-box on its slide on the end of the ram; and the flat surface is then generated by reciprocating the tool across the work, and imparting a horizontal feed motion to the work-table. When two surfaces are to be machined at right angles, the larger surface is placed horizontally, and is machined; the smaller surface is then machined by feeding the tool-downwards in the short slide on the ram end. If this slide is not long enough to feed the tool across the smaller face, then the work must be machined in two operations, being reset at 90° to its original position after the first surface has been machined.

When two faces are disposed at an angle which is not a right angle, then the larger face is machined; and, if the second face is narrow, the tool-box slide is turned to the desired angle. If the second face is too wide for this method, then the work must be set at an angle on the table, or a tilting table may be used.

The shaping of a regularly angled component, such as a hexagon nut, or a part with any number of equally disposed flats or slots, is best performed with the component held in an *indexing fixture* or *dividing head*. The principle of a direct dividing head is shown in fig. 20.6.

A headstock and tailstock each have a central parallel tongue on their machined base, thus allowing them to be lined up by means of one of the table grooves. The tailstock has a movable centre, which can be locked in a suitable position. The headstock has a spindle which can be rotated but cannot be moved endways; this spindle can also be locked at any point of its rotation. One end of the spindle has a nose of similar design to the nose of a lathe spindle, thus allowing catchplates or chucks to be mounted. A loose or 'live' centre can be inserted in the spindle socket. The other end of the spindle has a key.

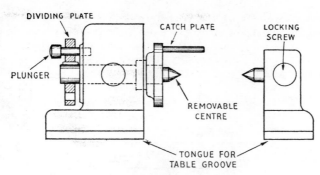

Fig 20.6 Dividing head

Index or dividing plates are provided. These are circular steel discs, with a central hole and keyway, and are a light press fit on the spindle. Each plate has a ring of circular holes, equally spaced out. These holes are at the same radius as a single hole which is drilled into the end face of the dividing head. When any hole in the plate is opposite the hole in the dividing head, a push-fit plunger can be pushed through the plate and into the dividing head, thus fixing the spindle and any work attached to it. Suppose a dividing plate with twelve holes is mounted, then the spindle can be 'indexed' $\frac{1}{12}$, $\frac{1}{6}$, $\frac{1}{4}$, $\frac{1}{3}$, and $\frac{1}{2}$ of one turn and any work will be indexed the same amount. Thus twelve slots could be machined in a cylindrical job mounted between centres, or six flats could be machined on a nut clamped in a chuck.

The accuracy of the work is dependent on the accuracy of the pitching of the holes in the dividing plate, and the absence of 'play' in the spindle, the plate, and the plunger. The plates can be bored to suit the spindle, and the plunger holes may then be set out and bored by the button method illustrated in fig. 16.18. One central disc should be used for all the plates, so that the pitch circle diameter will not vary; the hole in the dividing head can then be drilled from one of the plates. It can also have a hardened steel bush driven tightly in, as a safeguard against wear. A set of plates as follows will cover a very wide range of work: sixteen holes, fifteen holes, fourteen holes, thirteen holes, twelve holes, eleven holes, ten holes, nine holes.

It may also be noted that a gear-wheel might be fitted in place of the dividing plate, and, if this wheel is connected to the feed mechanism, the work can be rotated before each cutting stroke. A shape closely approaching a cylinder can thus be generated, if the rotation is very slow. If a form tool with a suitable radius is used, the component can then be formed to a true cylinder.

20.2.3 Shaping-machine alignments. The following are certain of the alignment tests which may be applied to the shaping machine. The

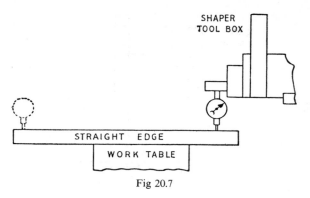

Fig 20.7

machine should first be tested for level, with a precision spirit level on the main sliding surfaces and the work-table. Figure 20.7 shows the test for determining whether the ram movement is parallel to the top of the work-table. In an old machine, the work-table will be dented and marked; these defects must be smoothed as far as possible, with a suitable file and a straight-edge placed on the table. The ram movement is then tried relative to the straight-edge throughout the full-stroke. It is best if the outer end of the straight-edge is found to be slightly high—say up to 0·035 mm per metre—as the weight of the work will tend to depress the outer end of the table. When the ram is in the outer position, as shown dotted in fig. 20.7, it is as well to try the vertical 'play' between the ram and its slides, since the weight of the ram will cause it to sag during the test; but when cutting, the cutting force will tend to lift the ram in most operations. If the machine-table has sides with T-slots for clamping work, then the ram movement must also be tried to see that it is parallel to these sides.

In surfacing a piece of work, the feed motion is given to the table, and fig. 20.8 shows the test for this motion. The straight-edge is placed on the table, which is then moved from end to end of its travel. The shaper tool-box and dial-indicator are kept stationary during this test.

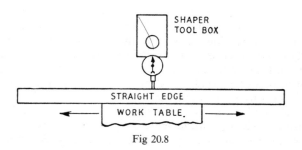

Fig 20.8

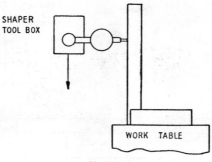

SHAPER
TOOL BOX

WORK TABLE

Fig 20.9

Figure 20.9 illustrates the test for the short slide on the end of the ram. The graduated scale must, of course, be carefully set to zero. The same test may also be used for the upwards movement of the table, which is controlled by the screw-jack operating on the saddle. In making this latter test, the ram-slide will, of course, be kept stationary.

20.3 The slotting machine
The slotter illustrated in fig. 20.10 may be likened to a vertical shaper, since the reciprocating motion is vertical. The nature of the machine and the type of work performed have led to certain specialised features being included. The quick-return motion for the ram is of a different type from that of the shaper; it is more compact, but rather more complicated. The length of stroke and stroke position can both be varied as in the shaper, but generally the slotter has a shorter stroke than the shaper.

It would be wrong, however, to consider the slotter as simply a shaper turned on end. In certain classes of work, the slotter would be difficult to replace, and some examples will be given a little later. Furthermore, the slotter is not a light general-utility machine like the shaper, but is sometimes required to remove large amounts of metal. A special range of slotters, known as 'puncher' slotters, are of very rugged construction: equipped with a powerful motor, they can machine out metal at a remarkable speed.

Certain of the advantages of the vertical boring mill may be noted in the slotter. The table is horizontal, and thus the work may be manoeuvred in comfort. The table is mounted directly over a bed casting, and fairly heavy work may be placed on it without serious distortion.

The work-table is usually circular, and can be revolved by hand or power feed. It is graduated round its outer edge, and work can thus be mounted and turned to predetermined angular positions. The circular table is mounted on a pair of slides arranged on a saddle, and this saddle itself moves on another pair of slides on the bed casting. Thus, the work can be revolved, and also moved in two directions at right

Fig 20.10 Slotting machine   *Butler Ltd*

angles to each other, providing both rectangular and polar coordinate systems, an unusual feature. The depth of cut is adjusted by one motion, and the feed is put on with either the other straight-line motion or the circular motion. The tool simply reciprocates in one plane, as in the shaping machine.

20.3.1. The cutting tool may be mounted on the front of the ram (fig. 20.11), on the bottom of the ram, or, alternatively, in a bar, like a boring bar (figs. 20.12 (*a*) and (*b*)). A cutting tool that is mounted on the front of the ram tends to deflect away from the workpiece, because of its large overhang, and must be of large and rigid section. A cutting tool used in this way is unconventional in shape, as the tool breast is at the end of the tool; fig. 20.13 illustrates a typical slotting tool for this mounting.

A cutting tool to be mounted on the bottom of the ram, or from a bar, is similar to a lathe tool and a shaper tool. This form of mounting gives a better support to the tool, but when the mounting is directly from the bottom of the ram, the ram must enter the hole being slotted, and so the alternative, bar-mounted tool is used for slotting small holes.

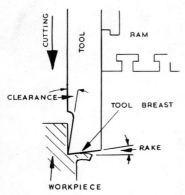

Fig 20.11 Tool mounted on front of ram

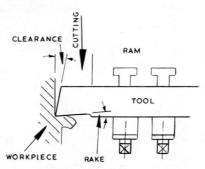

Fig 20.12(*a*) Tool mounted on bottom of ram

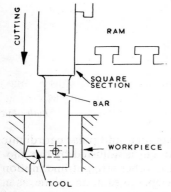

Fig 20.12(*b*) Tool mounted in bar

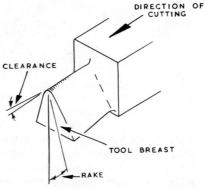

Fig 20.13 Slotting tool for front-mounting

A relieving tool (fig. 20.14(*a*)) is used to produce large internal surfaces. When this tool is used, a starting hole is first drilled, and then opened out by the relieving tool, which 'nibbles' at the hole. Reference to fig. 20.14(*a*) will show that the relieving tool is circular in section, and is therefore able to cut in every direction at right angles to its axis as shown in fig. 20.14(*b*).

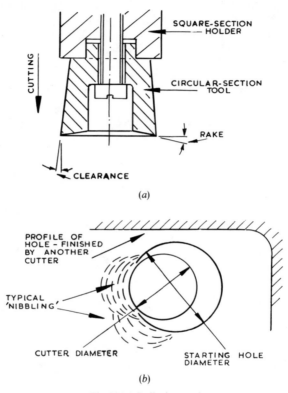

(*a*)

(*b*)

Fig 20.14 Relieving tool

20.3.2. Clapper boxes are not usually fitted to the heavier slotting machines, so there is a tendency for the tool to rub on the surface during the return stroke. A clapper box is often fitted to the lighter machines, as an attachment, as shown in fig. 20.15(*a*). The tool holder is mounted so that, under gravity, it swings, and causes the tool to move from the vertical surface being cut. During the cutting stroke, the resistance to cutting causes the tool holder to take up the position shown in fig. 20.15(*b*), but during the return stroke, gravity causes it to take up the position shown in fig. 20.15(*c*).

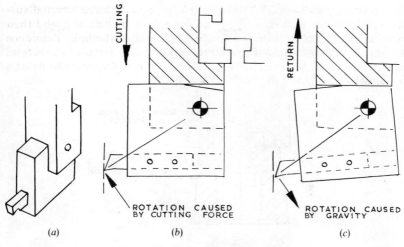

(a)   (b)   (c)

Fig 20.15 Clapper box

20.3.3. Slotting machines are used to machine slots in bores, as well as in external vertical surfaces, and to produce large internal surfaces, as shown in fig. 20.14(*a*). By the use of the circular table, a circular, or part circular, vertical face can be generated by machining a large number of small flats, as shown in fig. 20.16.

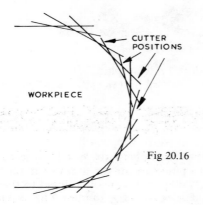

Fig 20.16

20.3.4 Slotting-machine alignments. These are similar to alignments for shaping machines. The datum is the table, which must be flat and level, and its movements accurate. The ram movement must be square, in both directions, with the table.

20.4 Planing machines

A large planing machine is shown in fig. 20.17. The bed is a very rigid iron casting, on the top of which are two slides. The reciprocating table has two slides on the under-side which rest on the bed-slides. The flat top of

Fig 20.17 Planing machine   *Butler Ltd*

the table has T-slots for clamping bolts. The bed is approximately twice as long as the table, so that the table is fully supported throughout its stroke. Two tool-boxes are carried on a cross slide or 'rail', which can be moved up and down on two strong columns attached to the bed. The size of a planer is indicated by the length of the stroke and the maximum height and width which will pass the rail and its supports.

The under-side of the table carries a rack which engages with a helical pinion. This pinion is driven by a motor situated at the side of the bed. Since the table, together with the part being machined, must be accelerated quickly to the maximum speed at the start of the stroke, and retarded equally quickly at the end of the stroke, considerable variation occurs in the power input to the pinion. Furthermore, the return stroke of the table should be made as quickly as possible, while the speed of the forward or cutting stroke must be varied according to the material being machined.

To meet these unusual demands, a special electrical lay-out is required, and the following is a very brief outline of the system used. A standard a.c. or d.c. motor is used to drive a d.c. generator which supplies current to the table driving-motor. The voltage of the generator field is variable, and the field can be reversed. By varying the generator field, the speed and power output of the table motor can be varied over a wide range. The maximum power is required when the table is being accelerated at the start of the stroke, and heavy continuous power input is required when a heavy cut is being taken. High speed but lower power are required in making the return stroke. At the end of the short acceleration periods, the field strength is automatically adjusted to the stroke conditions. One of the principal difficulties with the old belt-driven planer was that of retarding the table at the end of the stroke. When a heavy casting or forging was on the table, the momentum acquired was considerable, and was difficult to dissipate. In the case of the modern planer, the electric drive forms its own brake, the generator field is reversed, and the surplus energy due to retardation is passed back through the generator set to the electrical supply lines.

It is often necessary to plane two or more small surfaces spaced well apart, as shown in fig. 20.18. The table can be moved quickly to bring each face to the cutting tool, and then abruptly slowed down to the correct cutting speed. The variation in speed and torque of the motor is controlled from the table; the edge of the table is arranged to carry movable tappets, which throw over suitable switches; these in turn alter the generator field by relay systems. Thus, a pair of tappets is set to reverse the table at each end of the stroke, and further tappets may be set to cause changes in the speed of the cutting stroke at appropriate points.

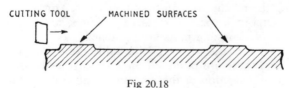

Fig 20.18

20.4.1. The tool-feed is put on before the start of each cutting stroke, during the over-run period. It is done by moving the tool-box along the rail, a separate motor being provided for this function. The lead-screws for the tool-boxes are shown inside the rail in fig. 20.17. This motor starts up automatically when the tool clears the work, just before the reversal of the table. The tool-boxes are mounted on short slides, which normally are vertical to the table; after a cut has been made across the width of the work, the tool-boxes are returned, and a new cut is put on by lowering the tool-box in the slide. For machining the sides of the work, two further tool-boxes may be mounted on the side columns of the planer. In this case, the feed motion is parallel to the side columns (i.e. vertical to the table), and the cut adjustment is horizontal to the table. These side tool-boxes are clearly shown in fig. 20.17.

The rail is raised and lowered to suit the height of the work by a motor, and since the rail must be locked while the cut is being taken across the width of the work, a further small motor is fitted, to tighten the nuts which secure the rail to the side columns.

During the return stroke of the table, the tip of the tool must not be allowed to rub along the surface just cut, and accordingly the tool is lifted clear during the stroke, by means of a solenoid.

20.4.2. The tools used are generally similar to lathe tools, but, as there is a distinct shock when the tool nose enters the work, the top rake is often a negative angle, although considerable side rake may be used: tools with the usual top rake are liable to snap at the very tip, as this is the first point to contact the work. For similar reasons, it is advisable to use tools of very heavy cross-section in the planing machine.

A further point arising from the cutting arrangements is the necessity of clamping the work so as to resist the sudden heavy load which occurs at the beginning of each cut. If possible, the work should be backed up by a definite abutting face, or 'stop' as it is termed, so as to resist the shock. Clamping the work is one of the main points in the craft of planing, and the clamping of a tricky job is the hall-mark of a good planer operator. The accuracy of planed surfaces is often impaired by unwise clamping; long work, particularly castings, and welded structures, is usually slightly distorted, and while it may pull down flat to the table when bolted up, and be machined flat while fastened down, after the clamps have been released, the job will spring back, thus making the machined surfaces either convex or concave. The remedy is to support the part by suitable packings, so that no distortion occurs when the clamping bolts are tightened.

Since the force of the work and the table press downwards on the bed slides, and these are mounted on a massive bed-casting, there is little danger of deflection of the machine itself; consequently very accurate flat surfaces can be produced by careful work on the planer. When wear does take place, it is usually in the guiding surfaces.

The planing machine is used for similar work to the shaping machine, but upon larger workpieces.

20.4.3 Planing-machine alignments. The planing machine requires a very substantial foundation, and the utmost care should always be taken when the machine is first installed. In any subsequent checking work, it is essential to determine that the machine base is still level, and has not moved as a result of subsidence of the foundations. Careful checking of the table in all positions with a precision spirit

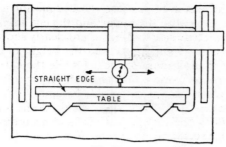

Fig 20.19

level is the first requirement. If inaccuracies are disclosed, these must be corrected before proceeding to other tests.

Providing the machine is level, a straight-edge may be laid on the table under the cross-rail. A dial-indicator is mounted in the tool-box, which is then traversed across the table, thus checking the accuracy of the tool-feed motion. The straight-edge is now placed lengthways to the table, which is moved along the slides, thus moving the straight-edge under the stationary dial-indicator. If these two motions are correct, the machine will generate a flat surface.

If tool-boxes are fitted on the side columns, these should traverse a path at right angles to the table. The three tests are illustrated in figs. 20.19, 20.20, and 20.21 respectively.

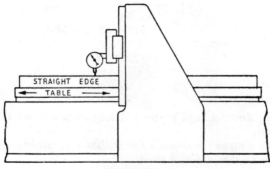

Fig 20.20

20.5 Landing groove
A feature which is common to the shaper, the slotter, and the planer is the necessity for providing room for tool over-run. In the examples just quoted, the procedure would be to pack up the work clear of the table, but in other cases it is necessary to machine close up to an abutment, as shown in fig. 20.22. This is possible only if a 'landing groove' is provided, as shown; this may be contrasted with milling

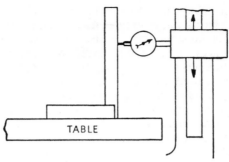

Fig 20.21

operations. When using an end mill, no 'landing groove' is needed, but profiles with sharp corners (e.g. a rectangular hole) cannot be machined. On the other hand, in horizontal milling, the cutter cannot approach nearer to an abutment than a distance equal to its own radius.

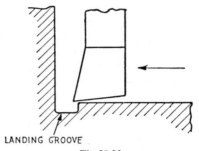

LANDING GROOVE

Fig 20.22

Summary

1 Shaping, slotting, and planing machines are basic reciprocating machines.
2 The return stroke is usually faster than the cutting stroke, to reduce the non-productive time.
3 A mechanism is usually introduced to prevent the tool from rubbing on the machined surface during its return stroke.
4 The shaping machine is usually used for the machining of small, rectangular plane surfaces. The workpiece is usually held in a vice, or clamped directly to the table, but an indexing fixture or dividing head may be used if slots, etc. are being machined.
5 Alignment checks on a shaping machine usually start by determining the flatness and level of the table, so that it can be used as a datum to check the accuracy of the ram movements.

6   The slotting machine is like a shaping machine with a vertical movement. As its name implies, the slotting machine is usually used to machine slots; but it can also be used to produce large internal surfaces, and also to generate large, part-circular surfaces.

7   The procedure when testing the slotting machine for alignments is similar to that used for the shaping machine.

8   The planing machine is used for similar work to that done by the shaping machine, but upon very large workpieces. In order to obtain maximum rigidity, it is usual for the table to move, and the cutters to be stationary during the cutting operation.

9   As in the shaping machine and the slotting machine, the table is used as the datum for alignment checks, and its accuracy is determined first.

10 When designing for machining using reciprocating machines, it must be remembered that a 'landing groove' must be incorporated.

Questions

Set A

1   What defects would you expect to find in work machined on a planer (*a*) with a worn cross slide, (*b*) with worn table guideways?

2   Two mild-steel bars, each 300 mm long and 25 mm square in section, are fastened to a planer table. One is lightly machined with a single-point tool in the usual way; the other is lightly machined with a flat-nose tool 35 mm wide, no cross-feed being used. What differences might be found in the two surfaces, and why would this difference occur?

3   A small rectangular block machined on three faces on a shaping machine at one setting has two vertical faces slightly inclined to each other. What defect in the shaping machine would produce this defect?

4   A casting has two machined faces which are known to be parallel to each other. It is placed on a shaping machine, with one face clamped down to the machine-table, and the other face is then machined again. It is discovered that the two surfaces are no longer parallel to each other. How would this defect arise, and how can its reoccurrence be prevented?

5   The rectangular face of a forging is 300 mm × 200 mm, and is to be machined on a shaping machine. The over-run at each end of the stroke is to 35 mm, and the average cutting speed is 0·3 m/s. The ratio cutting time/return time is 9/7. Calculate the minimum cutting time at 0·4 mm feed per stroke.

6   The stroke-wheel of a shaping machine revolves at 40 revs/min. The shaper stroke is 400 mm, and the ratio cutting time/total time is 7/12. What is the average cutting speed in metres per second?

Set B (questions requiring further study)

7   Consider the construction of a double-standard planing machine
    with reference to rigidity. To what extent is the capacity limitation
    associated with this type of machine overcome by the openside
    planing machine?

8   Explain how an involute gear form is generated using a reciprocat-
    ing cutter.

Chapter 21
Milling Machines

21.1. Milling is a cutting operation in which each tooth of a multi-toothed rotating cutter engages the workpiece in turn, and removes a relatively small amount of metal in the form of a chip. Milling operations can be broadly classified as *end-cutting* and *peripheral-cutting*, which were illustrated by figs 15.16 and 15.17. Milling is usually used to produce plane surfaces, or, by suitable combination of cutter and workpiece movements, circular or part-circular surfaces. Vertical milling machines are also used for drilling, reaming, and boring.

21.2 Types of milling machine
Milling machines can be classified into *knee-and-column machines*, and *bed-type machines*.

21.2.1 Knee-and-column machines. As their name suggests, these machines consist of two main parts, the column and the knee. The column is a massive casting that contains the drive, lubrication, and transmission systems, and supports the knee, which is carried on slides at the front of the column. The knee is a casting which in turn carries the table; it can be raised and lowered as required, and locked in position. The two basic machines in this group are the *horizontal milling machine* and the *vertical milling machine*, illustrated in figs 21.1 and 21.2.

In the horizontal machine, the cutter is usually mounted on an arbor with its axis horizontal, and peripheral-cutting cutters are used. Figure 21.1 does not show the arbor and cutter in position, but the arbor is supported by the overarm (the casting carrying the name Cincinnati) at its extreme end, and is driven by the spindle (the end of the spindle is seen projecting from the column, immediately below the name Cincinnati). End-cutting cutters can be held in a short arbor, and used to machine vertical surfaces. When this operation is done, the overarm is unlocked, and pushed back to give more room for the workpiece and the operator.

In the vertical milling machine, the cutter is held in an arbor with its

Fig 21.2 Horizontal milling machine
Cincinnati Milling Machine Co.

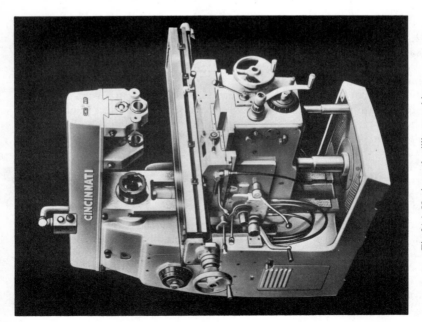

Fig 21.1 Horizontal milling machine
Cincinnati Milling Machine Co.

axis vertical; it is more usually end-cutting, but special shank-mounted peripheral-cutting cutters can be used. The vertical milling machine is also used for drilling, reaming, and boring; and it can be used as a form of jig-boring machine, if the table is positioned under the cutter by using stops and end bars (end bars are discussed in section 23.3.4).

The *universal milling machine* is similar to the horizontal milling machine, but the table can be swung about a vertical axis, and locked in position. It is used in conjunction with a dividing head (section 21.6.4) to generate helices, and is associated with the tool-room, and similar small-production shops.

21.2.2 Bed-type machines. Although the knee-and-column machines are quickly set, they tend to lack rigidity. In the bed-type machine, this lack of rigidity is overcome to a large extent by having the table supported directly by the bed of the machine (fig. 21.3). From this photograph, it will be seen that the bed-type machine is a form of horizontal milling machine in which vertical adjustment is by movement of the spindle and overarm; horizontal adjustment is usually by positioning the cutter along the arbor. Adjustment for depth of cut is usually a fairly long operation; but this machine is used for production work, where the machine is set up for the production of a large number of similar components, without the need to apply a large number of 'cuts', as is usual in the case of small-production runs.

Fig 21.3 Bed-type milling machine   *Cincinnati Milling Machine Co.*

21.3 Types of milling cutters

Milling cutters are classified according to the cutting action (peripheral-cutting and end cutting), the mounting (from the cutter bore, or from the cutter shank), and according to the method of regrinding (form cutters are reground in a different manner from other cutters, and are designed accordingly). The following are representative of the many types of milling cutters.

N.B. The rake and clearance angles for end-cutting cutters and for peripheral-cutting cutters were illustrated in figs 15.16 and 15.17.

21.3.1 Roller cutters. These are peripheral-cutting, and are used for the milling of large plane surfaces. Figure 21.4 shows a roller cutter with straight teeth. This type of cutter tends to cause vibration, because the

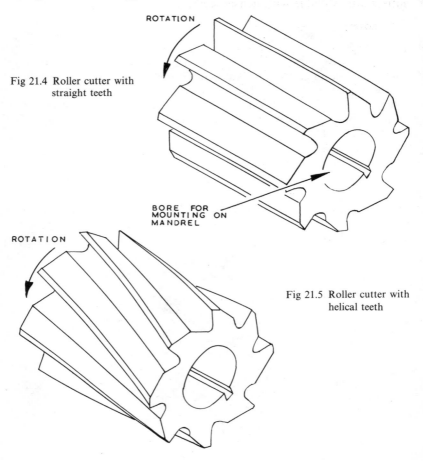

ROTATION

Fig 21.4 Roller cutter with straight teeth

BORE FOR MOUNTING ON MANDREL

ROTATION

Fig 21.5 Roller cutter with helical teeth

cutting action is intermittent. A smoother cutting action is obtained by making the cutting edges helical, as shown in fig. 21.5, so that each tooth commences its cut before the previous one has finished producing its chip. The disadvantage associated with this type of cutter is that a thrust is set up along the axis of the arbor, but this can be nullified by using two cutters of opposite but equal helix angle, and mounting them back to back.

21.3.2 Side-and-face cutters. Although a narrow roller-type cutter could be used to produce a groove, a large number of passes would be required. This operation can be speeded up by using a cutter with cutting edges on its sides, in addition to those on its periphery. Figure 21.6 shows a typical side-and-face cutter. Variations of side-and-face cutters are available with helical teeth.

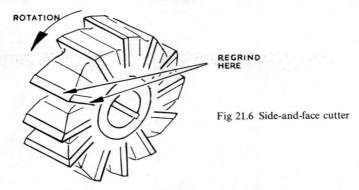

Fig 21.6 Side-and-face cutter

21.3.3 End-milling cutters. Figure 21.7 shows a typical end-milling cutter. The example shown is end-cutting and side-cutting, and is used to produce grooves and profiles

Fig 21.7 End-milling cutter

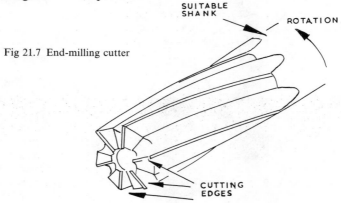

21.3.4 Form-milling cutters. Form-cutting was discussed in section 15.9.1. The cutter shown in fig. 21.8 is a peripheral-cutting form cutter, used to produce a gear, treating each tooth space in turn as a 'special' groove. It will be seen that the form cutter is reground by the removal of metal from the face of each tooth. (Compare fig. 21.8 with fig. 21.7, which shows that other cutters are reground by the removal of metal from their periphery, and, if necessary, from their sides.) The form cutter cannot be reground by the removal of metal from the periphery, because this would cause the form to be incorrect: in the example shown, the tooth gap would become wider as a result of regrinding. The teeth must also be given a clearance to prevent rubbing. The teeth are therefore given *form relief*, as shown in fig. 21.9, so that the radial form, at, say, OA, OB, OC, and OD, remains the same, provided the same amount of metal is removed from each tooth during regrinding.

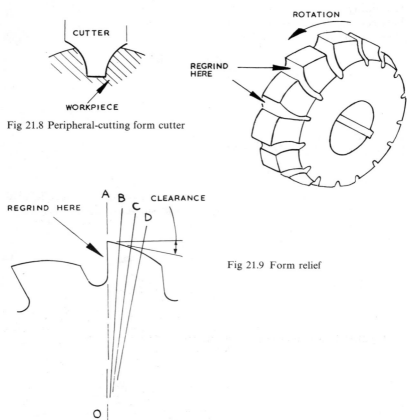

Fig 21.8 Peripheral-cutting form cutter

Fig 21.9 Form relief

21.4 Up-cut milling and down-cut milling

Figures 21.10 and 21.11 show the difference between these two methods of milling. Examination of these diagrams will show two very important differences between the methods: the paths taken by each cutter relative to the workpiece are different, and the cutting action also differs according to the method used. The path taken by the cutter teeth must be taken into account when designing the teeth (this is dealt with in more specialised books on tool design), and cutting action must be considered, in conjunction with the material to be cut, the clamping system, and the milling machine. Up-cut milling is particularly useful when milling a casting, because the characteristic hard 'case' is attacked from underneath. It is also useful when milling ductile materials, where 'built-up' edge (see section 15.2.3) tends to be large at the end of each chip, and a poor finish would be produced if the remaining metal were not removed by the next tooth. (Comparison between the two methods will show that, in the case of up-milling, the start of the chip produces the finished surface; while, in the case of

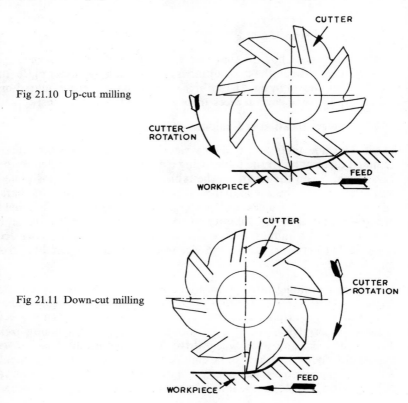

Fig 21.10 Up-cut milling

Fig 21.11 Down-cut milling

down-milling, the end of the chip produces the finished surface.) The forces during up-milling tend to lift the workpiece from the machine table, but those during down-milling tend to press the workpiece down on to the table. Down-cut milling is therefore better in this respect, provided the leadscrew is in good condition (leadscrew backlash causes snatching and can be dangerous).

21.5 Straddle milling and gang milling

The rate of metal-removal can be increased if more than one cutter is used at a time. In straddle milling, shown in fig. 21.12, two cutters are

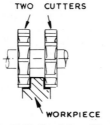

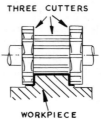

Fig 21.12 Straddle milling   Fig 21.13 Gang milling

mounted on the arbor, so that two faces are milled simultaneously. The distance between the two cutters is controlled by a spacer piece. In *gang milling*, shown in fig. 21.13, three or more cutters are mounted on the arbor, allowing several faces to be machined simultaneously.

21.6 Workpiece location and holding

21.6.1 Machine table and machine vice. Large workpieces are often clamped directly on to the table, using clamps and bolts located in the T-slots which run the length of the table. The workpiece is positioned on the table with the aid of dial-indicators, spirit levels, and sine bars, in conjunction with jacks and wedges. Smaller workpieces are held in a machine vice if the quantity to be produced does not justify the manufacture of a milling fixture (see section 21.6.5). Special jaws are often made to convert a machine vice into an inexpensive milling fixture.

21.6.2 Rotary milling table. This attachment, used extensively on the vertical milling machine, consists of a base, supporting a circular table which can rotate around a vertical axis. The table is marked in degrees around its periphery, and can be rotated by means of a handwheel, through a worm and wormwheel drive. The table usually has T-slots from which the workpiece can be clamped in position. This attachment is used for machining holes spaced on pitch circles, and also for milling radii and profiles. When the latter operations are performed, the workpiece is positioned on the table, and fed against an end mill, by means of the handwheel.

21.6.3 Dividing chuck. This attachment consists of a three-jaw self-centring chuck, attached to a base piece, so that its axis is vertical. The chuck is marked in degrees, and can be positioned as required by means of a plunger. The dividing chuck is useful for milling features such as the flats on bolt heads.

21.6.4 The dividing head. The dividing head is used for the accurate spacing of, for example, holes on a pitch circle, and slots in the periphery of a disc. To do this, it is necessary to hold the workpiece during the milling operation, and to be able to move the workpiece to the new position between the milling of each slot, hole, etc. The use of a simple direct dividing head is discussed in section 20.2.2, but such a system is limited by the number of index plates available. The simple dividing head described here is a gearbox which includes means of attaching a chuck or faceplate to hold the workpiece. Figure 21.14 shows, in simplified form, the essentials of a simple dividing head. The spindle supporting the workpiece is driven by a wormwheel (usually with 40 teeth) which meshes with a single-start worm, rotated by a crank.

In the 40 : 1 gear system quoted above, 40 turns of the crank are required to rotate the workpiece once. Therefore, if n equally spaced divisions are required, the workpiece must be rotated $1/n$ revs between each machining operation. Therefore $40/n$ turns of the crank are re-

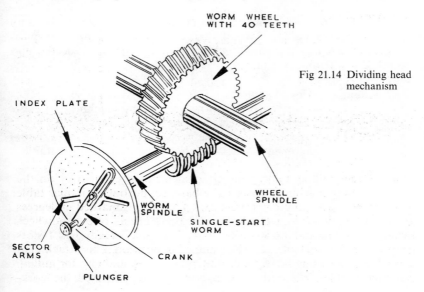

WORM WHEEL
WITH 40 TEETH

Fig 21.14 Dividing head
mechanism

INDEX PLATE

WHEEL
SPINDLE

WORM
SPINDLE

SINGLE-START
WORM

SECTOR
ARMS

CRANK

PLUNGER

quired to turn the workpiece $1/n$ rev. The number of whole turns and fractions of a turn can be determined from the foregoing. The fraction of a turn can be easily obtained by use of an index plate, as shown in fig. 21.14. The index plate contains a wide range of concentric hole-circles, and a suitable circle is selected to suit the fraction required. The crank is adjusted so that the plunger is in line with the selected hole circle, and the index plate is locked relative to the body of the dividing head. The plunger is located in a hole when the first slot, etc. is machined, and then withdrawn, allowing the crank to be given the required number of turns and part turn (or part turn only), being located in a hole during the next machining operation. To save time and the possibility of error when counting the holes, a pair of sector arms are incorporated, and these can be set to include the required number of holes.

Angular division can be obtained by considering that 40 turns of the crank produce one rotation of the workpiece, i.e. 360°, so 1 turn of the crank produces 360°/40, i.e. 9°.

The indexing required for $\theta°$ is $\theta°/9°$. The fraction of a turn required is obtained by use of the index plate, as already described.

A more sophisticated dividing head, called a *universal dividing head*, is used to obtain awkward divisions that cannot be obtained by using a simple dividing head. It is also designed so that the worm spindle can be driven by gear train from the machine leadscrew, enabling the work-piece to be rotated while the table is in motion. Such an arrangement can be used to mill helices (helical milling is discussed in more spe-cialised books on machine tools).

21.6.5 Milling fixtures. Workpiece and cutter positioning is speeded up by the use of a milling fixture. Figure 16.22(a) illustrates a typical milling fixture, and fig. 16.22(b) shows how the fixture is located and clamped to the machine table.

21.7 Milling-machine alignments
The following notes refer to the horizontal milling machine, but other types of milling machine are dealt with in a similar way.

As the table is the location for the workpiece, it is used as a datum for most of the alignment checks. The level and flatness of the table is

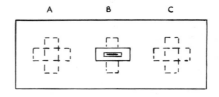

PLAN   Fig 21.15

checked in two directions at three places, using a spirit level, as shown in fig. 21.15.

The spindle is checked by rotating it against a dial-indicator mounted on a stand, placed on the table (fig. 21.16). Check A is for axial slip or float, and check B is for correctness of the outside diameter of the spindle. The relationship between the spindle internal taper and the spindle outside diameter is checked as shown in fig. 21.17: a 'master' mandrel is placed in the taper, and slowly rotated against a dial-indicator mounted from the table, this check is made in two places, A and B.

The table is now checked for parallelism with the axis of the taper; a stationary mandrel is located in the spindle taper, and the dial-indicator is mounted on the stand, and placed on the table. The distance between the table and the mandrel is checked with the dial-indicator in two positions, A and B (fig. 21.18). The table movement is checked relative to the machine spindle, as shown in fig. 21.19: the dial-indicator is mounted from the spindle taper. The accuracy of the table

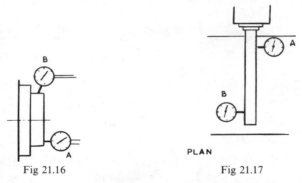

Fig 21.16   PLAN   Fig 21.17

traverse relative to the machine spindle is checked by mounting the dial-indicator from the table, and checking against the stationary mandrel, mounted from the taper. The table is traversed, first being checked for errors in the vertical plane (fig. 21.20), and again for errors in the horizontal plane (the dial-indicator then being placed against the side of the mandrel, in the horizontal plane).

The accuracy of the centre T-slot is now checked to ensure that it is

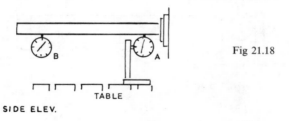

Fig 21.18

TABLE

SIDE ELEV.

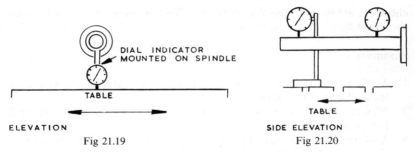

ELEVATION   SIDE ELEVATION
Fig 21.19   Fig 21.20

parallel with the table movement (the T-slots are used to locate fixtures, etc. on the table, and must therefore be accurate). To do this,
tenon blocks are located in the slot, and the dial-indicator is mounted
from the spindle (fig. 21.21); the table is then moved longitudinally.
The squareness of the T-slot relative to the spindle axis is checked by
locking the table, and checking the slot in two places, A and B. To do

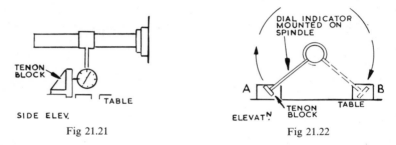

SIDE ELEV.   ELEVAT͟N.
Fig 21.21   Fig 21.22

this, a tenon block is used, and checked with the dial-indicator, mounted from the spindle (fig. 21.22); the dial-indicator is swung from position A to position B by rotation of the spindle.

The accuracy of the column ways for the knee is checked by mounting the dial-indicator from the spindle, and raising and lowering the
knee, the accuracy being checked by placing a square on the table, and

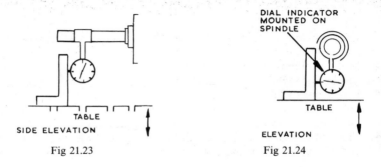

SIDE ELEVATION   ELEVATION

Fig 21.23   Fig 21.24

checking errors with the dial-indicator. This is done in two planes, as shown in figs 21.23 and 21.24.

Summary

1   Milling usually implies cutting, using a multi-toothed rotating cutter and a moving table.
2   Milling cutters can be broadly classified into end-cutting and peripheral-cutting.
3   Milling machines are usually used to produce plane and part-circular surfaces, but vertical machines are also used for drilling, reaming, and boring.
4   Milling machines can be classified into (*a*) knee-and-column, and (*b*) bed-type machines. The former are further classified as vertical, horizontal, and universal machines.
5   Milling cutters are classified according to cutting action, method of mounting, and method of re-sharpening.
6   The workpiece may be held directly on the table, in a vice, on a rotary table, in a dividing chuck, in a dividing head, or in a fixture.
7   The alignment procedure follows the usual pattern whereby the table accuracy is first examined, then the spindle accuracy, and finally the relationship between the spindle movements and the table movements.

Questions

Set A
1   (*a*) Illustrate, with the aid of sketches, the main types of standard milling cutters, and their application.
    (*b*) Explain the advantages and/or disadvantages of coarse-tooth, quick-spiral milling cutters.
2   Specify in some detail the cutters and accessories necessary for use with a plain horizontal milling machine, in order to make full use of its capabilities.
3   Describe, using explanatory sketches where necessary, the construction and uses of the dividing head, as used on a plain horizontal milling machine.
4   Make sketches to show the cutter and machine movements that can be arranged on the plain horizontal milling machine.
5   It is usual to provide a universal milling machine in a tool-room, but, in the workshop, vertical machines and plain horizontal machines are more commonly used. Suggest reasons for this.
6   Calculate suitable settings on the dividing head for indexing 76, 6, and 112 divisions, using a 40 : 1 gear ratio dividing head, and an

indexing plate with 28, 30, 33, 34, 38, 42, 45, 46, 48, and 54 holes.

7 (*a*) Divide 7° into four equal parts, and calculate a suitable indexing on the dividing head.
(*b*) Divide 11° 12′ into five equal parts, and calculate a suitable indexing on the dividing head.
(Dividing head as in question 6.)

Set B (questions requiring further study)

8 Discuss in some detail the cutting action of a peripheral-cutting milling cutter.

9 Compare the cutting action of a peripheral-cutting milling cutter when up-cut milling with that when down-cut milling, and explain how the direction of cutting influences the actual rake and clearance angles, and the forces involved.

10 List the principal types of form-milling cutter, and add brief notes on the use of each type mentioned.

11 Discuss the various types of end-mill, the purposes for which they are used, and the type of machine to which they are fitted.

12 (*a*) Describe the various methods by which a surface of reasonable flatness can be milled. Explain what deviation from flatness you would expect with each method.
(*b*) Explain the relationship between table feed rate and cut per tooth in slab milling.

Chapter 22
Grinding, Honing, and Lapping

22.1. Grinding, honing, and lapping are similar in that they are all cutting processes using abrasive cutting material, but they differ in the form taken by the abrasive used. *Grinding* employs abrasive which is bonded in the form of a wheel, *honing* employs abrasive which is bonded in the form of sticks held in a special holder, and *lapping* employs abrasive which is loose but in suspension in a liquid.

22.2 Grinding

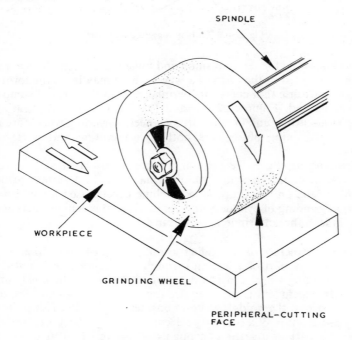

Fig 22.1(*a*) Peripheral-cutting grinding wheel

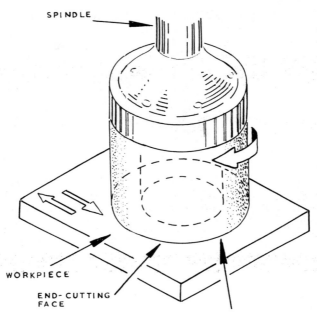

SPINDLE

WORKPIECE

END-CUTTING
FACE

Fig 22.1(*b*) End-cutting grinding wheel

Grinding is used for semi-finishing and finishing, and employs abrasive particles bonded in the form of a wheel which may be in the form of a thin or thick disc that cuts at its periphery, or in the form of a cup that cuts at its end. Figures 22.1(*a*) and (*b*) illustrate the application of peripheral-cutting and of end-cutting wheels. Grinding wheels are used for the machining of surfaces both by generating and by forming methods.

Grinding machines for general work can be classified as external grinding machines, internal grinding machines, and surface grinding machines; the universal grinding machine can be used for internal or external grinding of cylinders and cones. Special machines include cutter grinders, thread grinders, and gear grinders.

22.2.1 The structure of a grinding wheel, and its cutting action. Figure 22.2 illustrates part of a section through a grinding wheel, and shows that a grinding wheel consists of (*a*) the *abrasive*, (*b*) the *bond*, and (*c*) the *voids*. The function and the selection of the abrasive and the bond, and the size of the voids, are best considered after discussing the self-sharpening action of a correctly selected grinding wheel. Figure 22.3(*a*) illustrates part of a section through a grinding wheel at the start of cutting; the cutting points are indicated. As the cutting proceeds, the

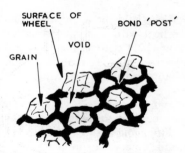

Fig 22.2 Grinding wheel structure

points become dulled, and eventually the abrasive particles become cracked along the cleavage planes, since the workpiece material resists the cutting action. This produces new cutting points, as illustrated in fig. 22.3(*b*). This process continues until the abrasive grains become worn down level with the bond; and at this point the bond allows the remainder of the worn grains to be torn from the wheel, exposing new grains which were previously below the surface of the wheel. When these grains are exposed, the voids form the clearances between the

(*a*)   (*b*)

Fig 22.3 Self-sharpening action

grains. The selection of the grinding wheel demands the correct selection of the type of abrasive, the size of the grains, the type of bonding agent and its strength, and also the size of the voids. The behaviour of a grinding wheel is affected by the workpiece material, the cutting speed, the depth of cut, and the feed rate. The grinding wheel is selected, and then small changes in its action can be affected by small changes in the cutting conditions.

22.2.2 Wheel loading and wheel glazing. The term *wheel loading* implies that workpiece chips are embedded in the cutting face of the wheel, reducing the rate of cutting because the depth of penetration is reduced. It is caused by using a grinding wheel with voids which are too small to accommodate the chips, and it may be cured, to some extent, by increasing the work speed (see section 22.2.8), although it usually demands the use of a different wheel for its complete cure.

    The term *wheel glazing* implies that the grains are worn down level with the bond, which has held them too long for efficient cutting. It is caused by using a wheel with a bond strength which is too strong (termed 'too hard'), a wheel with grains that are too fine, or by the inefficient use of dressers. This may require a change of wheel, but can often be cured by changing the cutting conditions.

22.2.3 The abrasive and the grain size. It has already been explained that the abrasive grains perform the cutting. Abrasives are classified as (a) *natural abrasives*, and (b) *manufactured abrasives*. The principal natural abrasives are diamond, emery, corundum, and quartz; they contain impurities that may hinder the cutting action, and promote non-uniformity of wheels, and hence, of performance. The only natural abrasive to be used for precision work is diamond, which is used for grinding ceramics and die steels; diamond wheels are of a different structure from those using other abrasives. Manufactured abrasives are (a) aluminium oxide, and (b) silicon carbide; the latter is completely synthetic.

Aluminium oxide (Al_2O), also known as fused alumina, is produced from bauxite, using an electric furnace. It is of reddish-brown colour, and is tough and sharp, and used in the grinding of high tensile-strength materials such as alloy steels, high-speed steels, annealed malleable iron, and tough bronze. A special form of aluminium oxide, which is white in colour, has a tendency to fracture more easily than regular aluminium oxide, and therefore presents new and sharper cutting edges to the workpiece more easily; this abrasive is used when grinding hardened tool steels.

Silicon carbide (SiC) is an artificial abrasive produced in an electric furnace by the combination of silicon and carbon (in the form of sand and coke). It is usually of greenish-black colour, and is harder and more brittle than aluminium oxide, and therefore fractures more easily, producing a more rapid self-sharpening. Silicon carbide is used to grind hard materials which demand the rapid resharpening of the wheel. It is also used to grind low tensile materials such as bronze, aluminium alloys, copper, and non-metallic materials, because these materials do not readily fracture the tougher aluminium oxide. A special form of silicon carbide is used to grind and resharpen cemented carbide-tipped tools.

The classification of grain sizes. The fused alumina or silicon carbide is crushed to produce smaller particles, which are separated by sifting through screens, or by flotation methods. The size of the grains is expressed as the size of the screen opening through which the grains just pass; grit sizes between 6 and 24 are termed 'coarse', those between 30 and 100 are termed 'medium', and those between 120 and 700 are termed 'fine'.

22.2.4 The bonding material. The bonding material must hold the grains together to form the wheel, but must release them when they become too blunt to continue cutting. The four basic bonding materials are (*a*) vitrified, (*b*) resinoid, (*c*) rubber, and (*d*) shellac.

  (*a*) *Vitrified bond* is the most common bond, and allows high stock removal rate.
  (*b*) *Resinoid bond* is used for cool cutting at high speeds, and with a high rate of stock removal.
  (*c*) *Rubber bond* is strong and tough, and used for thin wheels, and where a good finish is required.
  (*d*) *Shellac bond* is used for cool cutting, and for thin wheels.

22.2.5 The grade of a grinding wheel. The grade of a wheel indicates the strength of the grains, and the holding power of the bond; and is controlled by the thickness of the bond 'posts' which hold the grains together. A grinding wheel that wears down readily is termed a 'soft wheel', and that which wears down slowly is termed a 'hard wheel'. The wheel grade is indicated by a letter—D indicating a soft wheel, and, at the other extreme, V indicating a hard wheel. Figure 22.4(*a*) illustrates weak 'posts', and fig. 22.4(*b*) illustrates strong 'posts'.

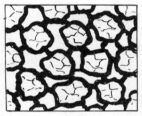
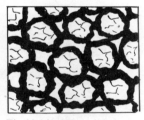

Fig 22.4(*a*) Weak bond posts   Fig 22.4(*b*) Strong bond posts

22.2.6 The structure of a grinding wheel. In section 22.2.1, the importance of the voids was explained, with reference to the self-sharpening action of a grinding wheel. For a given post strength, the void size is controlled by the spacing of the grains. Figure 22.5(*a*) illustrates a wheel with a 'dense' spacing, and fig. 22.5(*b*) illustrates a wheel with an 'open' structure. The structure of the wheel is indicated by a number—1 indicating a dense structure, and 9 indicating an open structure.

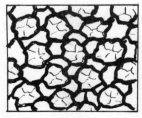

Fig 22.5(*a*) Wheel with dense spacing   Fig 22.5(*b*) Wheel with open spacing

22.2.7 Area of contact. The stress that acts upon a grinding wheel during cutting is given by force/area of contact, and so the stress becomes less as the area of contact is increased. When the area of contact is large, the wheel tends to act 'harder' than when the area of contact is small, and this must be taken into account when selecting the grade of the wheel to be used for a specific operation. The area of contact also affects the choice of structure, since more chip clearance is necessary when the area of contact is large, and also the choice of grain size, since many fine cutting points are required when the area of contact is small.

Figures 22.6 illustrate the arc of contact (AB) when grinding using a peripheral-cutting wheel. When cutting in this way, the area of contact is the arc of contact multiplied by the width of contact, and is thus proportional to the arc of contact. It will be seen from figs. 22.6 that, for a given depth of cut, the area of contact is least when external grinding, and greatest when internal grinding, owing to the workpiece

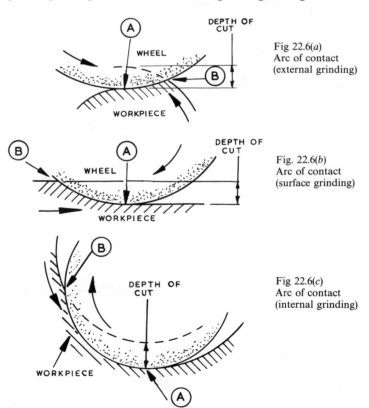

Fig 22.6(*a*)
Arc of contact
(external grinding)

Fig. 22.6(*b*)
Arc of contact
(surface grinding)

Fig 22.6(*c*)
Arc of contact
(internal grinding)

geometry. This explains why a softer wheel is used when performing an internal grinding operation than when performing an external grinding operation upon the same material.

Figures 22.7 illustrate the area of contact when grinding using an end-cutting wheel, and show that the area of contact depends upon the shape of the wheel, the shape of the workpieces, and the packing of the workpieces upon the table.

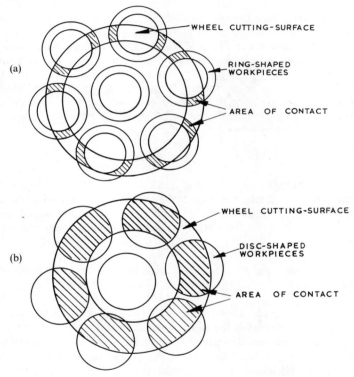

Fig 22.7 Area of contact when grinding using an end cutting wheel

22.2.8 Changes in work speed and wheel speed. If the work speed (feed towards wheel) is increased, the predominant effect is to produce a thicker chip, as shown in figs 22.8, so the wheel tends to act softer, as the stress acting upon the grains is greater. Change of work speed is one way of changing the cutting action of a grinding wheel.

Increasing the wheel speed usually causes the wheel to act harder, as, from the time that each grain starts to cut a chip to the time when it completes that chip, the work will have moved a smaller amount, and so the chip will be thinner. It must, however, be emphasised that the

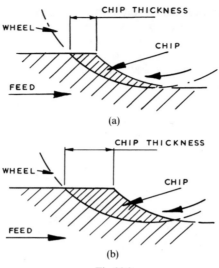

Fig 22.8

spindle speed is usually fixed, but that the cutting speed of a large-diameter wheel is greater than that of a smaller-diameter wheel, even if the spindle speed is the same. Similarly, as the wheel wears down during its working life, the cutting speed becomes slower, and so the wheel acts softer.

22.2.9 Wheel selection. Many factors must be taken into account when selecting a wheel; the following indicates some of these factors.

Choice of abrasive. This depends upon the workpiece material. Aluminium oxide is used for high tensile-strength materials, and silicon carbide for low tensile-strength materials, and hard materials.

Grain size. If the work size or the work surface finish is important, a fine grain is used; but if a high rate of stock removal is important, a coarse grain is used.

Grade. If the material being ground is hard, or of low tensile-strength, a soft grade is used; if soft, or of high tensile-strength, a hard grade is used.

Structure. It must be noted that the 'structure' determines the size of the clearances, and the number of cutting points. A soft workpiece material needs an open structure (large clearances), and a hard workpiece material requires a dense structure (more cutting points).

Bond. For general work, a vitrified bond is used; but, for special work, and thin wheels, one of the other bonds is used, as stated in section 22.2.4.

22.2.10 Wheel classification system. Figure 22.9 illustrates the wheel classification system used by the manufacturers of grinding wheels. It will be seen that letters and numbers are used alternately, to avoid confusion. The sequence is abrasive (letter), grain size (number), grade (letter), structure (number), and bond (letter).

ABRASIVE	GRAIN SIZE		GRADE	STRUCTURE	BOND
Aluminium	6	80	D (Soft)	1 (Dense)	Vitrified = V
oxide = A	8	90	E	2	
Silicon	10	100	F	3	Resinoid = B
carbide = C	12	120	G	4	
	14	150	H	5	Shellac = E
	16	180	I	6	
	20	220	J	7	
	24	240	K	8	Rubber = R
	30	280	L	9 (Open)	
	36	320	M		
	46	400	N		
	54	500	O		
	60	600	P		
	70	700	Q		
			R		
			S		
			T		
			U		
			V (Hard)		

Fig 22.9 Wheel classification system

22.2.11 Wheel mounting and wheel balancing. Before mounting it upon the spindle, the wheel must be checked for soundness. It must then be mounted according to the maker's instructions, which aim at ensuring that the wheel is not subjected to excessive stresses, but that it is secured to the spindle. The wheel must be put in static balance before running it; this is usually done by adjusting balance weights which are incorporated into the spindle, but lead may be removed from the bush that lines the wheel.

22.2.12 Wheel dressing and truing. Dressing is defined as any operation which is performed upon the wheel face to change the nature of the cutting action; it is often done after glazing or loading has taken place. It is carried out at operating speeds or lower, and coolant is used if coolant is to be used during the grinding operation for which the wheel is being prepared.

Truing is defined as any operation upon any part of the wheel to produce concentricity or parallelism of faces, or to prepare the wheel to perform a forming operation.

Dressing and truing may be done using an abrasive wheel, a knurled steel wheel, or a star-shaped wheel (like a spur); wheels of this type are fed in radially, and driven by the grinding wheel. It may also be done using an abrasive stick (usually when forming by hand), or by diamond mounted in a suitable holder and traversed across the face of the wheel.

22.2.13 Grinding-machine movements. Figures 22.10(*a*) to (*d*) illustrate the machine movements for external, internal, and surface grinding. Surface grinding is done using a peripheral-cutting wheel, or an end-cutting wheel. The table may be a reciprocating table or a rotating table.

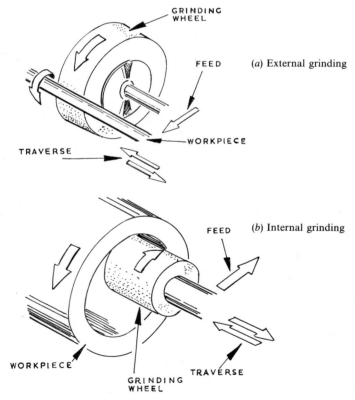

Fig 22.10 Grinding-machine movements

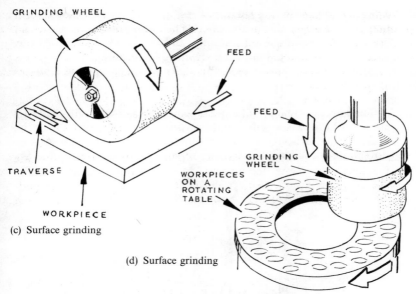

(c) Surface grinding

(d) Surface grinding

Fig 22.10 Grinding-machine movements

22.2.14 Grinding-machine alignments. Cylindrical grinding machines, both external and internal, are similar to lathes, and their alignment follows a similar pattern. The slides are first checked for level and flatness, then the workpiece and wheel spindles, and finally the relationship between the workpiece and the wheel spindle movements are checked.

The surface grinding machines are first levelled and checked for table flatness, then the wheel spindle, and finally the relationship between the wheel spindle movement and the workpiece table are checked.

22.3 Honing

Honing is used to correct local irregularities such as ovality, waviness of axis, or non-parallelism of cylindrical features, and to develop a particular texture. It cannot correct malposition of the axis, or gross errors along a cylinder of large length compared with that of the hone. The amount of metal removed by the process is usually quite small.

In many respects, honing is similar to grinding, but it differs in that the abrasive is in the form of sticks that are evenly spaced about the surface to be honed; this means that the heating caused by cutting will also be evenly spread about the surface.

22.3.1 The abrasive. The abrasive is aluminium oxide, silicon carbide, or, for special operations, bonded diamond grit; the grain size is similar to that used for grinding. The bond is usually vitrified, but may be resinoid if rough honing is to be done, or when cast iron or certain non-ferrous materials are finish-honed. The action of the abrasive and the bond is the same as when grinding, and the abrasive, bond, grade, and structure are selected as when selecting for grinding.

The abrasive sticks are cemented to shoes which are held in a holder called the 'hone'.

22.3.2 The hone. A typical hone arrangement is shown in fig. 22.11. It consists of a hollow flanged cylinder, with radial slots into which the shoes are located. About six of these shoes are commonly used. A cone adjustment device is used to push the shoes radially outwards, and the

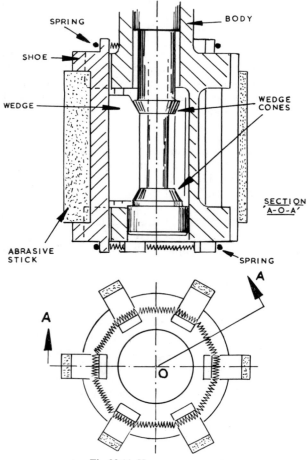

Fig 22.11 Hone arrangement

shoes are retained by a simple arrangement such as coil springs. An abrasive stick is cemented to each shoe. The hone is fixed to a honing head that causes it to rotate and reciprocate. The hone is made to float, so that it follows the 'mean' axis of the feature being honed; this is usually done by making the hone itself floating, but, as an alternative, the workpiece-holding device can be made floating.

22.3.3 Cutting action (fig. 22.12). Cutting is by the combination of pressure normal to the workpiece surface and motion tangential to the workpiece surface. The pressure is obtained by the expansion of the hone, and the motion by the rotation of the hone (in the case of external honing, the workpiece rotates instead). The rotational speed depends upon the workpiece material and the finish required, and is usually selected by experiment, starting with a cutting speed of about 3 m/s, and then adjusting to suit the requirements. The reciprocating movement provides the generating action, distributes the wear over the whole length of the sticks, and helps to clear the swarf. The speed of reciprocation compared with that of rotation depends upon the type of surface that is to be generated, but 0·3 m/s is a typical speed. During the cutting, a lubricant such as paraffin is introduced.

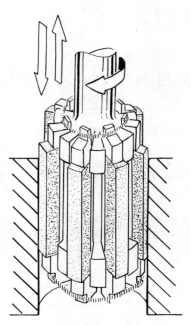

Fig 22.12 Hone cutting action

When the stroke of the machine is set, an over-run is allowed for (see fig. 22.13), so that each stick does not keep retracing its path, causing localised errors.

The combination of the continuous rotation in one direction and the reciprocating action produces the characteristic criss-cross texture. If this texture is not required, the continuous rotational movement is stopped, and an intermittent rotational action is used instead. (This intermittent action is made non-uniform, to prevent the abrasive sticks from eventually retracing their own paths.)

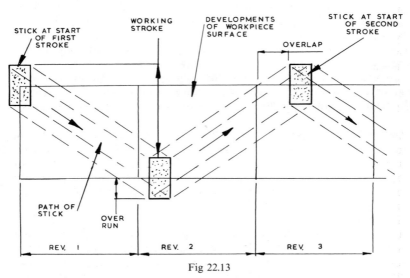

Fig 22.13

22.3.4 Honing machines. Honing machines are classified as (*a*) internal machines, and (*b*) external machines. Internal machines are of the vertical type for honing normal length holes, but long holes are honed by horizontal machines. A horizontal machine is usually used for external honing.

22.3.5 Materials suitable for honing. Most metals, and some non-metallic materials, can be honed. The softer materials are more difficult to hone, as they tend to cause loading.

22.4 Lapping
Lapping is fundamentally an abrasion process in which two surfaces are made to conform, one to the other, using abrasive particles held in suspension and applied between the two surfaces. Lapping can be classified as (*a*) hand lapping, and (*b*) machine lapping.

22.4.1 Hand lapping. Hand lapping is of two types. In the one type, the two surfaces that are to mate in service are rubbed together, with the abrasive between them, so that any irregularities are removed, and the two surfaces fit closely. In the other type, the mating surfaces are each made to conform to a master surface known as a *lap*. The 'grinding in' of internal combustion engine valves is an example of the first type, and the preparation of location surfaces of components that do not come together until the assembly stage is typical of the second type.

The lap for hand lapping is of a softer material than that to be lapped, so that its surface tends to become impregnated with the abrasive particles. The abrasive material is of very fine grit size, and is usually aluminium oxide or silicon carbide; though for fine finishes on small components, diamond dust, rouge (ferric oxide), green rouge (chromium oxide), or boron carbide is used. The abrasive particles are held in suspension in paraffin, or, for soft materials, in soluble oil or water. The speed when hand lapping is not important, but the pressure must not be too great, otherwise the workpiece surface will become scored.

22.4.2 Machine lapping. Machine lapping is used to produce extreme accuracy of dimension, improved geometric accuracy, and improved surface quality. The lap is usually similar to that used when hand lapping, and the abrasive is applied in suspension. Processes that are more like grinding are often used in production, and use either an abrasive lap, or a lap with abrasive-coated material attached to it.

Machine lapping is illustrated in fig. 22.14(*a*), which shows the laps rotating in opposite directions, with the workpieces between them, in a workholder. It is essential that the workpieces have random motion over the laps, and so they are only lightly constrained in the workholder, which is given an eccentric motion as it rotates. About twelve

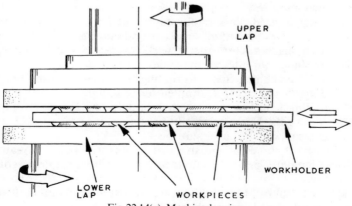

Fig 22.14(*a*) Machine lapping

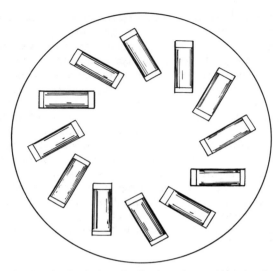

Fig 22.14(*b*) Workpiece distribution when machine lapping

workpieces are lapped together (fig. 22.14(*b*)), so that the pressure of the upper lap is equalised, and so that an undersized workpiece will not affect the lapping action on the remainder.

Summary

1   Grinding, honing, and lapping are all cutting processes that use an abrasive cutting material, but they differ in the form taken by the abrasive. Grinding uses the abrasive in the form of a wheel, honing uses it in the form of sticks, and lapping uses loose abrasive in suspension.

2   Grinding is used for semi-finishing and finishing. The grinding wheel may be end-cutting or peripheral-cutting.

3   Grinding machines for general work may be classified as (*a*) external machines, (*b*) internal machines, (*c*) surface machines, and (*d*) universal machines. Special grinding machines are used for gear grinding, thread grinding, and cutter grinding.

4   A grinding wheel consists of the abrasive, the bonding material, and the voids. For correct cutting action, it is essential that the wheel wears down during cutting.

5   The correct choice of abrasive, size of abrasive, bonding material, bond strength, and void characteristics is important for correct cutting.

6   The behaviour of the wheel during cutting depends upon the area of contact, the work speed, and the wheel speed.

7 The grinding wheel must be correctly mounted and balanced for safety and accuracy of cutting.

8 Grinding machines are checked for alignment in a similar way to other machine tools, the cylindrical machines being treated like lathes, and the surface machines like milling machines.

9 Honing is used to correct local irregularities, or to produce a special texture.

10 The hone assembly consists of about six sticks of abrasive, suitably held. It is given rotation and reciprocating action, but is floating, so as to take up the mean axis of the feature being honed.

11 Lapping is a process in which two parts are made to conform by rubbing them together, with the abrasive between them. The two parts may be those that are to mate upon assembly, or, alternatively, one may be the workpiece and the other a master surface, called a lap.

12 Lapping may be done by hand or by machine.

Questions

Set A

1 (a) What are the basic components of a grinding wheel?

(b) What is the characteristic of natural abrasives that limits their use in abrasive tools?

(c) Name the two main manufactured abrasives, and discuss their characteristics.

(d) List the main bonding materials, and discuss their characteristics and applications.

(e) What is implied by the terms 'hard' and 'soft' in relation to an abrasive cutting tool?

2 (a) Write a short account of the cutting action of a grinding wheel, giving due regard to the self-sharpening action.

(b) The grade of a grinding wheel is varied according to the type of machine operation—i.e. cylindrical external, surface, or internal. In this respect, explain the factors involved.

3 (a) Explain how departure from ideal conditions affects the cutting action of a grinding wheel.

(b) Explain how variation of the following will affect the performance of a grinding wheel: (i) wheel speed, (ii) work speed, (iii) rate of infeed, and (iv) traverse rate.

4 Explain how grinding wheels are classified, and enumerate, with explanatory notes, the factors which influence the selection of a wheel for any specific purpose.

5 Compare grinding, honing, and lapping with respect to the form taken by the abrasive, the cutting action, and the application of each.

Set B (questions requiring further study)

6 (*a*) With the aid of suitable sketches, describe the essential features of a universal grinding machine.

(*b*) Why, when grinding between centres, are both centres dead?

7 Write notes on the following terms used in conjunction with grinding: (*a*) 'sparking out', (*b*) spot grinding, (*c*) grit size, (*d*) grinding allowance, (*e*) wheel balancing, (*f*) loading, (*g*) glazing, (*h*) wheel dressing.

8 Discuss the question of surface finish with respect to cylindrical and surface grinding, mentioning points of special importance.

9 Outline the scope of the tool and cutter grinding machine, and describe two typical operations done on the machine.

Chapter 23
Engineering Metrology (1)
Basic Measurement Methods

23.1 Introduction

Metrology is the science of measurement. Engineering metrology is mainly concerned with the measurement of engineering products, and the basis of this measurement is length.

Engineering products consist of solids formed by the combination of surfaces; and so when these products are measured it is necessary to consider the accuracy of surfaces and then their relationship.

This basic chapter is therefore divided into (a) length measurement, (b) surface measurement, (c) surface relationship measurement.

23.2 The British Standards Institution

Reference is made throughout this book to British Standards, and it is appropriate to make reference to the British Standards Institution at this stage.

The British Standards Institution is the recognised body in the United Kingdom for the preparation and promulgation of national standards, and represents the United Kingdom in the International Organisation for Standardisation and similar organisations.

The scope of standards work includes: glossaries of terms and symbols; methods of test; specifications for quality, safety performance, or dimensions; preferred sizes; and codes of practice.

When it is considered advisable to produce a standard, the British Standards Institution provide the facilities to enable representatives of all interested parties to meet to decide upon the main feature of the standard, and then to draw up the standard and promulgate it. British Standards are indicated by the letters 'BS', followed by the reference number, and finally the year of introduction. For example, 'BS 870 : 1950. External Micrometers'.

A British Standard is a recommendation; it may be used by choice, or its use may be demanded by a regulation or byelaw.

23.3 Standards of Length

In medieval times, the necessity of having definite standards of length was appreciated, and several crude standards were set up. Today, the definition of length has reached a very high standard. The purpose of having accurate standards is to enable different people to make articles of similar size.

Two rods might be loosely stated to be of equal length. Trial by rule might confirm this statement, but the two rods could vary in length to the extent of 0·00002 mm, say. That such a difference could possibly be important may seem absurd, yet the detection of such small differences is of basic importance in modern engineering practice.

The implications of precision measurement are very wide, and can be only briefly discussed. The engineer as a scientist is concerned with the exactitude of his methods: the great importance of similarity of observation is now one of the main principles of physics.

From the workshop point of view, the question of interchangeability requires careful consideration in all standard articles. When a part is to be built into a machine, it may be necessary for its size to be correct to 0·002 mm if it is to function correctly. Such parts have to be measured, and the measuring instrument has to be made. In the making of the measuring instrument, an accuracy of 0·0002 mm may be needed. Such an accuracy can be obtained only if there is some standard of much greater accuracy, and hence the need for a length standard with an error not exceeding 0·00002 mm.

It can also be demonstrated that, if the best results are to be obtained from a given amount of work in the workshop, accurate measuring instruments and gauges are essential. Anyone who has worked in a workshop where the micrometers and other measuring devices are not corrected regularly knows that a great deal of time and energy is wasted, and a careless attitude is generated by this unwise procedure.

23.3.1. Until recently, the standards of length were metal bars, and the length was defined by the distance between two lines on the bar. The Imperial Standard Yard is a bronze bar of 1 inch section, and 38 inches long; the bar is counterbored in two places to receive two gold plugs, so that their top faces are in the plane of the neutral axis of the bar, to minimise the effect of sag. The datum lines are engraved on the top faces of the plugs, and the distance between the lines defines the yard when the temperature is 62°F. The bar is carefully supported to minimise sag when in use. The International Prototype Metre is a bar of platinum–iridium alloy of H-like section, with the datum lines engraved on the web of the section. These standards are no longer in use, but are preserved.

The bar standards are unique, and, when used as the standards of length, copies had to be made for distribution. It will be appreciated that it is impossible to attain perfection, and so errors were bound to be made. The situation was further aggravated by the gradual deterioration of both the standard and the copies, and, although regular comparison was made, the system was poor.

23.3.2. The metre is now standardised in terms of the wavelength of light radiation, because this can be produced without error, does not deteriorate, and material copies of the standard do not have to be made for distribution.

The metre is now defined as 1 650 763·73 wavelengths of the orange radiation in vacuum of krypton-86 isotope. The radiation can be produced by discharge lamp, and so the fundamental standard can be produced as required; the wavelengths are counted by using interferometry (Interferometry is introduced in Chapter 24, but absolute measurement using this system is beyond the scope of this book).

23.3.3 Line standards and end standards. It has already been stated that the former length standards defined length as the distance between two lines; such standards are called *line standards*. A length can also be defined as the distance between two parallel plane surfaces; such a standard is called an *end standard*. With the exception of the rule, most engineering measuring devices depend upon end standards. An end standard consists of a rectangular block of steel, with the end faces hardened, ground, and lapped, so that they are flat and parallel, and the correct distance apart.

23.3.4 End bars. End bars are cylinders of 22 mm diameter with parallel end faces so forming an end standard. They are mainly used for reference, and to calibrate other measuring equipment.

BS 5317: 1976 provides for three grades. The reference grade is intended for use in the Standards Room, and is calibrated using interferometry (like the more accurate Slip Gauges, it forms the link between the International Standard and the engineering measuring devices); the calibration grade 1 is intended for use in the Tool Room, and the least accurate grade, calibration grade 2, is intended for use when measuring jigs and gauges, and certain workpieces. The calibration grades are designed to be screwed together to produce long lengths.

When an end bar is used with its axis in the horizontal plane it must be supported so that its end faces are parallel; the two support points that produce this condition are called the *Airy points* after their originator, Sir George Airy, who was the Astronomer Royal when the work on the Imperial Standard Yard was done. The Airy points are 0·5773 L apart (where L is the length of the bar) and are indicated on end bars of length greater than 150 mm; when end bars are combined they should be supported at support points that are 'central' and 0·577 L apart (where L is the length of the combination).

23.3.5 Slip gauges (more correctly called *gauge blocks*). These are of rectangular section, 9 mm × 30 mm for sizes up to 10 mm, and 9 mm × 35 mm for the larger sizes, and are made in a hardened high-grade cast steel. Each gauge can be used individually, or, alternatively, a number can be assembled to produce a composite gauge. The gauges are assembled by *wringing*, a combined sliding and twisting action which causes the gauges to adhere strongly, and to produce an overall length that is, for practical purposes, the sum of the individual sizes in the combination. The gauges must be separated by a wringing action, to prevent their damage.

BS 4311 : 1968 provides for five grades of gauge block:

grade II, for preliminary setting up, or for comparatively rough checking;

grade I, for the production of tools and gauges;

grade 0, for gauge inspection, and precision work;

grade 00, the most accurate gauge, as regards both size and the flatness and parallelism of the gauging faces;

calibration grade, used to calibrate other gauges, and for setting comparators. This grade has a similar tolerance on flatness and parallelism of the gauging faces to the grade 00, but the tolerance on length is greater. The gauges are calibrated, and the actual sizes are recorded on a calibration chart for the set; these deviations are taken into account when the set is used. The increased tolerance reduces the cost.

Grade 00 and calibration grade pieces are calibrated by interferometry, and are therefore the link between the international standard and engineering measuring devices.

A number of sets of gauges are recommended in the British Standard; the recommendations are based upon information regarding the most popular sets, though other sets are produced. One series is based upon 2 mm, and the other upon 1 mm; the 2-mm series is recommended, as gauges in this series are less likely to suffer deterioration in flatness than the similarly sized series based upon 1 mm. The 1-mm-based series are M32/1, M41/1, M47/1, M88/1, M112/1, and M46/1 (an M41/1 set plus 5 slips: 40, 50, 70, 80, and 90 mm), the symbols indicating metric, number of pieces in the set, and 1-mm-based. The 2-mm-based series are M33/2, M46/2, and M88/2; three auxiliary sets can be used with the 2-mm sets to enable them to cover sizes below 2 mm.

Set M46/2 is a typical 2-mm-base set:

Size or series mm	Increment mm	Number of pieces
2·001—2·009	0·001	9
2·01—2·09	0·01	9
2·1—2·9	0·1	9
1—9	1·0	9
10—100	10·0	10
	total	46

Building up a size Slip gauges should be built up systematically, as shown in the following example. To build up 58·343 mm using the M46/2 set:

		mm
eliminate the last decimal place		2·003
eliminate the second decimal place		2·04
eliminate the first decimal place		2·30
eliminate the remaining whole number		2
	remainder	50
	total	58·343

Protector slips Wear of gauge faces can be reduced very considerably by using protector slips made of steel or tungsten carbide. A pair of protector slips is used, and one piece is wrung on to each end of the 'build up'. Protector slips are usually 2 mm long, and are marked with the letter P on one measuring face.

The care of slip gauges Slip gauges should be kept in a special box when not in use, and should be cleaned before and after use. Wringing should not be done in the presence of abrasive dust, pieces must not be kept wrung together for long periods of time, and should be separated by a wringing action.

The application of slip gauges Mention has already been made of slip gauges as length standards and for setting comparators; they are also used in conjunction with other measuring devices, such as a sine bar, measuring balls, and measuring rollers, to carry out measurement using trigonometrical methods.

23.3.6 Feeler gauges. Sets of thin pieces of steel held together in a holder are termed feeler gauges. A range of thickness from about 0·030 mm to about 0·6 mm is provided, and the gauges can be combined to produce a variety of sizes. The accuracy of feeler gauges is not equal to that of slip gauges, and care must be taken to prevent the thinner feelers from becoming damaged.

23.4 The measurement of length
The foregoing have been 'fixed size' pieces of equipment, and intermediate sizes have been obtained by combination. When lengths, depths, heights, and diameters are to be measured, it is more convenient to use equipment that can be used for intermediate sizes, without the need to 'build up'. It must be emphasised that equipment that can be used for a variety of sizes cannot be as accurate as 'fixed dimension' equipment, and the choice of method must be carefully considered.

23.4.1 The engineer's rule. In this case, the sizes are indicated by fine lines scribed on a steel strip, and so this is a *line measurement* system. For best results, the rule should be used with a magnifying glass; setting and measurement with an accuracy of about 0·25 mm can often be achieved using an engineer's rule.

The main cause of error when using the rule is parallax error, which is caused by the incorrect positioning of the eye in relation to the mark being used. Figure 23.1 illustrates this point in exaggerated form. The

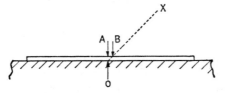

Fig 23.1 Parallax error

arrow A indicates the mark on the rule which coincides with point O on the work. If, however, the rule is viewed from the point X, then B will appear to be the coincident mark. It will be obvious that, for a given position of the eye, the error increases with rule thickness; rules are often made thin, or bevelled to reduce the thickness near the markings.

The rule is often used with inside and outside calipers to measure bores and shaft diameters when the tolerance is of the order of 1 mm.

23.4.2 The vernier caliper. The vernier caliper (shown in fig. 23.2) can be regarded as a development of the engineer's rule; the measurement being by the *end system* using a fixed jaw that is part of the beam carrying the main scale, and a movable jaw that can be locked in any desired position. A second movable member is introduced to assist in the correct setting of the movable jaw; this member is locked in any position and the movable jaw is moved relative to it by means of the fine adjustment screw.

The vernier caliper has the following merits:

(*a*) a large range of sizes can be covered by one caliper.
(*b*) the only wearing parts are the jaws and providing these are undamaged, there is no loss of accuracy as a result of continued use.

But there are some limitations:

(*a*) except for small sizes, hexagonal or round bars cannot be measured on the diameter.
(*b*) because of its shape, the 'feel' is not as good as that of the micrometer caliper (the micrometer caliper is discussed in section 23.4.4, where it is described as an alternative to the vernier caliper).
(*c*) the jaws are comparatively light, and may be sprung out of alignment.

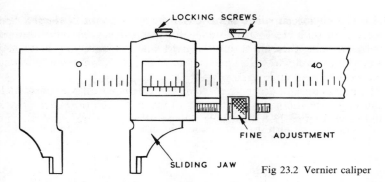

Fig 23.2 Vernier caliper

This instrument is called a vernier caliper because it uses the vernier principle to enable the scale to be read with greater accuracy; the graduations must be very accurate because the system depends upon the co-incidence of the markings.

Figure 23.3 illustrates the vernier system; this system, which was invented in 1631 by the French mathematician Pierre Vernier uses two scales: scale A is of any length, and is graduated in 1 mm and 0·5 mm divisions, and scale B is a short sliding scale with twenty-five equal

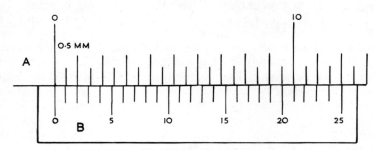

Fig 23.3 Vernier scales

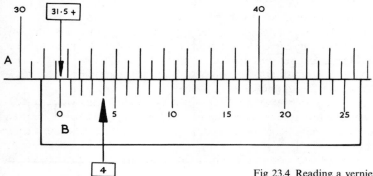

Fig 23.4 Reading a vernier scale

divisions which occupy the same length as twenty-four of the 0·5 mm divisions on scale A. The difference in length between a division on scale A and one on scale B will therefore be

$$\frac{12}{24} \text{ mm} - \frac{12}{25} \text{ mm} = 0{\cdot}5 - 0{\cdot}48 \text{ mm} = 0{\cdot}02 \text{ mm}$$

If the two scales are set so that the zero lines coincide, and then moved so that the fifth lines coincide, the short scale movement will be

$$5 \times \frac{12}{24} - 5 \times \frac{12}{25} = 5(0{\cdot}5 - 0{\cdot}48) \text{ mm} = 5(0{\cdot}02) \text{ mm}$$

Similarly, if the short scale is moved until the tenth lines coincide, the total movement from the zero setting will be 10(0·02) mm.

If the scale is moved to the position shown in fig. 23.4, the movement will be 31·58 mm. It will be seen that the zero of scale B is slightly beyond the 31·5 mark; counting along the scale B, it is seen that the fourth mark coincides with a mark on scale A, therefore 4(0·02) mm is added to the 31·5 mm, giving the reading 31·58 mm.

23.4.3 The vernier height gauge and the vernier depth gauge. The Vernier Height Gauge (see fig. 23.5) is basically a vernier caliper but with an accurate base instead of the fixed jaw, and is used in conjunction with a surface plate as shown in fig. 23.6 which shows two

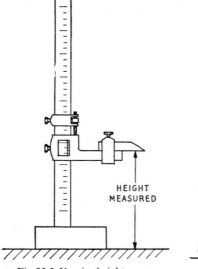

HEIGHT
MEASURED

Fig 23.5 Vernier height gauge

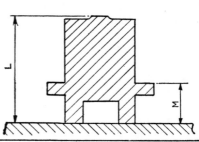

Fig 23.6

heights, 'L' and 'M' to be checked. Owing to the hole, and the small diameter of the boss and the projecting collar, these dimensions could not be checked with a micrometer or a vernier caliper, but are readily checked with the height gauge if the component is mounted on the surface plate as shown. The sharp extremity of the gauge finger is also used as a scriber when marking out work.

The vernier depth gauge. Figure 23.7 shows the main features of the vernier depth gauge. The projection of the blade from the stock gives the depth setting. This instrument also uses the fine-setting system used in the vernier caliper and vernier height gauge.

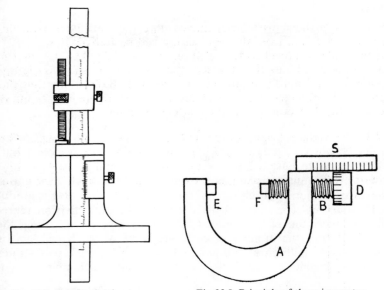

Fig 23.7 Vernier depth gauge   Fig 23.8 Principle of the micrometer

23.4.4 The micrometer. The principle of the micrometer is shown in fig. 23.8. The movable spindle B can be screwed in or out of the tapped hole in the frame A, to alter the gap between faces E and F. The number of complete rotations of the spindle can be seen from scale S; the position of drum D relative to the scale gives this number. The fractions of rotations are indicated by the evenly graduated markings around the circumference of D, the markings being read off against a datum (in this example, the scale S). The alteration of the gap between E and F for every rotation and fraction of a rotation depends upon the lead of the screw-thread on spindle B. The screw-thread is the vital part of the micrometer, and must be accurate as regards lead, diameter, and shape; the tapped hole in which it rotates must also be accurate. It is very difficult to produce an accurate lead, and it will be appreciated that the error associated with lead error increases with the length of the screw-thread—this is known as progressive error. For this reason, the range of a micrometer is only 25 mm; one micrometer is used for sizes between 0 and 25 mm, another for sizes between 25 and 50 mm, and so on. Figure 23.9 illustrates the principal features of a typical micrometer.

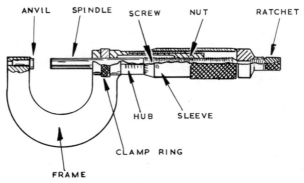

Fig 23.9 Micrometer features

Metric micrometers have a screw of 0·5 mm lead, so that the gap is altered by 0·5 mm for each turn of the thimble. The thimble is graduated, around its rim, into 50 divisions, and so each division represents an alteration of 0·01 mm in the gap. A divided line along the barrel indicates the number of complete turns of the barrel, and is graduated into millimitres and half millimetres. Figure 23.10 illustrates how the micrometer is read; it will be seen that the thimble has un-

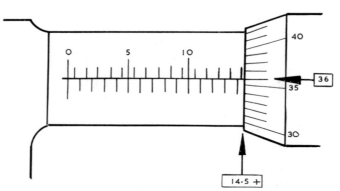

Fig 23.10 Reading a micrometer

covered 14·5 mm-divisions and part of a division. The part of a division is indicated by the markings on the thimble, and will be seen to be 36 divisions (representing 36 hundredths of a millimetre). The complete reading is therefore 14·5 + 0·36 = 14·86 mm.

The micrometer is an alternative to the vernier caliper—it is easier to obtain 'feel' and is more accurate and reliable. However, one vernier caliper can cover a range of sizes.

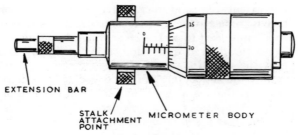

EXTENSION BAR

STALK
ATTACHMENT   MICROMETER BODY
POINT

Fig 23.11 Inside micrometer

Figure 23.11 illustrates an inside micrometer; a set consists of a micrometer head and a range of bars. The inside micrometer must have radiused ends to fit inside the holes to be measured, and so is much more sensitive as regards 'feel'. The bottom of a deep hole can be reached by means of a 'stalk', screwed into the body of the micrometer, but this tends to upset the balance of the micrometer, and makes feel even more difficult.

A micrometer depth gauge is illustrated in fig. 23.12. This instrument is used in the same way as a vernier depth gauge, but is easier to read, as the divisions can be wider, due to the magnification effect of using a screw-thread.

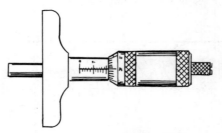

Fig 23.12 Micrometer depth gauge

23.5 Comparators
The measuring devices dealt with so far are all measures in themselves, and the measurement is made without reference to any other datum.

Very often, it is necessary to know the variation of size, rather than the actual size. For example, if a number of rollers, nominally 12 mm in diameter, is to be checked, it is necessary only to set the instrument to 12 mm, and to know the amount by which each roller differs from that size. Such relationships as roundness and concentricity can be checked similarly. Again, the devices dealt with have relied upon the accuracy to which a long piece of steel can be divided, or the accuracy to which a screw-thread can be produced. The screw-thread difficulty is overcome, to some extent, by using micrometers with a range of only 25 mm—but there is some error even in a screw-thread of that shortness. This problem is minimised to a very great extent by using a comparator, setting it to the desired dimension, using slip gauges, and then measuring only the variation. By so doing, the error is reduced considerably, because the slip gauges are 'fixed size' devices, and the only progressive error is that between the set size and the size of the part being examined. Comparators are considered in Chapter 24, but the dial-indicator, which is a simple comparator, has already been mentioned, and will be discussed at this point.

23.5.1 The dial-indicator. The mechanism of this instrument is shown in fig. 23.13. The plunger slides in and out of the body, and the motion is recorded by the pointer on the dial, which is divided into divisions.

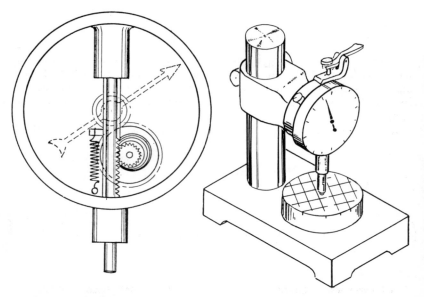

Fig 23.13 Dial-indicator mechanism   Fig 23.14 Mounted dial-indicator

Usually, the dial scale is marked from zero on each half of the circle, and the dial can be rotated relative to the pointer, so that a zero setting can be made for any position of the plunger. The total plunger movement is about 12 mm or 1 mm, according to the division of the dial. The dial-indicator has a lug at the back of the body, so that it can be mounted on a stand or other fixture. Figure 23.14 shows a dial-indicator mounted on a stand over a small flat table on which the work to be measured can be placed. One use of this arrangement is illustrated in fig. 23.15.

A very important feature of this indicator is that the contact pressure of the plunger is maintained by a light spring, and is quite independent of the 'feel' of the operator.

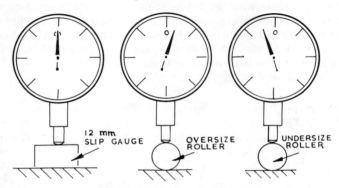

Fig 23.15 Use of a comparator

The dial-indicator can be set up as a comparator, as shown in fig. 23.15, which illustrates the checking of 12-mm-diameter rollers. It can also be used to check a surface for flatness or roundness (see section 23.6) and to check the relationship between two or more surfaces (see section 23.7).

Another use of the dial-indicator is shown in fig. 23.16. This method

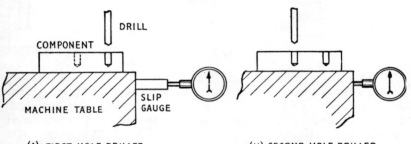

(I) FIRST HOLE DRILLED   (II) SECOND HOLE DRILLED

Fig 23.16 Hole setting with a dial-indicator

is used in certain precision-boring-machines; it is one way of eliminating the question of 'feel'. A component is to have two holes spaced 100
mm apart. It is placed on a boring machine with a sliding table. The
end of the table has a face which is a true plane. A 100-mm slip gauge
is placed between the table end and a dial indicator, as shown at (i).
The dial-indicator, which is attached to an immovable part, is set to
zero, and the first hole is bored. The slip gauge is removed, and the
table is moved over until the dial-indicator again reads zero, as shown
in (ii). The second hole is then bored.

A different type of dial-indicator has a dial that faces upwards when
in normal use, and a projecting plunger that can be inserted in positions where a normal dial-indicator would not be convenient. Figure
23.17 shows a plate with projecting studs. The plate is revolving in a
chuck, and it is necessary to know if the plate is set so that it is
revolving about the axis of the central stud. The extended plunger of
the gauge can be placed on the stud, without any danger of the remaining studs fouling the dial-indicator body.

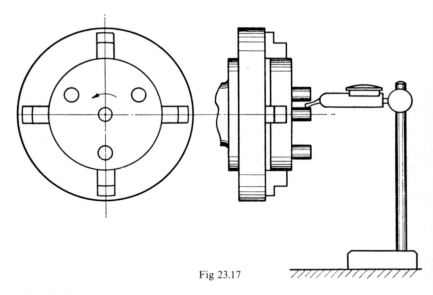

Fig 23.17

23.6 Surface measurement

Surfaces must be measured to ensure that they are of a sufficiently high
degree of accuracy before their relationship with each other is studied.
The measurement of surfaces can be divided into two related
studies—that of form (flatness, roundness etc.), and that of texture. The
study of texture is the subject of Chapter 25, but this really a 'finer'
study of form.

23.6.1 Flatness. A plane surface can be examined for flatness by using a dial indicator and a surface plate as shown in fig. 23.18; the surface plate is used to explore the surface being examined, and variation in

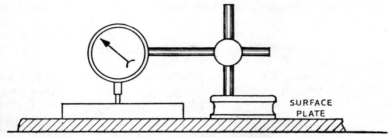

Fig 23.18 Checking a flat surface

the general trend of the needle movement indicates that the surface is not flat (compare this with the check for parallelism of faces in fig. 23.22).

Large surfaces can be checked using a spirit level (see 23.7.2) or by optical methods (see Chapter 24).

The flatness of the end face of a cylinder or of a shoulder face is checked at the same time as concentricity (see fig. 23.35)

23.6.2 Roundness and Axial Straightness of Cylindrical Surfaces. The term 'roundness' implies that a cylinder is of circular section; a circle is the locus of a point moving at constant distance (radius) from a fixed point. Therefore a section cannot be said to be circular if only its diameter is constant. Figure 23.19 illustrates the simplest *constant diameter figure*; the British 50 pence coin is another example of a constant diameter figure; a constant diameter figure has an odd number of sides

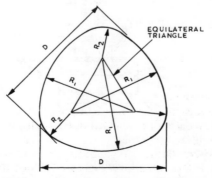

Fig 23.19 The constant diameter figure (simplest example)

greater that 1. The examples shown are clearly not round, but in practice parts submitted for examination may have so many 'sides' that they appear to be circular. Figure 23.20 shows checks for roundness; fig. 23.20(*a*) shows a workpiece mounted between centres, and rotated relative to a dial indicator; figs. 23.20(*b*) and 23.20(*c*) show variations that

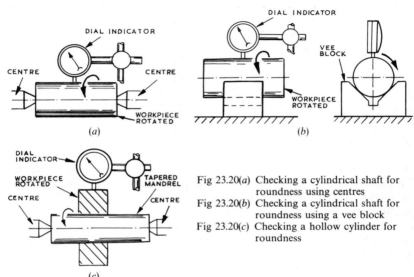

Fig 23.20(*a*) Checking a cylindrical shaft for roundness using centres
Fig 23.20(*b*) Checking a cylindrical shaft for roundness using a vee block
Fig 23.20(*c*) Checking a hollow cylinder for roundness

are used when a 'solid' workpiece without centres, and a hollow workpiece is to be checked for roundness.

The cylinder can also be checked for axial straightness using the same arrangement by keeping it stationary, and moving the dial-indicator along it in the same vertical plane as its axis (see fig. 23.21).

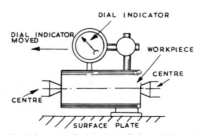

Fig 23.21 Checking a cylindrical shaft for axial straightness

23.7 Surface relationship
If surfaces are found to be sufficiently accurate, their relationship can be examined.

23.7.1 Parallelism of surfaces. The parallelism of surfaces can most conveniently be checked by placing the workpiece on a surface plate which then becomes an 'extension' of the lower surface, and the upper surface explored by a dial-indicator using the surface plate as a datum (see fig. 23.22).

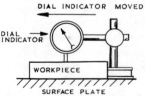

Fig 23.22 Checking for parallelism of surfaces

The parallelism of very accurate surfaces, such as those of slip gauges can be checked by optical methods (see Chapter 24).

23.7.2 Angular measurement. *Angle Slip Gauges.* These are the workshop standards for angles. They are considered in Chapter 24 (section 24.4.3) because they are usually used in conjunction with autocollimation.

The vernier protractor. The angle between two surfaces can be measured using the vernier protractor (fig. 23.23); the workpiece being placed on a surface plate using one of the surfaces as the seating face, and the vernier protractor also seated on the surface plate. The blade of the protractor is then adjusted so that it contacts the other surface that forms the angle being measured, and the included angle is measured

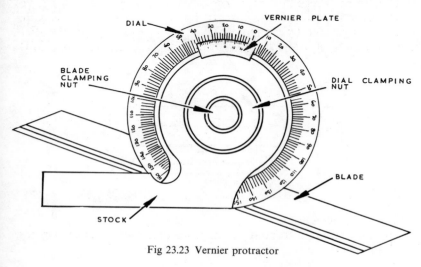

Fig 23.23 Vernier protractor

off directly. The usual graduation is in degrees, which may be sub-divided into half degrees.

For more accurate work, a vernier scale is fitted. The main scale is then divided into degrees, and the vernier scale is divided so that twelve divisions equal 23° on the main scale. Each vernier division thus represents $\frac{23}{12}° = 1\frac{11}{12}°$, or five minutes of arc less than 2°. To read the vernier, the whole number of degrees is noted, and then the number of divisions is counted up to the point where a line on the vernier scale coincides with a line on the main scale. Each division represents five minutes of arc, and these must be added to the reading. It is essential, in counting, to move *away* from the zero mark on the main scale. Figure 23.24 shows a reading of 6° 25′.

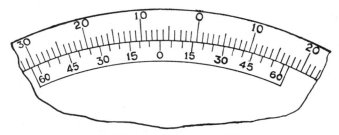

Fig 23.24 Vernier reading 6° 25′

The Sine Bar. This is a more accurate angle-measuring device, but is slower to use than the vernier protractor. Figure 23.25 illustrates a simple sine bar, consisting of a straight-edge, to which are attached two steel cylindrical plugs of equal diameters, projecting from the straight-edge. The axes of the plugs must be in the same plane, parallel to the top edge of the straight edge, and parallel to each other in the other plane. Figure 23.26 shows a more elaborate sine bar, which has

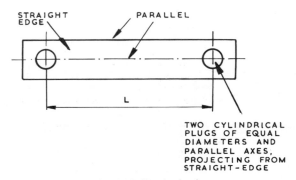

Fig 23.25 Simple sine bar

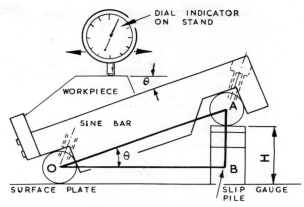

Fig 23.26 Sine bar principle

two rollers attached to the underside, and an end-stop to position the workpiece, which, if smaller than the sine bar, is seated as shown, on the top face. The sine bar is seated on a surface plate, and one end is raised, using a pile of slip gauges, until the other face of the workpiece, enclosing the angle to be measured, is horizontal. A dial-indicator is used to check that the face is parallel with the surface plate.

The value of angle θ is obtained from $\sin \theta = AB/OA$, where $AB = H$ (the height of the pile of slip gauges), and $OA =$ the distance between the roller centres (this distance is shown as L in fig. 23.25, and is usually 100 mm or 250 mm, to simplify calculation).

If the angular face of a large component is to be measured, the sine bar can be placed upside-down on the face (see fig. 23.27), and the

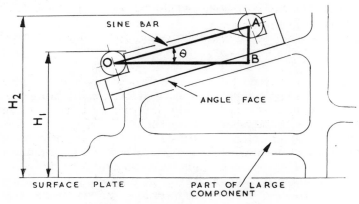

Fig 23.27 Sine bar used on large component

height of each roller measured by height gauge. From these measurements, the value of the angle can be calculated as before. If the angle is steep, the sine bar can be clamped to the component.

Owing to the characteristics of the sine function, the accuracy of sine bars becomes less as the angle being measured becomes larger. For this reason, the complements of angles above 45° should be tested, if possible.

The Spirit Level can be used to measure an angle relative to 'horizontal'; it can also be used to measure flatness by taking readings at several places, to produce a graph of flatness along the length measured.

The principle of the spirit level can be explained with reference to a circular glass tube of uniform cross section, which is almost full of liquid (see fig. 23.28). A small bubble of air is left in the tube; and, as

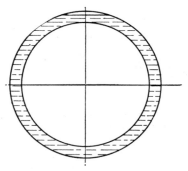

Fig 23.28 Spirit level principle

the tube is rotated, the liquid will remain at the bottom, and the air at the top. If the tube is 20 m radius, and is rotated through 1 minute of arc, its movement at the circumference will be

$$\frac{2 \times \pi \times 20 \times 1000}{360 \times 60} = 5 \cdot 82 \text{ mm approx}$$

If the tube is moved by this amount then the edge of the bubble will move by the same amount. A little consideration will bring the conclusion that an increase in tube radius will give a greater bubble movement for the same angular displacement.

Figure 23.29 illustrates the essential features of an engineer's block level. This instrument contains a small portion of a large-radius tube, called a vial. The upper inside surface is carefully ground to a definite radius, and the vial is mounted level, in a cast-iron block with a flat base. The outside of the vial has a series of graduations, so that the bubble movement can be accurately determined.

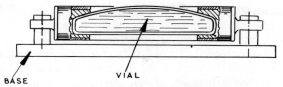

Fig 23.29 Engineer's block level

The general formula for determining the sensitivity of a level is illustrated in fig. 23.30.

Let x = movement of bubble, in mm,
R = tube radius, in metres,
θ = angle of inclination in seconds or arc.

Then
$$x = \frac{2 \times \pi \times R \times \theta \times 1000}{360 \times 60 \times 60} = \frac{2\pi R\theta}{1296} \qquad (1)$$

or
$$R = \frac{1296x}{2\pi\theta} \qquad (2)$$

If the length of the block = L metres, and it is tilted about its centre through θ seconds of arc, then

$$H = \frac{xL}{R} \text{ for small angles} \qquad (3)$$

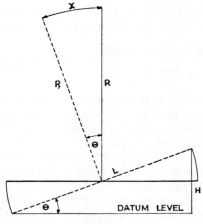

Fig 23.30

But from (2), substituting for R,

$$H = \frac{xL2\pi\theta}{1296x} = \frac{2\pi\theta L}{1296} \qquad (4)$$

Example. A level, 250 mm long, has a bubble movement of 3 mm in an inclination of twenty seconds of arc. State the tube radius, and the packing to be placed under one end for a bubble movement of 3 mm.

From (2) $\quad R = \dfrac{1296x}{2\pi\theta} = \dfrac{1296 \times 3}{2\pi \times 20} = 30\cdot94$ metres

From (4) $\quad H = \dfrac{2\pi\theta L}{1296} = \dfrac{2\pi \times 20 \times 250}{1296 \times 1000} = 0\cdot023$ mm

Measurement of angles using rollers and balls. The magnitude of angles can be determined by obtaining measurements using precision rollers or precision balls, in conjunction with a surface plate, slip gauges, and measuring instruments; these measurements can be used to calculate the magnitude of angles using geometry or trigonometry. Measuring rollers are easier to use than balls, as they are only unstable in one direction, but the latter must be used for tapered holes. The following examples show the principles involved.

Measurement of the included angle of an external taper (fig. 23.31). The tapered part is seated on a surface plate, which is the datum for

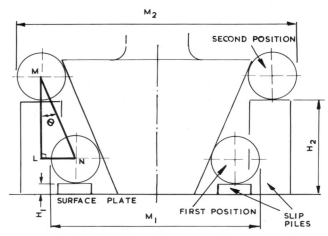

Fig 23.31 Measuring an external taper

heights. Two rollers of equal diameter are placed on slip-gauge piles of equal height, and the overall measurement (M_1) is taken. The rollers are then placed on two higher slip piles, and measurement M_2 is taken. A slip-gauge pile is used for the first condition, rather than seating the rollers directly on the surface plate, so that the effect of local variation of surface-plate flatness is overcome. In triangle LMN, length LM = $H_2 - H_1$, and LN = $(M_2 - M_1)/2$. Angle θ is half the included angle of the taper.

$$\tan \theta = \frac{\text{LN}}{\text{LM}} = \frac{M_2 - M_1}{2(H_2 - H_1)}$$

Measurement of the included angle of a large diameter tapered bore (fig. 23.32). The geometry is similar to that in the above example. It is necessary to use measuring balls, because of the curvature of the hole;

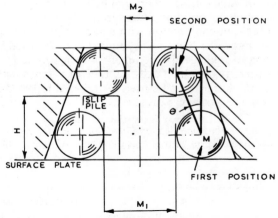

Fig 23.32 Measuring a large internal taper

a slip pile is not used for ball seating when measuring M_1, owing to the lack of space, but may be used to advantage when the diameter of the bore is large enough. As in the previous example, the included taper angle is 2θ where θ is given by:

$$\tan \theta = \frac{M_1 - M_2}{2H}$$

Measurement of the included angle of a small diameter tapered bore (fig. 23.33). In this example, it is necessary to use two balls of such a size that they can be placed in the bore in turn, to make contact with the side of the bore in places far enough apart to produce a 'non-local'

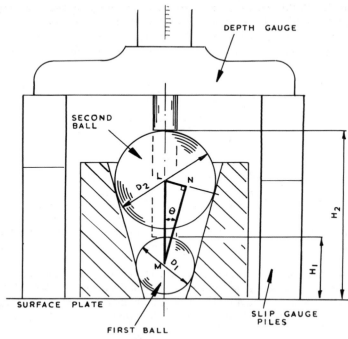

Fig 23.33 Measuring a small internal taper

taper measurement. It is usually convenient to use a depth gauge seated on two equal piles of slips, so that the two heights H_1 and H_2 are measured. If the outside of the part being measured is too large to allow a depth gauge to be supported on the slip gauges, as shown in fig. 23.33, the slip gauges can be placed on the top surface of the part. The disadvantage of this arrangement is that an additional machining operation is necessary to ensure that the top and bottom surfaces are parallel.

In triangle LMN, the included taper angle $= 2\theta$, length LN $= (D_2 - D_1)/2$, and LM $= H_2 - H_1 + (D_1 - D_2)/2$

$$\sin \theta = \frac{\text{LN}}{\text{LM}} = \frac{D_2 - D_1}{2(H_2 - H_1) + (D_1 - D_2)}$$

The *Try-Square* is used to check surfaces that are at right angles; it is discussed in detail in section 17.3.

23.7.3 Concentricity of Cylindrical Surfaces. The test for concentricity of cylindrical surfaces is similar to that for roundness, but in this case the relationship between two or more cylindrical surfaces is studied.

Figure 23.34 illustrates the arrangement for checking the concentricity of three cylindrical surfaces. The workpiece being checked is mounted between centres and rotated relative to the dial-indicator in each of the three positions in turn. An eccentric surface will cause the dial-

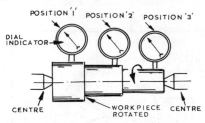

Fig 23.34 Checking for concentricity

indicator needle to reach maximum deflection at every complete rotation of the workpiece (a non-round, but concentric surface will cause the needle to fluctuate through the cycle).

23.7.4 Squareness of Shoulder and End Faces. The squareness of a shoulder or end face relative to a cylindrical surface can be checked at the same time as concentricity as shown in fig. 23.35. A non-square shoulder face will produce a cyclic deflection of the needle (in the same

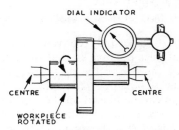

Fig 23.35 Checking a shoulder face for squareness with axis

way as does an eccentric cylindrical surface). The flatness of the face can also be checked at the same time – a non flat, but square shoulder face will, like a non-round cylindrical surface, cause the needle to fluctuate throughout the cycle.

Summary

1 Any system of measurement must be based upon a standardised unit.
2 The metre is now standardised in terms of the wavelength of light radiation.

3   Length can be expressed as the distance between two parallel
     plane surfaces (end measurement), or as the distance between two
     lines (line measurement).
4   End bars and slip gauges are end standards.
5   Length can more conveniently, but usually less accurately, be
     measured using a form of rule (line measurement). Greater pre-
     cision can be obtained by incorporating a vernier device. The
     vernier caliper, vernier height gauge, and vernier depth gauge are
     variations of the simple rule.
6   The micrometer uses a screw-thread as the basis of measurement.
     The range obtained by one micrometer is limited, because of the
     progressive error of a screw-thread.
7   A comparator is an accurate measuring device because it only
     indicates variation from a nominal size that is set using an end
     bar or slip-gauge pile.
8   Surfaces must be checked before their relationship can be exam-
     ined. Flatness of plane surfaces, and roundness and axial straight-
     ness of cylindrical surfaces are the principal considerations.
9   Surfaces can be most conveniently checked using a dial-indicator
     and surface plate.
10   Sufficiently accurate surfaces can be checked to ensure that their
     relationship is acceptable. Parallelism and angular relationship of
     plane surfaces, and concentricity of cylindrical surfaces are the
     principal considerations.
11   Parallelism and concentricity are most conveniently checked
     using a dial-indicator and surface plate.
12   Angles can be measured using a protractor, a sine bar, a spirit
     level, or by trigonometrical methods using balls or rollers, slip
     gauges, measuring devices, and a surface plate as the datum.

Questions

Set A
1   If the three holes shown in fig. 16.12 have been drilled, and paral-
     lel plugs, 25 mm diameter fitted, calculate the overall size of slip
     gauges to check the straight-line distances between the plugs, and
     suggest a 'build up' from the M 46/2 set.
2   A spirit level is 250 mm long. The bubble moves 0·25 mm when a
     feeler 0·0025 mm thick is placed under one end of the level. What
     is the radius of the tube?
3   You are required to check a number of try-squares. A true surface
     plate and a micrometer are available, but not a true square.
     Describe a suitable method.
4   What is secular change? How does it affect fine measurement, and
     how can it be minimised in a gauge?

5   Give the minimum number of slip gauges required to build up the following dimensions: 76·253 mm, 25·2 mm, 25·37 mm, 121·745 mm. A standard M 46/2 set is available.

6   Given a set of slip gauges, a short straight-edge, and a toolmaker's flat, suggest a suitable method of testing each of the following parts: a flat gauge 0·1-mm thick, a plug gauge 25-mm diameter, a 40-mm snap gauge.

7   Draw out, to a large scale, a portion of a rule marked in 0·5 mm divisions. Make a short vernier scale to give readings to 0·02 mm, and fix it to your main rule at the dimension 41·94 mm.

8   Discuss the relative advantages of a 300-mm vernier caliper, and a set of micrometers to cover the range 0–300 mm.

9   Make sketches of the following micrometer readings: 10·56 mm, 17·33 mm.

10   Make sketches of the following vernier readings: 6·37 mm, 10·25 mm.

11   What accuracy would you expect to obtain when measuring a round bar approximately 75 mm in diameter (*a*) with a rule and calipers, (*b*) with a 75·2-mm snap gauge and a set of feelers? Give reasons for your answers.

12   Explain carefully how you would measure a 40-mm-diameter hole, using inside calipers and an outside micrometer. State what degree of accuracy you would expect, and what precautions must be taken to ensure this accuracy.

13   It is decided to make a micrometer with thimble divisions 3 mm apart. If the micrometer has a spindle with the usual thread, what will be the diameter of the thimble?

14   Illustrate, with sketches, three uses of the vernier height gauge.

15   State the limit of accuracy of each of the following measuring devices, and explain briefly how you would make a check if the the accuracy were in doubt: a set of feelers, a steel rule, a vernier height gauge.

16   (*a*) Some micrometers have twenty divisions on the thimble. What will be the thread of the spindle?
     (*b*) What difference is to be noted between the anvils of an outside micrometer and an inside micrometer? Why is this difference necessary?

17   A taper gauge of 25 mm maximum diameter and 100 mm long has an included angle of 10°. Make a sketch showing a sine bar set up for checking the gauge, and state the size of slip gauges you would place under each roller.

18   Two flat gauges are placed on a toolmaker's flat. Two rollers of equal diameter are obtained, and one is placed on each gauge. The centre distance of the two rollers is 25 mm. A level with a tube radius of 40 m is placed on the rollers, and the bubble moves 3 mm

from the level position. The smaller gauge is known to be 19 mm high. What is the height of the larger gauge?

19 A shaft 75 mm in diameter has six splines equally spaced. The splines are each 9 mm wide, with parallel sides, and the diameter across the top of the splines is 90 mm. Explain how you would check the following points: (*a*) the diameter across the splines, (*b*) the diameter of the shaft, (*c*) the width of the splines, (*d*) the spacing out of the splines, (*e*) the parallelism of the splines to the axis of the shaft.

20 You are given a rectangular block of metal 25 mm × 12 mm × 9 mm thick. Outline three methods of determining the thickness of the block to fine limits. With each method, state the degree of accuracy, and explain what determines this accuracy.

21 A small eccentric is mounted on a shaft. The eccentric is supposed to be circular and to have a 'throw' of 0·5 mm. Describe the fixtures and instruments required, and outline a method of checking the eccentric.

22 Two shafts, each running in two bearings, are to be coaxial, and are to have their adjoining ends 6 mm apart. Explain carefully how they could be set in this position.

23 Make a sketch of an angular vernier reading of 3° 40′.

Set B (questions requiring further study)

24 (*a*) Make a sketch showing how an outside micrometer is adjusted for wear.
(*b*) Give the number of threads per unit of length on the spindle, and the number of thimble divisions of a micrometer reading to 0·01 mm.

25 Write a brief description of the manufacture of slip gauges.

26 Sketch and describe a bench micrometer fitted with a fiducial indicator.

27 Make a sketch, and explain the principle of a clinometer.

28 Briefly describe the use of slip-gauge accessories, and give three typical applications.

Chapter 24
Engineering Metrology (2) Comparators, Optical Projectors, Optical Flats, and Collimation

24.1 Comparators

A brief reference has been made to comparators (section 23.5) where it was explained that errors associated with measuring instruments that use a long scale or a screw thread as the measuring device can be reduced by measuring only the variation of size from a datum to which the instrument is set using a 'fixed size' setting piece, such as a slip gauge or end bar. A device that compares the size of a part with that to which it is set, and does nor *directly* indicate the actual size is called a comparator.

Comparators can be classified as follows:

(*a*) High precision comparators that are used in a Standards Room to calibrate slip gauges, end bars etc. by comparing them with a reference gauge (slip gauges and end bars can also be examined by optical methods as discussed in section 24.3). The Eden–Rolt Millionth Comparator and the Brookes Level Comparator will be discussed (section 24.1.1) as examples of this group of comparators.

(*b*) Comparators that are also used for general work on the shop floor, either as an alternative to using a direct measuring instrument (as already discussed) or as an alternative to limit gauges. Limit gauges are discussed in section 26.7, where it is stated that they usually only indicate if a workpiece is accepted or rejected by virtue of its size, and do not specify its actual size. A knowledge of how close a part is to being accepted or being rejected is necessary where the process is such that knowledge of the dimensional trend would enable correction to be made to machine settings, tools, and so on before the point at which workpieces are rejected. A comparator can be set to indicate 'control' limits of size in addition to indicating acceptance and rejection limits and their values.

24.1.1 High precision comparators

(*a*) *The Eden–Rolt Millionth Comparator* (developed at the National Physical Laboratory by E. M. Eden and F. H. Rolt in 1918). This instrument is a good example of high magnification being obtained by clever design, and using components that are not manufactured with great accuracy, and is still popular for the calibration of slip gauges; its usual capacity is up to about 50 mm, and its range varies from about 0·2 to 0·8 mm depending upon the model.

Figure 24.1 illustrates the main features of this comparator. The slip gauge being measured is placed between a fixed anvil consisting of a

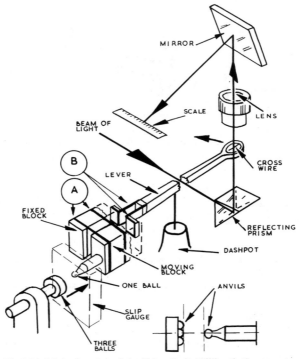

Fig 24.1 Main features of the Eden–Rolt Millionth Comparator

cluster of three balls in a chuck, and a moving anvil consisting of a single ball attached to a moving block; this anvil system is designed to ensure that the gauge being examined is correctly seated. The moving block moves parallel to the fixed block to which it is attached by two thin strips (strips 'A'), that produce a frictionless linear movement; this linear movement is converted into an angular movement by two strips (strips 'B'), one of which is attached to the moving block and the other to the fixed block, and both attached to the lever, about 0·5 mm apart. Figure 24.2 shows in more detail the arrangements for the linear movement and the angular movement.

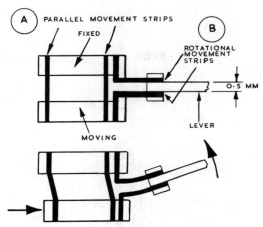

Fig 24.2 Angular movement produced from linear movement

The lever is about 200 mm long and made of aluminium alloy; it carries a cross wire at its end, and its movement is damped by a dashpot.

$$\text{The lever ratio} = \frac{\text{length of lever}}{\text{distance between the springs}} = \frac{200}{0\cdot5} = 400 : 1$$

The movement of the cross wire is viewed by projecting its image on to a calibrated scale, producing an optical magnification of × 50.

The total magnification is 400 × 50 = 20 000

The scale is calibrated to read directly to 0·0002 mm, but as the scale divisions are about 5 mm apart, the movement can be estimated to about 0·00002 mm.

(*a*) *The Brookes Level Comparator* (developed by A. J. C. Brookes at the National Physical Laboratory towards the end of the First World War). This high precision comparator, illustrated in fig. 24.3, consists of a precision spirit level mounted on an arm which also includes two ball contacts about 18 mm apart; the arm is supported by a column, but is free to tilt and take up its position when lowered on to the two parts that are being compared. The spirit level is calibrated so that the bubble indicates the difference between the heights of the two parts, which are placed on an accurately machined platen that can be rotated about a vertical axis. It is necessary to place the two parts on a platen that can be rotated because, as comparison is done using a spirit level, it is necessary to eliminate error caused by an incorrect position of the instrument; and as explained below, this error can be eliminated by reversal.

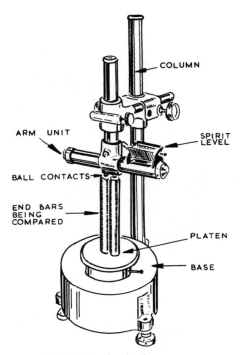

COLUMN

ARM UNIT

SPIRIT LEVEL

BALL CONTACTS

END BARS BEING COMPARED

PLATEN

BASE

Fig 24.3 Brookes level comparator

The operation of this comparator can best be described by considering the procedure when an end bar is compared with a reference grade
end bar. The two end bars are wrung on to the platen so that they are
approximately equal distances from the axis of the platen (indicated by
target rings on the platen), the arm lowered so that it rests on them,
and the difference in their 'levels' read from the spirit level. The arm is
raised and the platen rotated through 180° so that the end bars are
reversed. The arm is then lowered on to the end bars, and the difference between their 'levels' can be read off.

The difference between their heights is given by:

$$H = \frac{R_1 - R_2}{2}$$

where H = the difference between their heights. R_1 and R_2 are the two
readings.

As illustrated by fig. 24.4, this reversal eliminates the error caused by
instrument position, and 'doubles' the actual error (hence the halving
of the difference between the two readings).

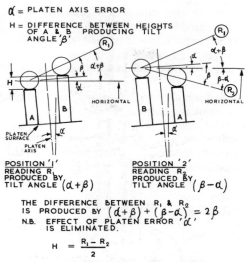

Fig 24.4 The reversal principle

The instrument is calibrated directly to 0·2 (0·0002 mm), but finer readings can be obtained by estimation; estimation combined with the 'error doubling effect' enables height variations of the order of 0·02 μm (0·00002 mm) to be detected.

This instrument differs from other comparators in that the part being examined is compared with the reference part by placing them close together on the instrument platen (when other instruments are used, the reference part is used to set the datum, removed, and replaced by the part being examined); errors caused by variation in the temperatures of the reference part and that being examined are almost completely eliminated by placing them near each other, on the platen at the same time and allowing sufficient time for their temperatures to become the same.

24.1.2 The basic requirements of a comparator for general work. A comparator for general work should satisfy the following basic requirements:

1. It should be of robust design and construction to withstand ordinary usage.
2. When the measuring head is mounted on a column, means of rapid adjustment and locking in position should be provided to enable a range of workpiece sizes to be readily accommodated.
3. Plunger contact pressures should be light and be uniform over the range of the instrument.

4. Means of lifting the plunger before inserting the workpiece should be provided to minimise wear.
5. The mechanism should be designed so that damage cannot be caused by excessive plunger movement.
6. The mechanism should be damped so that the pointer rapidly comes to rest.
7. Production comparators should include a workpiece location system, and limit indicators.

24.1.3 The classification of comparators for general work. It is convenient to classify these comparators according to the magnification method used as follows:
1. Mechanical
2. Optical.
3. Pneumatic.
4. Electrical.
5. Fluid displacement.

24.1.4 Mechanical comparators. The comparators in this group are of purely mechanical operation. The three principal models of this type are (a) the dial indicator, (b) the Sigma Vertical Comparator, and (c) the Johansson Mikrokator.

(a) *The dial indicator.* The dial indicator (see section 23.5.1) is a convenient comparator because it can be small if required, and has a large range—the needle can rotate several times, and the number of revolutions are indicated by a second needle and scale. Its extensive use has already been discussed in the sections in Chapter 23 referring to linear measurement, and the measurement of surface relationship, and also in the sections in this book referring to machine tool examination. The large range of the dial indicator introduces errors, and these, together with other errors are minimised by the design of the Sigma Vertical Comparator, and the Johansson Mikrokator, but at the expense of the large range of the dial indicator.

(b) *The Sigma Vertical Comparator.* This large mechanical comparator, shown in fig. 24.5, is a high magnification, small range instrument that includes design features that almost completely eliminate the errors that are inherent in the dial indicator; these errors are:
(a) Errors caused by wear of the plunger-bearing surfaces.
(b) Errors caused by the variation of the plunger contact pressure (the pressure increases with upward movement of the plunger because the spring force increases when it is pulled).
(c) Backlash error in the rack and pinion system used to convert the linear movement of the plunger into rotational movement.

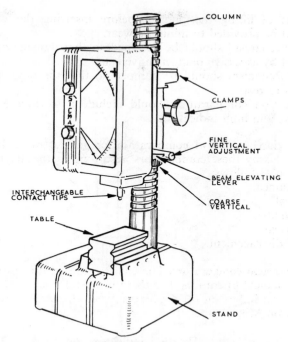

Fig 24.5 The 'Sigma' comparator

(*d*) Backlash in the gear train that magnifies the rotational movement.

(*e*) Errors caused by wear at the gear-bearing points.

Figure 24.6 illustrates the main features of the mechanism of the Sigma comparator. Starting from the plunger, and working through the mechanism, the principal features are as follows (the letters refer to fig. 24.6):

A. The plunger is a light-weight beam that is mounted on flat steel springs that are connected to fixed members secured to the back-plate of the instrument, providing frictionless movement with resisting pressure.

B. The plunger pressure is kept uniform over the range of the instrument by a magnet and keep-plate system. The increased downwards force caused by the upwards movement of the plunger is compensated by the increased attraction of the magnet as the keep-plate attached to the plunger approaches it.

C. The linear movement of the plunger is converted, without friction, into rotational movement by the crossed-strip hinge system. The

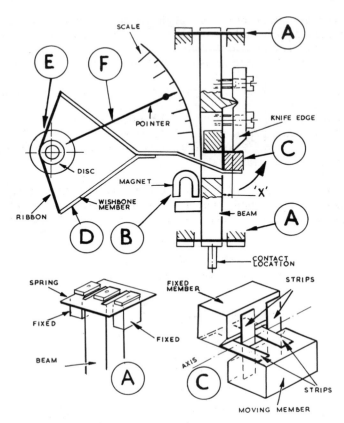

Fig 24.6 The main features of the mechanism of the 'Sigma' comparator

instrument is designed with an 'out of balance', causing the moving member of this system to rotate about the axis of the hinge and contact the knife edge that is attached to the plunger; vertical movement of the plunger permits the moving member to move, so that linear movement is converted into rotational movement without undue force on the mechanism. The distance 'X' affects the magnification, and is adjustable so that the instrument can be calibrated upon assembly instead of manufacturing the components to a high degree of accuracy.

D. The light-weight wishbone assembly attached to the moving member carries a metal ribbon that passes round the spindle, causing it to rotate when the moving member of the hinge system moves. The spindle is supported by two specially designed miniature ball bearings, which are the only two conventional rotational bearing-points in the mechanism.

E. The rotational movement of the spindle is damped by a metal disc attached to it and rotating in a magnetic field between a permanent magnet and a steel plate.

F. The indicating pointer is attached to a boss on the metal disc.

The measuring head is supported by a column, and is raised and lowered to suit the size of the workpiece being examined (see fig. 24.5). A number of models is available with magnifications from × 300 to × 5000, and scale ranges from ± 0·25 mm to ± 0·015 mm. The instrument is set to 'zero' by moving the scale relative to the pointer, and includes tolerance indicators.

(*c*) *The Johansson Mikrokator*. This comparator, illustrated in fig. 24.7 is a compact, small range instrument that includes several clever design features. The plunger is supported by thin sheet metal springs

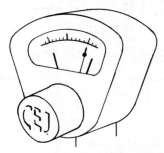

Fig 24.7 The Johansson 'Mikrokator'

(similar to the system used in the Sigma Vertical Comparator), but the magnification of the plunger movement, and its conversion into an angular movement of the pointer is done through the medium of a twisted thin metal band to which the pointer is attached.

Fig. 24.8 illustrates the main features of the mechanism. The band carries a light-weight pointer at its centre, and is twisted to form a left hand helix on one side of the pointer and a right hand helix on the other; one end is fixed to an adjustable support, and the other end to a right-angle spring knee which is attached to the top of the plunger. Upward movement of the plunger increases the tension on the band so that it rotates about its helix angle, and downwards movement of the plunger reduces the tension on the band so that it rotates in the opposite direction; the movement of the pointer that is attached to the band directly indicates the plunger movement, and is damped by running the band in a drop of oil in a split bush adjacent to the pointer. A range of models is available, with scale ranges from 2 μm to 400 μm (0·002 to 0·4 mm), with magnifications of up to × 5000.

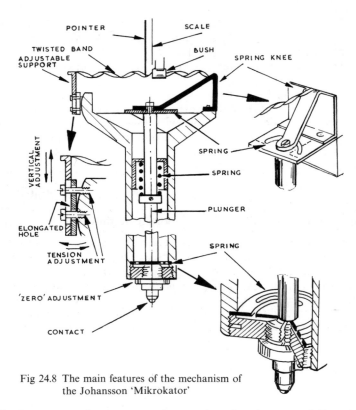

Fig 24.8 The main features of the mechanism of
the Johansson 'Mikrokator'

The instrument is set to zero by moving the plunger axially relative
to the body of the instrument, and is equipped with limit indicators. It
is calibrated by adjusting the length of the twisted band and the tension on it.

24.1.5 Optical comparators. As optical comparators utilise the regular
reflection of light at plane surfaces, the laws of regular reflection will be
recalled at this point. When a ray of light falls on a polished metal or
glass surface it is reflected in a single definite direction, but when it falls
on a sheet of white paper it is scattered in all directions. When reflection is in one direction, it is called *regular* or *specular reflection*, and
that in all directions is called *diffuse reflection*. Diffuse reflection can be
regarded as reflection at small regular reflectors that are arranged in a
random way.

The laws of regular reflection (see fig. 24.9).
   1. The incident ray and the reflected ray lie in one plane which is
      perpendicular to the reflective surface at the point of incidence.

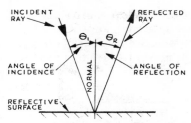

Fig 24.9 Regular reflection of light

2. The angle between the incident ray and the normal to the reflective surface at the point of incidence (called the angle of incidence, θ_1) is equal to the angle between the reflected ray and the normal (called the angle of reflection θ_R).

The effect of rotating a plane reflective surface (the optical lever). Figure 24.10 shows a ray incident at a plane reflective surface at an angle θ, and the reflected ray '1'. If the reflective surface is rotated from position '1', through an angle α to position '2', the normal to it is also rotated through angle α. If the incident ray is not moved, its angle of incidence is increased from θ to $\theta + \alpha$ as a result of rotating the reflective surface, and the angle of reflection is increased from θ to $\theta + \alpha$, causing it to rotate through an angle of 2α (see fig. 24.10); the reflected

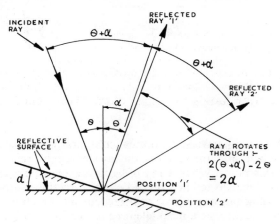

Fig 24.10 The optical lever

ray is therefore rotated through an angle twice that through which the reflective surface is rotated. The arrangement described is called an *optical lever*, and is a weightless lever system.

Optical comparators include an optical lever system, either to cause a spot of light to move relative to a fixed scale, or to cause the image of a scale to move past a datum line.

Figure 24.11 illustrates the principle of operation of a comparator in which a spot of light moves relative to a fixed scale. Movement of the plunger causes the mirror to rotate through a small angle, and the spot

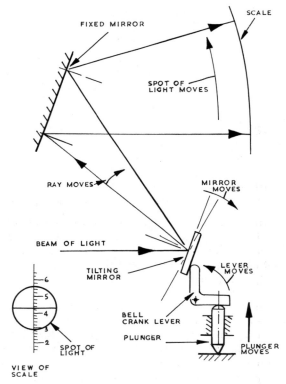

Fig 24.11 Principle of operation of an optical comparator (moving spot type)

of light to move relative to the scale on a curved screen; the magnification being obtained by the optical leverage and the distance from the point of incidence on the mirror to the screen (the bell crank lever may introduce an initial mechanical leverage if required).

Figure 24.12 illustrates the principle of operation of a comparator in which the image of a scale moves past a datum line. The light source is located for convenience at one side, and the beam is directed through the graticule aperture by a prism. It is directed by a 'fixed' mirror on to a tilting mirror, which is arranged so that the beam is reflected back along a slightly different path to reach the eyepiece after passing

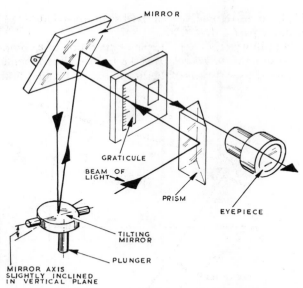

Fig 24.12 Principle of operation of an optical comparator (moving scale-image type)

through the datum aperture which is adjacent to the graticule aperture. Movement of the plunger causes movement of the image of the scale relative to the datum. This instrument is set to zero reading by altering the inclination of the 'fixed' mirror so that a different part of the scale is incident at the tilting mirror.

24.1.6 Pneumatic comparators. Pneumatic comparators indicate small variations of size by measuring their effect upon the flow of air through the comparator system. The flow of air through the system depends upon the size of the outlet jet which is controlled either by the gap between the gauging head and the workpiece surface, or by the movement of a plunger that contacts the workpiece; most models can operate using either method, but the former is preferred because there is no contact between the gauging head and the workpiece and therefore no risk of damage to the workpiece surface (these two methods are illustrated in fig. 24.13).

The two basic types of pneumatic comparator in use can be classified as (*a*) those that use the variation in back pressure caused by change of exit jet size, and (*b*) those that use variation of air flow rate caused by change of exit jet size.

(*a*) *Comparators that indicate variation of size by measuring variation of back pressure.* In these comparators, air is passed at a controlled pressure H, through a control jet on to a second chamber and on to

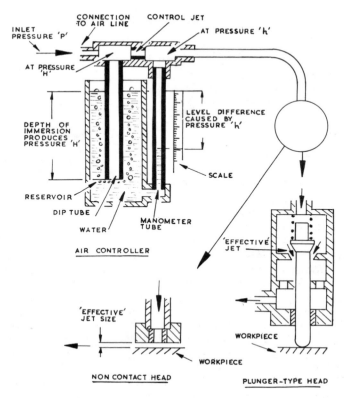

Fig 24.13 Pneumatic comparator ('Solex' type)

the measuring head, leaving it through the measuring jet. The 'effective' measuring jet size depends upon the size of the workpiece being
measured, and by careful selection of the control jet size and the
measuring jet size, small variations of the size of the latter will produce
a linear variation of the pressure h in the second chamber. The variation of pressure h can therefore be used to indicate variation of the
workpiece size, but the system must be such that the pressure H is
rigorously controlled.

In the *Solex* system (see fig. 24.13), the pressure H is controlled
by the controller unit, which includes a water reservoir, into which
a dip tube connected to the entry chamber is introduced. The depth
of immersion of this dip tube is adjusted to control pressure H in
the entry chamber, and provided the air line pressure p is greater
than the required pressure H, excess air will escape in the form of
bubbles (shown in fig. 24.13), and pressure H will be controlled. Varia-

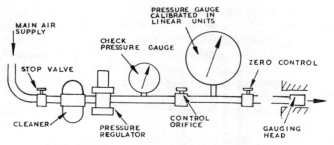

Fig 24.14 Pneumatic comparator ('Mercer' type)

tion of the back pressure *h* in the second chamber will cause the
water level in the manometer tube connected to the reservoir to
rise or fall, and the difference between the water levels in the reservoir and the manometer tube will indicate the variation of workpiece
size.

It has already been stated that the air escapes through the measuring jet in the measuring head. Fig. 24.13 shows the two basic types of
measuring head. The non-contact type includes a jet, but the 'effective'
jet size is the gap between the measuring head and the workpiece
surface; the measuring head can be similar in shape to a plug gauge or
gap gauge, but it is important to note that the gauging is not done by
contact, as in the case of conventional plug gauges and gap gauges.
The measuring head may be of the plunger type, and the measuring jet
size controlled by the plunger movement as shown in the diagram.

The size variation may be indicated directly by pressure gauges,
calibrated in linear units. The *Mercer Air Gauge*, which is shown in fig.
24.14 is typical of this type of pneumatic comparator, and can be used
with non-contact or plunger-type measuring heads.

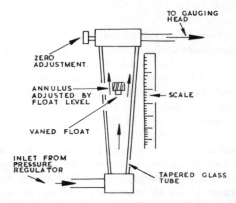

Fig 24.15 Pneumatic comparator (air flow type)

(*b*) *Comparators that indicate variation of size by measuring the variation of the rate of air flow through the system.* The basic measuring circuit of this type of comparator is shown in fig. 24.15. Controlled air is passed into a tapered glass tube and on to the gauging head, from which it escapes through the measuring jet. The rate of flow through the system depends upon the 'effective' jet size (the measuring heads used being similar to those used in the previous examples), and is indicated by the level of a float inside the tapered glass tube. The float will take up a position that produces the required annulus size to suit the flow rate that is required by the effective jet; the vanes on the float cause it to rotate and remain stable.

Variations of both types of pneumatic comparator are available for the simultaneous checking of several dimensions.

24.1.7 Electrical Comparators. Electrical comparators are based upon a Wheatstone bridge circuit. Figure 24.16 illustrates the Wheatstone bridge for a d.c. system; this consists of an arrangement of four resistances, R_1, R_2, R_3, and R_4, wired in a diamond-shaped circuit and

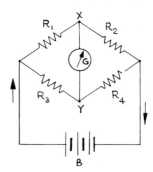

Fig 24.16 A Wheatstone bridge circuit

connected to a battery 'B'; a galvanometer 'G' is connected to X and Y. When the resistances are such that no current flows through the galvanometer, the bridge is said to be balanced, and $R_1 R_4 = R_2 R_3$; the a.c. bridge is similar to the d.c. bridge. Figure 24.17 shows the basic system of an electrical comparator; the plunger causes the iron armature in the magnetic field of the inductor coils to change the inductance value, and this is measured by the a.c. bridge circuit.

24.1.8 Fluid displacement comparators. Figure 24.18 illustrates this type of comparator. The capillary tube is of fine bore, and is attached to a chamber of relatively large cross-sectional area to which is attached a diaphragm which is deflected by pressure from the plunger; the chamber is filled with fluid. The ratio of the diameters of the cham-

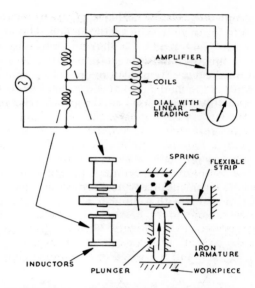

Fig 24.17 Basic system for an electrical comparator

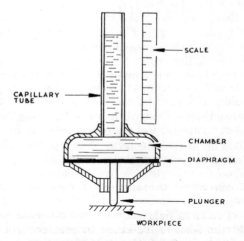

Fig 24.18 Fluid displacement comparator

ber and the capillary tube is such that a small movement of the plunger causes a large change in the level of the fluid in the capillary tube, and the change in level is read off from the scale as plunger movement. This type of comparator is not very popular because of the errors associated with the effect of temperature upon the level of the fluid, the effect of viscosity of the fluid, and the variation of the deflection of the diaphragm caused by its increased resistance with distance.

24.2 Optical projectors

Optical projectors are used to check profile gauges, hobs, screw threads, gears etc. by projecting the image of their profile on to a screen, where it can be compared with a master profile or measured.

The optical arrangement of a typical projector is shown in fig. 24.19. Projectors are available with a number of configurations that include

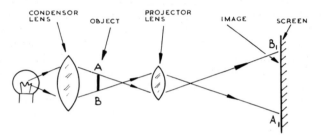

Fig 24.19 Optical system for projector

projection on to a screen that is behind the workpiece, on to a screen that is adjacent to the workpiece, on to a screen that is horizontal and on to a screen that is in front of the workpiece, slightly inclined to the horizontal and at 'desk' height. This latter type is very convenient to use, especially when features such as thread angles are to be measured. Optical projectors enable the profile as a whole to be examined but they tend to be large because optical magnification depends upon distance.

24.3 Optical flats

An optical flat is a thick circular disc of glass or fused quartz with two parallel flat surfaces. It is used either on its own or as part of an instrument called an interferometer to determine the accuracy, parallelism and distance between surfaces of a suitably high standard such as those of a slip gauge; in all these applications a phenomenon called *interference* of light waves is used.

24.3.1 The interference of light waves. Wave theory states that light is transmitted by vibrations in the ether; these vibrations being at right angles to the direction of the transmission as illustrated in fig. 24.20.

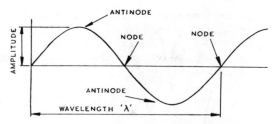

Fig 24.20 Light wave nomenclature

The *wavelength* is related to the frequency of the vibrations, and produces the sensation of *colour*, and the *amplitude* controls the *intensity*.

If a ray is split so that it consists of two rays, one travelling behind the other, the resulting intensity will be different from that of the separate rays; this difference is called *interference*. If the two rays are *in phase* (the positive antinodes coinciding), the resulting intensity is greater than that of each of the separate rays, and the interference is said to be *constructive*; if the rays are not in phase, the resulting intensity is less, and the interference is said to be *destructive*. If the two rays are out of phase so that the positive antinodes coincide with the negative antinodes, they will cancel each other out, and so produce a condition of darkness (*total interference*). This is illustrated in fig. 24.21. Interference is produced in practice by making one of the rays travel a greater distance than the other before they are reunited.

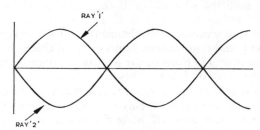

Fig 24.21 Light interference

If ray '2' in Fig. 24.21 is caused to travel a further distance equal to λ, there will be a further phase change, producing another condition of total interference, and so on. Since distance can be related to phase change, and hence to λ, interference can be used as a very accurate method of measurement of length. Interference is now used to define the metre in terms of the wavelength of light radiation, instead of defining it as the distance between two lines scribed on a length of metal.

24.3.2 The production of interference using an optical flat. Figure 24.22 shows an optical flat that is inclined at a small angle to a reflective flat

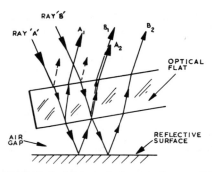

Fig 24.22 Optical flat producing interference of light

surface so as to enclose a small wedge-shaped air gap (the angle is shown exaggerated); a beam of monochromatic light, two rays of which are shown, is directed at the optical flat (a monochromatic light is of single wavelength, and is used so that the interference fringes will be sharp). Consider ray A: it will be partly reflected at the top surface of the optical flat, but most of it will pass through the optical flat, until it reaches the lower surface of the optical flat where part of it will be reflected (ray A_1) and the rest will pass through the air gap until it is reflected by the reflective surface (ray A_2). Ray B will behave in a similar way.

The part of ray A that is reflected from the reflective surface (ray A_2) will interfere with the part of ray B that is reflected from the lower surface of the optical flat (ray B_1). If the air gap below this point is equal to $\frac{\lambda}{4}$, the difference between the distances travelled by ray A_2 and ray B_1 will be $\frac{\lambda}{2}$, and total interference will be produced (indicated by a dark line, called an interference *fringe*). At every point where the air

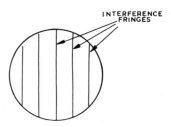

Fig 24.23 Interference fringes produced by an optical flat

gap is increased by $\frac{\lambda}{2}$, an interference fringe will be seen, as indicated by fig. 24.23; it should be noted that the fringes are produced here by the inclination of the optical flat and not by error in the reflective surface beneath it (since the latter has already been specified as a *flat* surface).

24.3.3 The study of slip gauge surfaces using an optical flat. If an optical flat is placed on a slip gauge and viewed using a monochromatic light source, the shape of its upper surface will be indicated by the shape of the interference fringes, as illustrated by fig. 24.24.

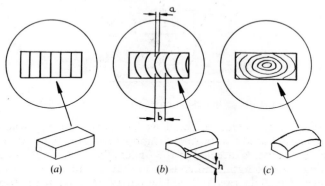

Fig 24.24 The study of a slip gauge surface using an optical flat

Figure 24.24(*a*) shows the fringes produced when the slip gauge surface is perfectly flat. Fringes are produced by the inclination of the optical flat; they are straight and parallel because the surface being studied is perfectly flat.

Figure 24.24 (*b*) shows the fringes produced when the slip gauge is not flat. In this example the slip gauge is 'ridged' as shown in the illustration. The variation in the distance between the lower surface of the optical flat and the upper surface of the slip gauge causes the fringes to be deformed. Here the 'bowing' of the fringes 'a' is directly related to the shape of the slip gauge (see fig. 24.24(*b*)); the actual value of 'h' can be determined by comparing 'a' with the fringe spacing 'b' – the latter representing a change in height of $\frac{\lambda}{2}$:

$$\frac{a}{b} = \frac{h}{\lambda/2} \qquad \therefore d = \frac{a}{b} \times \frac{\lambda}{2}$$

Figure 24.24(*c*) shows the appearance of the fringes when the surface is 'peaked' or 'valleyed'; the fringes can be read like a geographical contour map – each fringe indicating a change of 'level' of $\frac{\lambda}{2}$.

The fringes do not immediately indicate if the error is concave or convex, but if a very slight pressure is applied to the optical flat, the fringes will tend to move towards the point of pressure application if the surface is convex, and away from it if concave.

24.3.4 The study of the parallelism of slip gauge surfaces. If the surfaces are suitably flat, their parallelism can be checked by placing the slip

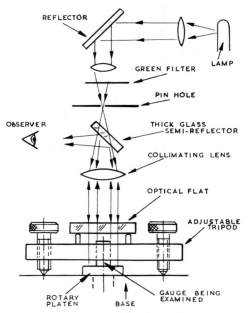

Fig 24.25 Slip gauge interferometer

gauge on an accurately produced reflective surface (called a 'platen'), beneath an optical flat, so that the fringes from the slip gauge surface can be compared with those from the platen. This is usually done using an interferometer; this instrument is like a low-powered microscope and enables the fringes to be clearly seen; it also incorporates a platen that can be rotated about a vertical axis, while the optical flat is fixed (see fig. 24.25). This instrument can also be used to check the flatness of the surfaces.

Figure 24.26(a) shows the appearance of the fringes when the slip

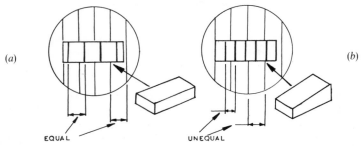

Fig 24.26 The study of the parallelism of slip gauge surfaces using an optical flat

gauge surfaces are parallel (in this case the top surface of the slip gauge will be parallel to the platen surface). It will be seen that the fringe spaces from the slip gauge and those from the platen are equal.

Figure 24.26(*b*) shows the appearance of the fringes when the slip gauge surfaces are not parallel (in this case the top surface of the slip gauge will not be parallel to the platen surface). It will be seen that the fringe spacings from the slip gauge and those from the platen are not equal.

When the slip gauge surfaces are more than about 25 mm apart (i.e. the slip gauge 'length' exceeds 25 mm), the fringes from the platen are not bright enough to be used for comparison purposes, and so a method must be used whereby only those from the top surface of the gauge are used. However, if only the number of fringes from the top surface of the gauge are considered, the method must eliminate the effect of the inclination of the optical flat, and the inclination of the platen axis (causing the platen surface to be inclined). The procedure for checking the parallelism of the gauge surface using this method is as follows:

1. With the slip gauge in position on the platen, count the number of fringes from its surface (F_1).

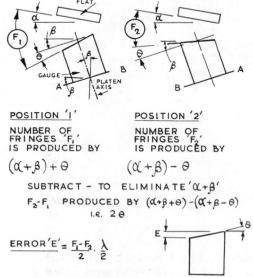

PLATEN INCLINATION 'β'
OPTICAL FLAT INCLINATION 'α'
GAUGE PARALLISM ERROR 'θ'

POSITION '1'

NUMBER OF FRINGES 'F_1' IS PRODUCED BY

$$(\alpha + \beta) + \theta$$

POSITION '2'

NUMBER OF FRINGES 'F_2' IS PRODUCED BY

$$(\alpha + \beta) - \theta$$

SUBTRACT – TO ELIMINATE '$\alpha + \beta$'

$F_2 - F_1$ PRODUCED BY $(\alpha + \beta + \theta) - (\alpha + \beta - \theta)$

i.e. 2θ

$$\text{ERROR '}E' = \frac{F_1 - F_2}{2} \cdot \frac{\lambda}{2}$$

Fig 24.27 The principle of parallelism examination by counting the number of fringes

2. With the slip gauge still on the platen, rotate the platen through 180° and count the number of fringes from the surface of the slip gauge (F_2).
3. Determine the error in the 'thickness' of the gauge from one end to the other, E from:

$$E = \frac{F_1 - F_2}{2} \times \frac{\lambda}{2}$$

The proof of this method is shown in fig. 24.27.

It will be seen in figs. 24.26(*a*) and 24.26(*b*) that the fringes from the slip gauge and those from the platen are not in line in the examples shown (in fact, alignment rarely occurs); this non-alignment is used when the 'length' of a slip gauge is determined absolutely (this is, by methods other than comparison with existing gauges). The absolute measurement of slip gauges is beyond the scope of this book.

24.3.5 The use of an optical flat as a comparator. The 'length' of a slip gauge can be checked against that of a calibration grade slip gauge using the arrangement shown in fig. 24.28.

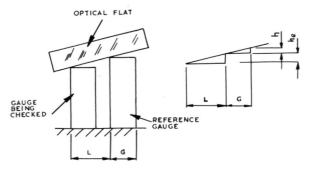

Fig 24.28 The optical flat as a comparator

From the fig.:

$$\frac{h}{G} = \frac{h_e}{L}$$

$$\therefore \quad h_e = h \times \frac{L}{G}$$

Let the number of fringes from the calibration grade slip gauge = n. Then $h = n \times \frac{\lambda}{2}$ and the difference between the 'length' of the calibration gauge, and the gauge being checked, h_e is given by:

$$h_e = \left(n \times \frac{\lambda}{2} \right) \frac{L}{G}$$

24.4 Collimation

A collimator is an optical instrument that can be used to measure small angular inclinations as illustrated in fig. 24.29. Light from a point source at the focus of a collimating objective lens is refracted by the lens as a parallel beam of light and is incident at a reflective surface. If the reflective surface is at right angles to the beam the rays that make up the beam will retrace their paths and the image will coincide with the object as shown in fig. 24.29(*a*). If the reflective surface is slightly inclined as shown in fig. 24.29(*b*) the rays will not retrace their

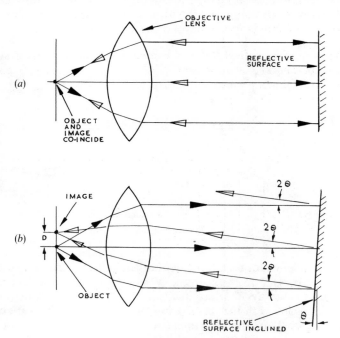

Fig 24.29 The principle of collimation

paths, and the image will be formed in the same plane as the object, but at distance 'D' from it. Distance 'D' depends upon the focal length of the lens and upon the angle of inclination of the reflective surface, and therefore can be used as a measure of the angle of inclination. The distance between the lens and the reflective surface does not effect distance 'D', but if the angle of inclination and this distance are large, some (and in extreme cases, all) of the rays will not re-enter the lens—the ray shown at the top of fig. 24.29(*b*) does not re-enter the lens after being reflected. The maximum distance between the lens and the reflective surface is, however, limited by the power of the light source used, because the image must be bright enough to be clearly seen.

The arrangement shown in fig. 24.29 is the basis of the more practical arrangement used in the *Autocollimator* and the *Angle Dekkor*.

24.4.1 The Autocollimator. The autocollimator is a combination of a telescope and a collimator; the optical arrangement of a typical autocollimator is shown in fig. 24.30. The light is directed by the condenser lens and the semi-reflector at the target wires that are at the focus of

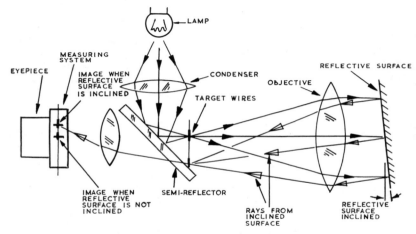

Fig 24.30 The topical arrangement of a typical autocollimator

the objective lens; these rays pass on to be refracted by the objective lens as a parallel beam that is incident at the reflective surface, which reflects the rays back to the eyepiece. When the reflective surface is at right angles to the rays that are incident at it, the image of the target wires will coincide with the target wires, but if the reflective surface is inclined by a small amount, the image will be seen alongside the target wires, and the distance between them will indicate the angle of incidence. Figure 24.31 gives a general impression of the instrument, and shows the levelling base with which it is usually used.

When the autocollimator is used, a datum is first obtained at which the image of the target wires coincides with the target wires; the reflective surface is then repositioned as required to make the check, and the distance between the target wires and the image as seen through the eyepiece is used to indicate the angle of inclination—the instrument is graduated so that the angle of inclination can be read off

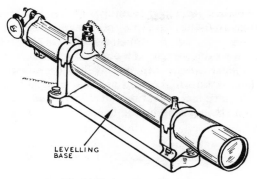

Fig 24.31 An autocollimator

directly. Figure 24.32 is a diagrammatic representation of the autocollimator, reflective surface and the view through the eyepiece. It will be
seen that the target wires are at right angles; this is so that inclinations in both the horizontal plane and the vertical plane can be

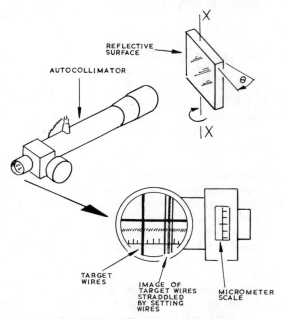

Fig 24.32 Reading an autocollimator

measured—the eyepiece being rotated through 90° when inclinations
in the vertical plane are to be measured. When a more accurate reading is required, the setting wires are adjusted so that they straddle the

target wires and the micrometer reading is noted. The setting wires are then adjusted so that they straddle the image of the target wires (as shown in fig. 24.32) and the micrometer reading is noted, the difference between the two readings being the angle of inclination.

Figure 24.33 illustrates how the autocollimator is used to check the flatness of a horizontal surface such as the top surface of a lathe bed. The reflector carriage incorporating the reflective surface is positioned at station 1 and the autocollimator lined up with it. The part of the

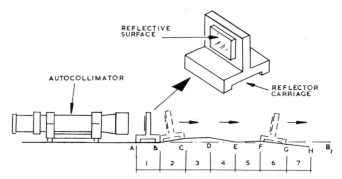

Fig 24.33 Using an autocollimator to check the flatness of a horizontal surface

lathe bed surface from 'A' to 'B' therefore is taken as the datum (line A to B_1 on fig. 24.33). The reflector carriage is moved along the surface in steps equal to its base length and a reading taken at each stage. A graph of the contour of the surface can be plotted and the linear errors from a true plane determined.

24.4.2 The Angle Dekkor. This application of the collimator, shown in fig. 24.34, is similar to the autocollimator, but includes a lapped base to which the barrel of the instrument is attached. The base can be used simply as a support for the instrument (in a similar way to the levelling base of the autocollimator) or as a datum face on which the part being examined is placed. The instrument includes an illuminated vertical scale whose image is formed at right angles to a similar scale in the field of the eyepiece, as shown in fig. 24.35. This system allows inclinations in the vertical plane and in the horizontal plane to be determined at the same time. The Angle Dekkor is not as sensitive as the autocollimator but is useful for a number of applications at short distance.

Figure 24.34 illustrates the Angle Dekkor being used to check the angle between one face of the groove in a Vee-Block and the base of the Vee-Block. The required angle (obtained by using a pile of angle

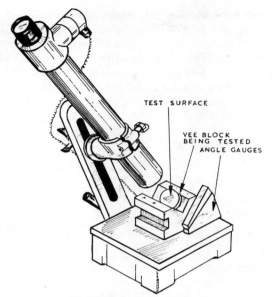

Fig 24.34 The Angle Dekkor

slips, see Section 24.4.3) is used as the datum, and the angle of the face being checked is compared with it. If the part being checked is not reflective enough, a suitably accurate reflective surface is attached to it with grease.

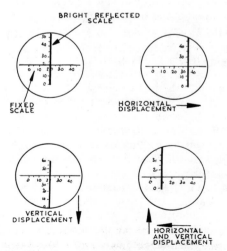

Fig 24.35 Views through the eyepiece of an Angle Dekkor

24.4.3 Angle slips (or combination angle gauges). The modern angle slips were devised at the National Physical Laboratory by Dr. G. A. Tomlinson in 1941, and consist of a number of hardened wedge-shaped blocks that are lapped so that they can be wrung together like ordinary slip gauges. They can, however, be wrung so that the angles between their surfaces can be added or subtracted, enabling a large number of angles to be obtained with a small number of gauges.

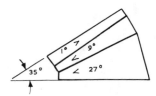

Fig 24.36 Building up an angle using angle slips

Figure 24.36 illustrates how a 35° angle can be obtained using three gauges in the set (27° + 9° − 1° = 35°). A typical modern set of angle slips is as follows:

degrees	1°	3°	9°	27°	41°
minutes	1′	3′	9′	27′	
fractional minutes	0·1′	0·3′	0·5′		

This enables angles from 0° to 81° 40·9′ in steps of 0·1′ to be obtained; by the addition of a second 9° block the range can be extended to 90° and by the addition of a square block it can be further extended to 360°. The steps can be reduced to 0·05′ if a block of that size if also included in the set.

Summary

1   A comparator is an instrument that indicates the variation of a size from a datum to which the instrument is set.
2   Comparators can be classified as (*a*) high precision and (*b*) general work comparators.
3   High precision comparators are used to calibrate slip gauges and end bars.
4   General work comparators are used either as an alternative to direct measurement or as an alternative to limit gauges.
5   General work comparators can be classified as: mechanical, optical, pneumatic, electrical, and fluid displacement types.

6 Optical projectors are used to check profiles by projecting their image on to a screen where it is compared with a master profile or is measured.

7 An optical flat is a thick circular disc of glass or fused quartz with flat, parallel surfaces, and is used for measurement involving interference.

8 Interference is the change of the intensity of light caused by light rays being out of phase. It enables length to be related to the wavelength of light.

9 Slip gauges can be checked for 'length' accuracy, flatness, and parallelism of the surfaces by interferometry.

10 Collimation can be used to measure small angular inclinations. The Autocollimator and the Angle Dekkor are instruments that use the collimation principle.

11 Angle slips are hardened, wedge-shaped blocks that can be wrung together to produce a wide range of angles.

Questions

Set A

1 What are the magnification methods used in comparators for fine measurement? Discuss fully the advantages and disadvantages of the various methods used.

2 Describe the principle of operation of a pneumatic comparator and describe the types of gauge-head that are used.

3 Describe an autocollimator, its field of view and its accessories, and give detailed examples of a number of purposes for which it can be used.

4 Show clearly what is meant by interferencce of light. How does the nature of the light-source affect the phenomenon? How may interference be used in length measurement, flatness measurement, and in the measurement of parallelism?

5 Show clearly, with the aid of sketches, the light-ray path differences which result when an optical flat lies at an angle to a lapped surface, so that a wedge-shaped air gap is present between the two surfaces.

6 Sketch the interference bands that are present when a flat is in contact with (a) flat, (b) convex, and (c) concave surfaces, and show how convexity can be distinguished from concavity.

7 Give an account of one type of comparator with which you are familiar. What are the disadvantages of using a comparator of high sensitivity on work which has a wide tolerance?

8 Describe briefly how the angle of a Vee block could be measured using angle slips and an Angle Dekkor.

9 (a) Explain, with the aid of simple sketches, the basic principles of
      (i) any type of pneumatic comparator
      (ii) any type of electric comparator
      Details of the actual instruments are not required.
   (b) State two advantages of each of the above gauging systems.

Set B (questions requiring further study)
10 Describe briefly, by means of sketches where necessary, how to
    check the following features before approving the purchase of a
    second-hand comparator:
       (a) the flatness of the platen
       (b) the sensitivity
       (c) the repeatability
       (d) the general condition.
11 Steel rollers produced in a centreless grinding machine have a
    tendency to be lobed. Explain, with the aid of a sketch how the
    roundness of the rollers may be checked using a pneumatic gauging
    unit.
12 Explain how the wavelength of light is used in the calibration
    of slip gauges with reference to an absolute length interferometer.
13 (a) Explain, with the aid of a sketch how a magnification of 2 is
    obtained by means of an optical lever.
    (b) Show the arrangement whereby a mechanical-optical com-
    parator can produce a magnification of 2000 : 1.
14 Explain how an alignment telescope can be used to check the
    alignment of three bearings spaced at two-metre intervals.
15 Describe a method of calibrating a polygon with 8 sides, by means
    of two precision autocollimators.
16 (a) Show, by means of a line diagram, the basic magnification
    principle of a simple optical lever.
    (b) State four advantages of using spring steel strips in a com-
    parator.
17 Explain how parallel strip hinges and a single strip hinge with a
    reflector may be incorporated in metrology equipment of high
    magnification.

Chapter 25
The Study of Surface Texture

25.1
The surface of parts produced by casting, working, and powder metallurgy will have irregularities associated with the manufacture of the dies etc. used in their production, and with the production process itself; irregularities will still be present after the parts have been machined.

25.1.1. Surface irregularities are of three types, as illustrated by fig. 25.1 which shows the profile of a nominally flat surface.

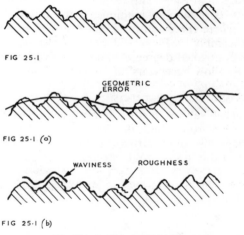

FIG 25·1

FIG 25·1 (*a*)

FIG 25·1 (*b*)

Fig 25.1 Surface irregularities

There is a general error, known as *geometric* (*or form*) *error* (illustrated separately in fig. 25.1(*a*). This error can easily be detected by straight edge, dial indicator etc.; it is caused by faulty machine alignment, faulty machine slides, a worn chuck or cutter spindle, worn bearings, incorrect machine setting and so on.

Superimposed upon this error (or upon an otherwise 'true' surface) there are two further sets of irregularities (shown separately in fig. 25.1(*b*)) that together tend to form a pattern or texture on the surface; this pattern is known as *surface texture*. The larger of these irregularities is known as *waviness*, and is caused by spindle or cutter deflection, machine vibrations, chatter, warping strains etc. Waviness has, in turn, irregularities superimposed on it known as *roughness*; roughness can be defined as 'irregularities in the surface texture which are inherent in the production process, but excluding waviness and form errors'.

25.2

The principal reasons for controlling surface texture are:
   (*a*) To reduce the initial wear of parts that are in contact (the 'running in').
   (*b*) To improve the fatigue resistance (surface irregularities are the seat of fatigue failure).
   (*c*) To allow fine geometric and dimensional tolerances to be held (this cannot be done if the surfaces involved have irregularities that are nearly as large as the tolerance allowed on their positions).
   (*d*) To reduce frictional wear (smooth contacting surfaces will wear less rapidly than rough surfaces).
   (*e*) To reduce corrosion by minimising the number and depth of crevices, where corrosion proceeds at a high rate.

This does not imply that a perfectly smooth surface is always ideal; for example, a controlled degree of roughness is usually required in a cylinder bore to allow 'reservoirs' of oil to be present.

25.3

The assessment of surface texture quality is the subject of British Standard BS. 1134, from which the definitions and the numerical assessment methods discussed in this chapter have been taken. Some of the terms used in this study are illustrated in fig. 25.2.

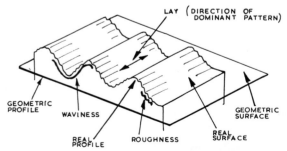

Fig 25.2 Illustration of some terms used in the study of surface texture

25.4 The study of surface texture

Examination methods are considered in more detail in section 25.6, where the methods are grouped into (*a*) optical methods, (*b*) tactual methods and (*c*) methods that use a stylus. The latter method can be used to produce a trace which gives a picture of the surface profile, and which can be used to produce a numerical evaluation of the texture (some machines produce a numerical evaluation without the need to produce a trace). Numerical evaluation of texture is useful when a known process is to be controlled; but it must be emphasised that it does not give a complete assessment of texture, because texture is three-dimensional and the numerical evaluation methods are based on two dimensions only. Furthermore, surfaces with quite different textures can have very similar numerical assessment values.

25.5 The numerical evaluation of surface texture

The most commonly used numerical value is the arithmetic average deviation of the surface from a datum, obtained by passing a stylus across the surface in a direction approximately at right angles to the lay, if the surface texture has a directional quality; the value so obtained is termed the R_a value. Figure 25.3 illustrates the graphical method used to determine the R_a value. The R_a value is usually quoted in μm units (1 μm = 0·000001 m, i.e. 0·001 mm), and the values specified on a drawing or similar specification should be selected from the preferred values shown in Table 25.1, which also shows the corresponding μ in values (1 μ in = 0·000001 in) because the reader may be familiar with equipment that produces μ in values, and the series of

Table 25.1 Preferred R_a values

| Nominal R_a values | | Roughness grade number |
μm	μ in	
50	2000	N 12
25	1000	N 11
12·5	500	N 10
6·3	250	N 9
3·2	125	N 8
1·6	63	N 7
0·8	32	N 6
0·4	16	N 5
0·2	8	N 4
0·1	4	N 3
0·05	2	N 2
0·025	1	N 1
0·0125	0·5	—

GRAPHICAL DETERMINATION OF R_a VALUE
(FOR NOMINALLY FLAT SURFACE)

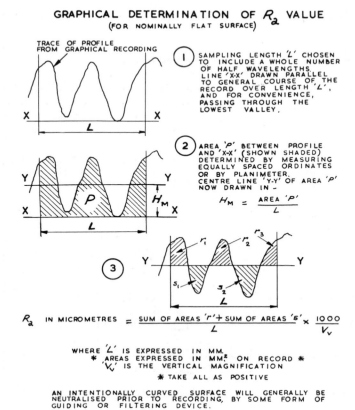

TRACE OF PROFILE FROM GRAPHICAL RECORDING

① SAMPLING LENGTH 'L' CHOSEN TO INCLUDE A WHOLE NUMBER OF HALF WAVELENGTHS. LINE 'X-X' DRAWN PARALLEL TO GENERAL COURSE OF THE RECORD OVER LENGTH 'L', AND FOR CONVENIENCE, PASSING THROUGH THE LOWEST VALLEY.

② AREA 'P' BETWEEN PROFILE AND 'X-X' (SHOWN SHADED) DETERMINED BY MEASURING EQUALLY SPACED ORDINATES OR BY PLANIMETER. CENTRE LINE 'Y-Y' OF AREA 'P' NOW DRAWN IN –

$$H_M = \frac{AREA \; 'P'}{L}$$

③

$$R_a \; \text{IN MICROMETRES} = \frac{\text{SUM OF AREAS } 'r' + \text{SUM OF AREAS } 's'}{L} \times \frac{1000}{V_v}$$

WHERE 'L' IS EXPRESSED IN MM.
✱ AREAS EXPRESSED IN MM.² ON RECORD ✱
'V_v' IS THE VERTICAL MAGNIFICATION

✱ TAKE ALL AS POSITIVE

AN INTENTIONALLY CURVED SURFACE WILL GENERALLY BE NEUTRALISED PRIOR TO RECORDING, BY SOME FORM OF GUIDING OR FILTERING DEVICE.

Fig 25.3

roughness grade numbers extracted from International Standard ISO/R I302 (Technical drawings: methods of indicating surface texture on drawings). Roughness grade numbers may be used on drawings to avoid misinterpretation of numerical values.

Table 25.2 shows typical surface roughness values produced by common production processes.

25.5.1. When the depth of irregularities is to be taken into account, an alternative numerical assessment method is used that takes into account the 'peak-to-valley' height; the system recommended in BS 1134 avoids exceptional 'peak-to-valley' heights by taking an average of ten values (the value so obtained is termed the R_Z value). Figure 25.4 illustrates the graphical method used to determine the R_Z value.

Table 25.2

SURFACE ROUGHNESS VALUES PRODUCED BY TYPICAL COMMON PRODUCTION PROCESSES
(AFTER BS 1134)

KEY   ■ AVERAGE APPLICATION   ▨ LESS FREQUENT APPLICATION

PROCESS	ROUGHNESS VALUES (μm R_a)												
	50	25	12.5	6.3	3.2	1.6	0.8	0.4	0.2	0.1	0.05	0.025	0.0125
SAND CASTING	▨	■	▨										
HOT ROLLING	▨	■	▨										
FORGING		▨	■	■	▨								
PERMANENT MOULD CASTING				▨	■	▨							
INVESTMENT CASTING				▨	■	■	▨						
EXTRUDING				▨	■	■	▨						
COLD ROLLING, DRAW^{G}				▨	■	■	▨	▨					
DIE CASTING					▨	■	▨						
FLAME CUTTING	▨	■	▨										
SAWING		▨	■	■	▨								
PLANING, SHAPING		▨	■	■	■	▨							
DRILLING			▨	■	■	▨							
CHEMICAL MILLING			▨	■	■	▨							
ELECTRO-DISCHARGE MACHINING			▨	■	■	▨							
MILLING		▨	▨	■	■	■	▨	▨					
REAMING, BROACHING				▨	■	■	▨						
GRINDING				▨	■	■	■	■	■	▨	▨		
HONING						▨	■	■	■	▨	▨		
LAPPING							▨	■	■	▨	▨	▨	

GRAPHICAL DETERMINATION OF R_z VALUE

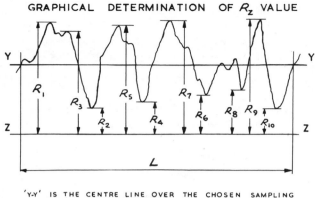

'Y-Y' IS THE CENTRE LINE OVER THE CHOSEN SAMPLING LENGTH (SEE FIG 25·3)
'Z-Z' IS ARBITRARY BASE LINE DRAWN PARALLEL TO 'Y-Y'
FIVE HIGHEST PEAKS AND FIVE DEEPEST VALLEYS
CONVENIENTLY MEASURED FROM 'Z-Z'

$$R_z = \frac{(R_1 + R_3 + \cdots R_9) - (R_2 + R_4 + \cdots R_{10})}{5}$$

Fig 25.4

25.6 The methods used to study surface texture

The methods used can be grouped as follows (*a*) optical methods, (*b*) tactual methods, and (*c*) methods that use a stylus. The method that is used depends upon the circumstances in which the study is to be made and the information that is required.

25.6.1 Optical methods

(*a*) *By studying in a Direction Normal to the Surface.* The image obtained by studying in this way depends upon the direction of illumination and the surface being studied. Figure 25.5(*a*) illustrates part of a

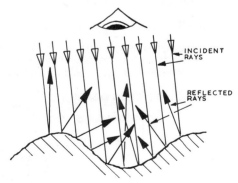

Fig 25.5(*a*) Ray traces when studying the
roughness of a surface

Fig 25.5(*b*) The appearance of
a rough surface

surface section, incident rays and reflected rays; where the rays are reflected back towards the observer's eye the surface will appear bright, and where they are reflected away from the observer's eye it will appear dark. The overall effect will be of lines that indicate the roughness spacing and the direction of the lay (see fig. 25.5(*b*)); this system can be used to compare a surface with that of a 'standard' by viewing them simultaneously—the magnification may be unity (unaided eye) or quite high, as required. This method does not give an indication of the depth of the irregularities.

An indication of the profile and depth of irregularities can be obtained by using a light slit system so that part of the surface is very brightly illuminated as illustrated in fig. 25.6(*a*). Because of the angle of reflection, the profile irregularities will cause the bright band to be distorted, giving an indication of the shape and depth of the irregularities (see fig. 25.6(*b*)); the depth of the irregularities can be measured by including a scale.

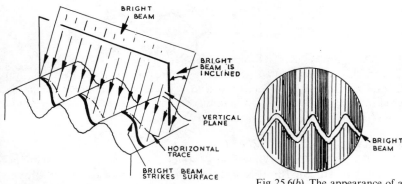

Fig 25.6(*a*) The principle of the light slit system

Fig 25.6(*b*) The appearance of a rough surface using the light slit system

Very smooth surfaces can be studied using a microscope that incorporates an optical flat. The use of an optical flat to check flatness is discussed in section 24.3 and this is an extension of the method. When a suitable high magnification is used, the fringes are seen to be distorted; a good indication of the depth of the irregularities can be obtained by comparing the distortion of the fringes with the fringe spacing, which indicates a depth of $\frac{\lambda}{2}$ (λ = the wavelength of the light radiation used); see fig. 25.7.

(*b*) *By studying a section to show the profile.* In this method the profile is studied by cutting the workpiece as shown in fig. 25.8 so that a direct study can be made. In order to prevent the profile from becoming blurred by burring during the cutting, the surface to be studied is plated before cutting. The depth of the irregularities can be 'mag-

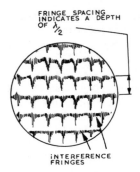

Fig 25.7 Surface irregularities indicated by interference fringes

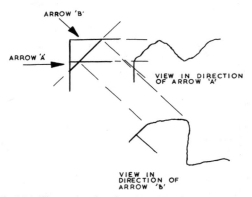

Fig 25.8 The study of surface irregularities by sectioning

nified' by taking the section at an angle and viewing it in the direction of arrow B.

25.6.2 Tactual methods. The surface texture can be gauged in the workshop by comparing it with a standard specimen. In a tactual examination this is done by the examiner using his fingernail as a stylus, passing it firstly across the workpiece and then across the standard, using the sensation of vibrations as a means of comparison. Metal standards are produced by electroforming and plastics standards by moulding; they are supplied in a range of textures, mounted in a suitable holder. This method is inexpensive and convenient to use, and is suitable for examining all but the finest texture because the fingernail is extremely sensitive and thin enough to follow surface irregularities very accurately, and because drawing instructions usually state the roughest surface that is allowed.

25.6.3 Methods that use a stylus. In these methods a stylus head is passed across the surface being examined, and the irregularities are explored by the stylus, which moves at right angles to the surface as it follows the irregularities.

A small surface finish indicator is produced by C. E. Johansson. This instrument is basically a very accurate dial indicator that, when slowly traversed across the surface being studied, indicates the depth of the irregularities. It is usually used to determine the peak-to-valley value (R_Z) but is also used to compare the surface being studied with a standard. Three models are produced, with scale divisions of 0·2, 1 and 2 μm. The instrument is usually traversed across the surface using a feeder that incorporates a micrometer so that distances as well as depths can be observed.

More elaborate instruments are used when the situation demands; these can be classified as (*a*) *mechanical instruments* and (*b*) *electrical instruments.*

The most important mechanical instrument is the 'Tomlinson' Surface Finish Recorder; it was developed in 1939 at the National Physical Laboratory, by Dr. G. A. Tomlinson, and was one of the first to be developed in this country. Figure 25.9 illustrates the principal

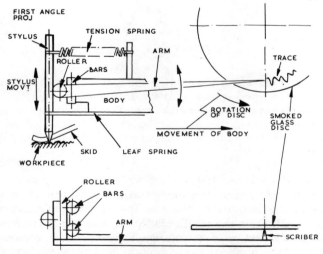

Fig 25.9 The principal features of the 'Tomlinson' surface finish recorder

features of this instrument. The body of the instrument, carrying the stylus head and scriber, is slowly traversed across the surface being examined, causing the stylus to move up and down, as it follows the irregularities; the stylus is held by tension spring against a horizontal roller to which is attached the scriber arm. The scriber produces a trace on the smoked glass plate—the magnification being up to 160 times, and obtained by making the roller of small diameter and the scriber arm long. After the test has been done, the glass plate is removed and the trace is magnified by projection; a typical optical magnification is × 100—this gives a vertical magnification of × 16 000 and a horizontal magnification of × 100 (the only horizontal magnification being the optical magnification). This instrument is inconvenient for industrial use.

Electrical instruments are more convenient for industrial use having a stylus with an electrical amplification system which produces a trace of the irregularities or a direct numerical assessment as required. These more modern instruments have been developed for measuring the surface texture of circular workpieces as well as flat workpieces.

When geometric errors are not to be included in the assessment, the stylus head is supported by a skid as illustrated in fig. 25.10. The size and mass of the skid is standardised in BS 1134.

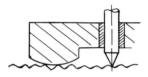

Fig 25.10 A stylus head skid

The length over which the study is made will affect the value of R_a and R_z; if the waviness is to be fully included, the examination must be over at least one waviness wavelength. The length over which the study is made is called the *sampling length* and is standardised by BS 1134 as:

0·08	0·25	0·8	2·5	8·0	25·0	millimetres
0·003	0·01	0·03	0·1	0·3	1·0	inch

Electrical instruments are designed to traverse the surface so that several sampling lengths are included. The recording meter cuts off at the end of each sampling length (called the *meter cut-off length*) and produces an average value for that length; the final value displayed is the average for all such values. The cut-off length is made equal to the corresponding sampling length, and is related to the finishing process used for the surface being examined (see table 25.3)

Many electrical instruments include a filtering device that can be set to exclude large irregularities from the recording. This is important when errors caused by the machine must be excluded so that the process itself can be studied.

Table 25.3

PROCESS DESIGNATIONS AND SUITABLE CUT-OFF VALUES (AFTER BS 1134)

TYPICAL FINISHING PROCESS	DESIGNATN	METER CUT-OFF (mm)				
		0.25	0.8	2.5	8.0	25
MILLING	MILL		■	■	■	
BORING	BORE		■	■	■	
TURNING	TURN		■	■		
GRINDING	GRIND	■	■	■		
PLANING	PLANE			■	■	■
REAMING	REAM		■	■		
BROACHING	BROACH		■	■		
DIAMOND TURNING	D.TURN	■	■			
DIAMOND BORING	D.BORE	■	■			
HONING	HONE	■	■			
LAPPING	LAP	■	■			
SHAPING	SHAPE		■	■	■	
ELECTRO-DISCHARGE MACHINING	EDM	■	■			
DRAWING	DRAW		■	■		
EXTRUDING	EXTRUDE		■	■		

25.7 The specification of surface texture

25.7.1. BS 1134 states that surface texture values should be expressed as numbers of micrometres R_a or R_Z.

For example: 0.4 μm R_a; 6·3 μm R_Z

These examples imply that the value accepted is between zero and the stated value, and that as the meter cut-off value is not stated, it is 0·8 mm.

25.7.2. If a minimum value and a maximum value are to be specified, they should be expressed as:

0·4
0·8 μm R_a or   0·4–0·8 μm R_a
6·3
12·5 μm R_Z or   6·3–12·5 μm R_Z

Again, as the value for the cut-off is not stated, it is implied that it is
0·8 mm.

25.7.3. Should the meter cut-off value be other than 0·8 mm, that value
should be indicated in parentheses following the surface texture value.
   For example: 0·2 μm R_a (2·5)
   The specification (either directly or by implication) of the meter cut-
off to be used in the assessment also denotes that the spacing of the
dominant peaks must not exceed that value.

25.7.4. When it is necessary to specify the direction of the lay, it should
follow that for surface texture, and where applicable, that for the meter
cut-off.
   For example: 6·3 μm R_a lay circular.
   BS 1134 gives six basic lays and appropriate symbols to use on
drawings. These six are: straight lay along the surface, straight lay
across the surface, crossed lay, multidirectional lay, approximately circular lay relative to the centre of the surface, and approximately radial
lay relative to the centre of the surface.

Summary

1   A surface will have irregularities associated with its production.
2   Irregularities can be classified as (*a*) geometric and (*b*) surface
    texture.
3   Surface texture consists of waviness and roughness.
4   Surface texture must be controlled because it affects the perfor-
    mance and the life of components.
5   Surface texture can be examined by (*a*) optical, (*b*) tactual, and (*c*)
    stylus methods.
6   Stylus methods can be used to produce a numerical assessment
    based on either the average surface deviation from a datum, or
    the average depth of irregularities.
7   Numerical assessment values and length over which the assessment
    is made are specified on drawings and instructions.
8   Numerical assessment is only part of the specification of surface
    texture; the shape of the profile and the direction of the lay is also
    important.

Questions

Set A
1   List the factors that produce surface irregularities, and state if they
    produce geometric errors, waviness, or roughness.

2 Produce a tabulated analysis of optical, tactual and stylus surface texture examination methods, in which you indicate the good and the bad features of each.

3 Explain, with the aid of diagrams, why a numerical assessment does not give a complete surface texture specification.

Set B (questions requiring further study)

4 As a project, examine some 'failed' or worn parts and determine if the surface texture had any influence upon the performance or failure of each.

Chapter 26
Dimensional Control

26.1

In the early days of engineering, the mating of parts was achieved by machining one part as nearly as possible to the required size, machining the mating part nearly to size, and then completing its machining, continually offering the other part to it, until the desired relationship was obtained. If it was inconvenient to offer one part to the other part during machining, the final work was done at the bench, by a fitter, who scraped the mating parts until the desired *fit* was obtained, the fitter therefore being a 'fitter' in the literal sense. It is obvious that the two parts would have to remain together, and, in the event of one having to be replaced, the fitting would have to be done all over again. In these days, we expect to be able to purchase a replacement for a broken part, and for it to function correctly without the need for scraping and other fitting operations.

When one part can be used 'off the shelf' to replace another of the same dimension and material specification, the parts are said to be *interchangeable*. A system of interchangeability usually lowers the production costs, as there is no need for an expensive, 'fiddling' operation, and it also benefits the customer in the event of the need to replace worn parts. It also, however, demands that the dimensions of mating parts be specified, and that dimensional variations, due to machine and operator shortcomings, be taken into account. Some form of inspection must be introduced to ensure that the manufacture is controlled; this is particularly important, because dimensional errors may not be revealed until some time has elapsed, and often many miles from the place where the machining was done.

26.2 Tolerance and limits of size

Since it is accepted that it is virtually impossible to manufacture a part without error, or, in the rare event of a part being without error, to be able to proclaim it to be perfect (because the measuring instruments are subject to errors), it is necessary to indicate the maximum errors permitted. The draughtsman must indicate the largest and smallest sizes that can be permitted without the part functioning incorrectly.

The extreme dimensions are called the *limits of size*, and the difference between them is called the *tolerance*. The magnitude of the tolerance depends upon the type of operation involved, the skill of the machinist, the accuracy of the machine, and the size of the part. For a given grade of tolerance, the actual tolerance must be increased with size. The tolerance should be as large as possible, to keep the cost to a minimum.

The method of indicating, on a drawing, the permitted tolerance depends mainly upon the type of operation involved, but local preference must also be taken into account. The following examples will illustrate some of the methods used.

26.2.1 Unilateral limits. These are usually used when the distance between two faces, or the diameter of a hole or shaft is specified. For example, when a diameter is being ground, the machinist would prefer to aim at the largest size permitted, so that, in the event of him reaching a diameter that is just a little larger then the maximum size permitted, he can take another cut, knowing that he can use up the whole of the tolerance before the job is rejected. A draughtsman might dimension a nominal 75-mm diameter shaft as: ϕ 75·012 − 0·012, or, alternatively, as $\phi\,^{75·012}_{75·000}$. The advantage of the first method is that the size to aim at is clearly indicated, but the advantage of the second method is that there is no chance of the operator making an arithmetical error when working out the unspecified limit. Similarly, a nominal 75-mm hole might be dimensioned as ϕ 75 + 0·012, or alternatively as $\phi\,^{75·012}_{75·000}$; the same reasoning applies as for shafts.

26.2.2 Bilateral limits. These are usually applied when, for example, the position of a hole is specified. The machine operator may position the hole nearer the datum or further from the datum than intended, and, as the operator is in no position to change the situation when the hole has been started, he must aim between the two limits of position, so that the maximum error can be made without causing the part to be rejected. The centre distance between two holes would therefore be specified as, for example, $100 \pm 0·02$ mm.

26.2.3 Dimensioning to improve accuracy. When a part is dimensioned as shown in fig. 26.1, the overall length may vary between 545 and 545·90 mm, i.e. a tolerance of 0·90 mm. It will be seen that the overall tolerance is the sum of the individual tolerances; this accumulation of tolerances can be avoided by dimensioning each step from one datum, as shown in fig. 26.2. It will be seen that, if one end face was chosen as the datum, it will be difficult to hold the tolerance on the 160-mm length; one end of the 160-mm length is therefore used as the datum.

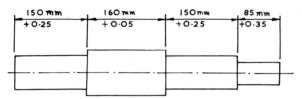

Fig 26.1 Dimensioning causing accumulation of tolerances

When calculations are made, it is necessary to add the tolerances, even if the dimensions are subtracted; the reader should verify that the tolerance on the 85-mm length is 0·5 mm. If the tolerance on the 85-mm length must be reduced to 0·35 mm, as in fig. 26.1, the tolerances on the 310- and 395-mm lengths must be reduced, so that their sum does not exceed 0·35 mm.

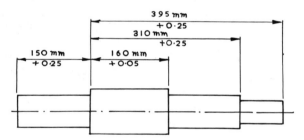

Fig 26.2 Dimensioning from a datum

26.3 Fits
Fits are concerned with the relationship between two parts. Consider a shaft and hole combination: if the shaft is larger than the hole, the condition is said to be of *interference*; and if smaller than the hole, the condition is said to be of *clearance*. The interference may be such that the two parts can be assembled only by shrinking, or it may be very slight, so that the parts can be assembled by hand-operated press. Similarly, the clearance can be slight, so that the shaft can rotate easily in the hole, or be large, so that there is ample clearance for bolts to pass through.

In order that the precise condition is ensured, the limits of size of both the shaft and the hole must be stipulated.

26.3.1 Classes of fit. These are classified as follows.
Clearance fit. When the limits of size of both the hole and the shaft are such that the shaft is *always* smaller than the hole, the fit is said to be a clearance fit.

Interference fit. When the limits of size of both the hole and the shaft are such that the shaft is *always* larger than the hole, the fit is said to be an interference fit.

Transition fit. When the limits of size of both the hole and the shaft are such that the condition may be of clearance *or* interference, the fit is said to be a transition fit.

26.3.2 Hole-based system and shaft-system. In order to obtain a range of degrees of clearance, and degrees of interference, it is necessary to use a wide variation of hole sizes and shaft sizes. For example, a manufacturing company could be making a number of parts, all of a nominal 25-mm diameter, but which are all slightly different in actual limits of size, to suit the actual fit required of each pair of parts. This situation could mean that a large number of drills, reamers, gauges, etc. were required.

It is logical that, to reduce this number, a standard hole could be used for each nominal size, and the variation of fit be obtained by making the mating shaft smaller or larger than the hole. This is known as a *hole-based system.* Alternatively, a standard shaft could be used for each nominal size, and the variation of fit be obtained by making the mating hole larger or smaller, as required. This is known as a *shaft-based system.* A hole-based system is usually preferred, because it standardises 'fixed size' equipment such as reamers and plug gauges; but a shaft-based system is usually also provided, because sometimes it is more convenient to employ a common shaft to which a number of components is assembled, each with a different fit, and sometimes it is convenient to use bar stock without further machining.

26.4 Systems of limits and fits
It is convenient to establish a standardised system of limits and fits, not only to eliminate the need for the draughtsman to determine the limits each time an assembly is detailed, but also to standardise the tools and gauges required. A system of limits and fits should cater for a wide range of nominal sizes, to satisfy the various needs of industry, and should cater for a wide range of quality of work. The system should, if possible, be tabulated, to save the user the trouble of having to calculate the limits of size to suit the class of fit, the quality of the work, and the size of the part.

26.5 British Standard 4500:1969. ISO limits and fits
This standard replaces BS 1916, which was for both metric and inch sizes. Apart from being completely metric, BS 4500 is essentially a revision of BS 1916 to bring the British Standard into line with the latest recommendations of the International Organization for Standardization (ISO). The system refers to holes and shafts, but these terms do not only apply to cylindrical parts but can equally well be

applied to the space contained by, or containing, two parallel faces or tangent planes. The system is tabulated, and covers sizes up to 3150 mm.

26.5.1 Terms used in BS 4500. Figure 26.3 illustrates the principal terms used in this standard. It will be seen that the term *deviation* is used to indicate the position of the limits relative to the *basic size* (nomi-

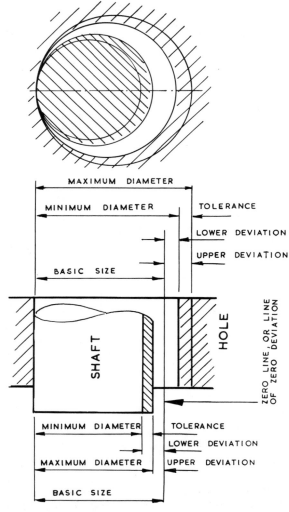

Fig 26.3 Terms used in BS 4500 (ISO limits and fits)

nal size). The basic size is the same for both the hole and the shaft. The zone on the diagram between the lines indicating the maximum and minimum diameters is called the *tolerance zone*; it is defined by its magnitude (the *tolerance*) and by its position relative to the zero line. The tolerance zone is useful when illustrating limits and fits, and is used in figs. 26.4, 26.6, and 26.7.

26.5.2 Grades of tolerance. In order to cater for a wide range of quality (grades) of work, there are 18 grades of tolerance in the system, indicated by number: IT 01, IT 0, IT 1, ... IT 16. (IT stands for ISO series of tolerances, and the higher the number the larger the tolerance for a given size range.) Grades 14 to 16 do not apply for sizes up to and

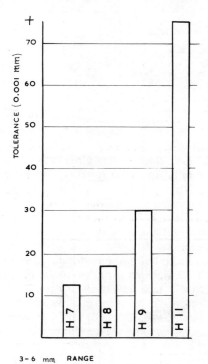

3-6 mm RANGE

Fig 26.4 Selected tolerance grades

including 1 mm, and grades 01 to 5 do not exist for sizes above 500 mm. Grades 6 to 11 are the commonly used grades. Figure 26.4 compares the magnitude of some of the tolerance grades for the size range 3–6 mm. The H applies to a hole with a lower deviation of zero (this is explained in later sections).

26.5.3 The effect of size upon tolerance. The tolerance must be increased with the size, because it is more difficult to manufacture and measure a large size than a small size. The connection between tolerance and diameter is illustrated by the curve in fig. 26.5. In order to produce a tabulated system, the increase of tolerance must be in steps (see fig. 26.5 again); and to prevent confusion regarding the tolerance to use in the case of diameters where the steps occur, the steps are made in little-used sizes. The tolerance is therefore dependent upon the grade of work and the magnitude of the dimension.

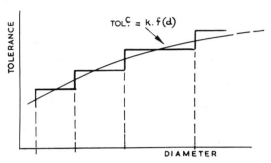

Fig 26.5 The connection between tolerance and diameter

26.5.4 Fundamental deviations. It has already been seen (fig. 26.3) that the *fit* depends not only upon the *tolerance* on the mating parts, but upon the position of the *tolerance zone*. The tolerance zone, relative to the *basic size*, is indicated by the deviation. To provide for a large range of fits, the system includes twenty-seven deviations for holes (indicated by capital letters), and twenty-seven deviations for shafts (indicated by small letters). In order to avoid confusion, the letters i, l, o, q, and w are not used, but some two-letter combinations are used.

In the case of the deviations of holes, the letter indicates the *lower deviation* relative to the zero deviation line (or basic size), the A hole having the greatest positive deviation (i.e. oversized), the H hole having a zero deviation, and the Z, ZA, ZB, and ZC holes having, in turn, the greatest negative deviations (i.e. undersized). The H hole is the one used in the hole-based system. The limits for holes can be designated as follows: A7, H7, ZC6, etc. From this, the lower deviation and the tolerance grade are implied; knowing the size, the actual tolerance, and hence the upper deviation, can be obtained from the tables.

In the case of the deviations of shafts, the letter indicates the *upper deviation* relative to the zero deviation line, the a shaft having the greatest negative deviation (i.e. undersized), the h shaft having a zero deviation, and the z, za, zb, and zc shafts having, in turn, the greatest positive deviations (i.e. oversized). The h shaft is the one used in the shaft-based system. The limits for shafts can be designated as follows: a7, h7, zc6, etc. From this, the upper deviation and the tolerance grade are implied, and, knowing the size, the actual tolerance, and hence the lower deviation, can be obtained from the tables.

In addition to the twenty-seven deviations for holes, and the twenty-seven deviations for shafts, there is a JS hole and a js shaft. In both cases, there is no deviation, but the tolerance is disposed equally about the zero deviation line. These deviations are used when a symmetrical bilateral tolerance is required.

26.5.5. Figures 26.6 and 26.7 illustrate the tolerance zones for some typical fits. Figure 26.6 illustrates a hole-based system, the hole being an H7 hole, the six fits illustrated being designated as H7-s6, H7-p6, H7-n6, H7-k6, H7-h6, and H7-f6 respectively. The tolerances shown are for the 3–6-mm range.

Figure 26.7 illustrates a shaft-based system, the shaft being an h6 shaft, and the six fits illustrated being designated as h6-S6, h6-P6, h6-N6, h6-H7, and h6-F7 respectively; the tolerances are for the 3–6-mm range.

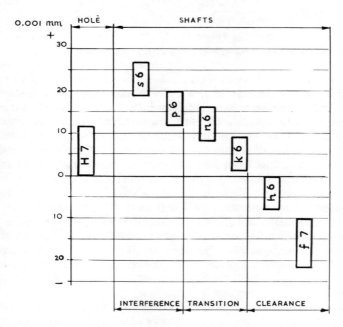

Fig 26.6 Selected hole-based fits

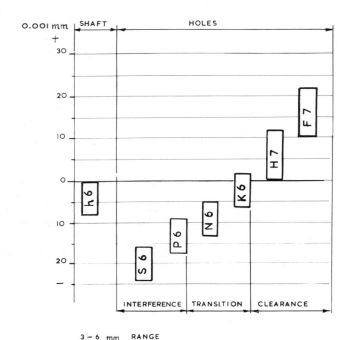

Fig 26.7 Selected shaft-based fits

26.5.6. It will be appreciated that BS 4500 covers a very wide range of tolerance grades, sizes, and fits. It is intended that each engineering concern will abstract from the standard the tolerance grades to suit the class of work done, and the size range to suit the size of the products. Again, a selection of the deviations most likely to be required would also be selected, and, from this information, the standard to be used in the work done would be drawn up.

26.6 Dimensional control

It has already been stated, in section 26.1, that interchangeability demands that some form of inspection be introduced, to ensure that the manufacture is controlled. The type of inspection system used depends upon the quantities involved, and the 'feedback' from the inspection department to the manufacturing department. The following are the principal systems in use.

(a) *Complete measurement.* This system is used when the quantities involved are very small, and the cost of gauges is not justified.

(b) *Statistical quality control.* This technique can be applied when a regular 'feedback' regarding the performance of a machine is required.

If, for example, a certain diameter must be held to a fine tolerance, a patrol inspector would visit the machine at calculated intervals of time (determined by the rate of production), so that a percentage of the output could be examined. At each visit, a certain number would be measured, and the average diameter calculated; this size would be indicated on a diagram. When the machine is performing correctly, the sizes would tend to be scattered about the 'target size', but if the machine starts to perform incorrectly, there will be a 'drift', the direction of the drift depending on the nature of the error. Control dimensions are determined, and, at the point when the drift reaches one of these, the machine is stopped, and the tools reground or reset, so that the process can continue.

(c) *The use of limit gauges.* In this system, every component is inspected with the aid of a gauge which indicates whenever the dimensions being inspected are within the limits specified. There is no indication regarding how 'good' or how 'bad' the parts are. The gauges are subjected to a manufacturing tolerance of the order of one-tenth of the workpiece tolerance, and the actual working tolerances are therefore reduced.

A workpiece may be subjected to statistical quality control at one operation and limit gauging at another operation.

26.7 Limit Gauging

It has already been stated that the permissible extremes that a size may be are called the limits of size. The limit that is associated with the greatest amount of metal is called the *maximum metal limit*, and that which is associated with the least amount of metal is called the *minimum metal limit*. The largest shaft size permitted is the maximum metal limit, and the smallest shaft permitted is the minimum metal limit. Similarly, the largest hole size permitted is the minimum metal limit, and the smallest hole size permitted is the maximum metal limit.

A limit gauge (or pair of limit gauges) consists of a 'Go' member that will pass over or through a correct feature, and a 'Not Go' member that will not pass over or through a correct feature. The 'Go' member checks the maximum metal limit, and the 'Not Go' member checks the minimum metal limit.

26.7.1 The Taylor Principle (stated in 1905 by William Taylor, of Messrs Taylor, Taylor and Hobson).

As stated already, the 'Go' member is used to check the maximum metal limit; the 'Go' member must be full form, because, as shown in fig. 26.8(c) a 'Go' member that is not of full form, will accept an incorrectly shaped workpiece. Taylor stated that *the 'Go' gauge should incorporate the maximum metal limits of as many dimensions as it is convenient and suitable to check in one operation.*

THE TAYLOR PRINCIPLE

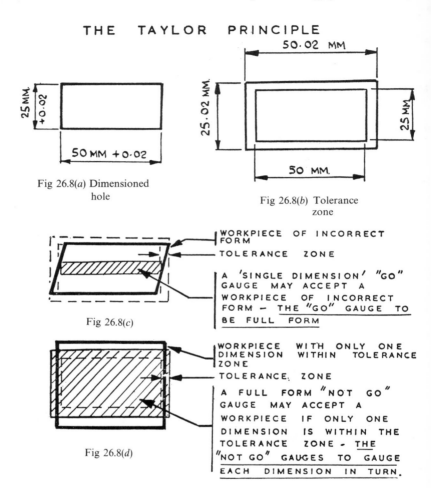

Fig 26.8(*a*) Dimensioned hole

Fig 26.8(*b*) Tolerance zone

Fig 26.8(*c*)

WORKPIECE OF INCORRECT FORM

TOLERANCE ZONE

A 'SINGLE DIMENSION' "GO" GAUGE MAY ACCEPT A WORKPIECE OF INCORRECT FORM — THE "GO" GAUGE TO BE FULL FORM

Fig 26.8(*d*)

WORKPIECE WITH ONLY ONE DIMENSION WITHIN TOLERANCE ZONE

TOLERANCE ZONE

A FULL FORM "NOT GO" GAUGE MAY ACCEPT A WORKPIECE IF ONLY ONE DIMENSION IS WITHIN THE TOLERANCE ZONE - THE "NOT GO" GAUGES TO GAUGE EACH DIMENSION IN TURN.

Taylor also stated that *the 'Not Go' gauges should be separate, and check the minimum metal limit of each dimension in turn.* This is because, as shown in fig. 26.8(*d*), if more than one dimension is checked at a time by the 'Not Go' member, it will accept an incorrect workpiece as long as one dimension is within the limits.

26.7.2 Plain plug gauges. These are used for gauging holes. Figure 26.9 illustrates a basic double-ended solid plug gauge; this type is now being replaced by renewable-end gauges, to reduce costs. The renewable-end gauges are similar to the solid-type, but the gauging members are attached to a handle, often of aluminium alloy or plastics.

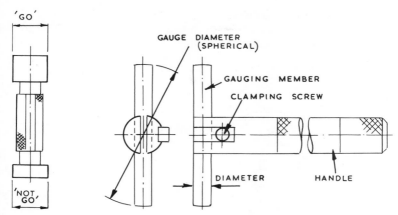

Fig 26.9 Plug gauge   Fig 26.10 Spherical-ended rod gauge

BS 1044 gives details of types of these gauges to suit a wide range of hole sizes. Gauges for large-diameter holes must be lightened, for ease of use; fig. 26.10 illustrates a typical spherical ended rod gauge used for these larger diameters.

Plug gauges do not fully satisfy Taylor's Principle when gauging long holes because they would be awkward to use if the 'Go' member was of full length; they are also, for convenience, produced with a full form 'NOT GO' member.

26.7.3 Gauges for shafts. Shafts are gauged by ring gauges or plain gap gauges, or a combination of these two types. Figure 26.11 shows a typical ring gauge, and fig. 26.12 shows a typical plain gap gauge; the

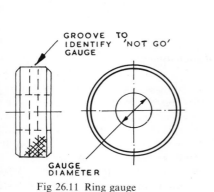

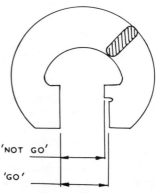

Fig 26.11 Ring gauge   Fig 26.12 Plain gap gauge

gap gauge must be used when a recess diameter is gauged. In order to enable a gap gauge to be used for another component, at the end of a 'run', an adjustable gauge, as shown in fig. 26.13 may be used. Figure 26.13 also shows two variations of gauging members.

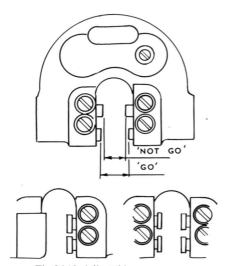

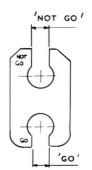

Fig 26.13 Adjustable gap gauge   Fig 26.14 Thickness gauge

'Go' ring gauges do not satisfy Taylor's Principle when gauging long shafts (see note regarding plug gauges), and it is not practical to produce a 'NOT GO' ring gauge to satisfy the principle.

Only the 'NOT GO' part of a gap gauge satisfies the Taylor Principle.

26.7.4 The gauging of screw-threads. External screw-threads are usually gauged by using a plain gap gauge for the major (outside) diameter, and a thread gap gauge for the effective diameter. The gauging members of the thread gauge are specially formed, so that the angle of the thread helix will not give incorrect gauging. Internal screw-threads are usually gauged with a plain plug gauge for the minor (inside) diameter, and a double-ended screw plug gauge for the effective diameter.

26.7.5 Thickness, length, and recess gauges. Figure 26.14 shows a typical thickness gauge, but gauges for length, width, and position of recesses are similar. They are all made from gauge plate, and have a 'GO' end and a 'NOT GO' end.

26.7.6 Stepped taper-plug, and taper-ring gauges. Figure 26.15 shows a stepped taper-ring gauge, and fig. 26.16 shows a stepped taper-plug gauge. Both of these gauges are used to gauge the large diameter of the

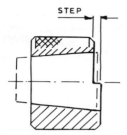

Fig 26.15 Stepped taper-ring gauge

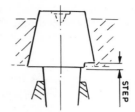

Fig 26.16 Stepped taper-plug gauge

tapered feature; the datum is the workpiece face, and one step-face must be lower than the workpiece face, and the other above it. The step is $X \times Y$; where Y is the tolerance on the diameter, and the taper on diameter is X in 1.

26.7.7 Receiver gauges. These are used to verify that a part will assemble correctly with its mating part. Figure 26.17 illustrates a receiver

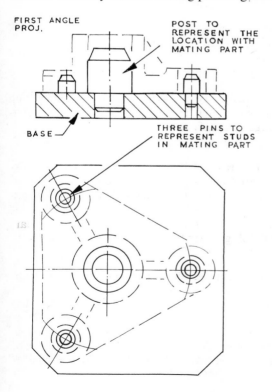

FIRST ANGLE
PROJ.

POST TO
REPRESENT THE
LOCATION WITH
MATING PART

BASE

THREE PINS TO
REPRESENT STUDS
IN MATING PART

Fig 26.17 Receiver gauge

gauge for a workpiece to be located on a spigot that is part of the mating part, and secured by three studs. The receiver gauge includes a post, to represent the spigot, and three pins, to represent the three studs. If the workpiece is accepted by the gauge, it will assemble correctly with its mating parts.

26.7.8 Indicating gauges. Limit gauging does not usually indicate the error of the part being gauged, but this can often be done by incorporating a dial-indicator into a gauge, as shown in fig. 26.18, which shows how a dial-gauge can be used to provide information regarding the length of the part being inspected.

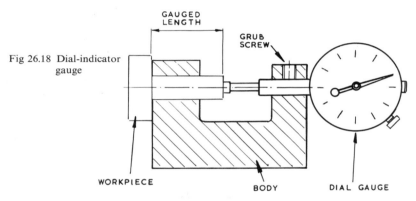

Fig 26.18 Dial-indicator gauge

GAUGED LENGTH

GRUB SCREW

WORKPIECE

BODY

DIAL GAUGE

Summary

1   Modern engineering demands interchangeability, to reduce overall production costs, and to allow a spares system to be operated.
2   As some manufacturing error must be expected, the maximum error allowed (tolerance), and extremes of size permitted (limits of size) must be indicated on drawings.
3   The relationship between two mating parts is called a fit. Systems usually cater for three classes of fit: clearance, interference, and transition.
4   Fits may be based upon a nominal hole size (hole-based) or upon a nominal shaft size (shaft-based).
5   The British Standard for ISO limits and fits (BS 4500) caters for eighteen classes of tolerance (quality of production), twenty-seven deviations for holes, and twenty-seven deviations for shafts. It is expected that a manufacturing concern will develop its own system, by abstracting information from the standard, to suit the type of work to be done.

6   Careful dimensioning can often produce a high degree of accuracy without the increased cost associated with small tolerances.
7   Dimensional control can be by complete measurement, statistical quality control, or by limit gauging. The choice depends upon the quantity to be produced, and the degree of certainty demanded.
8   Limit gauges can be of the 'accept or reject' type, or be indicating.

Questions

Set A
1   Give a suitable size, with limits, for the bore of a cast-iron bush which is to be a light interference fit on a shaft $75 + 0.1$ mm diameter. State the maximum and minimum interference.
2   A shaft is to be 100 mm in diameter, with a total tolerance of 0.025 mm. Give the shaft dimension (*a*) with unilateral limits, (*b*) with bilateral limits. If a bush $100.07 + 0.02$ mm is placed on the shaft, what will be the maximum and minimum clearances?
3   A hole $40 + 0.02$ mm diameter is bored in a plate, and a plug is to be fitted into it. The plug must be a close clearance fig. The maximum clearance is to be 0.05 mm. Give the plug size, with suitable limits.
4   A spindle is to be $50 + 0.05$ mm long, and is to have two diameters. The smaller diameter must have a length of $25 + 0.02$ mm. Sketch the spindle, and dimension your sketch. State the maximum and minimum lengths of the larger diameter.
5   A bar is to be machined $45.4 + 0.075$ mm in diameter, and then ground to $45 + 0.12$ mm in diameter. Calculate the maximum and minimum amounts to be removed by grinding.
6   A certain component which is mass produced in a machine-shop is to be $25 + 0.007$ mm in diameter. Large quantities are constantly rejected by the inspection department, but the shop foreman always disputes the matter. If you were asked to investigate the difficulty, how would you proceed?
7   A hole is $30 + 0.025$ mm in diameter, and a shaft which fits it is $29.1 - 0.025$ mm in diameter. Answer the following questions.
    (*a*) Is this a transition fit?
    (*b*) Are the limits unilateral?
    (*c*) What is the total tolerance on the shaft?
    (*d*) What is the nominal size?
You should add brief explanations where you consider these are necessary.
8   The pin shown in fig. 26.19 is to have the 40-mm dimension checked. Sketch a simple receiver gauge for this operation, and explain which parts of the gauge must be accurately made, and how the gauge is set before the pin is inserted.

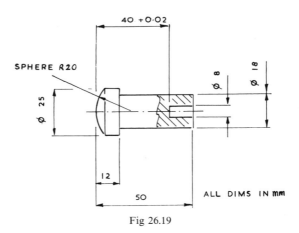

Fig 26.19

9   In the small wheel shown in fig. 26.20, it is important that the keyway is on the same centre line as one of the holes. Sketch a suitable receiver gauge to check this point.

Set B (questions requiring further study)
10   Make sketches of a limit gauge for a taper hole, and a limit depth gauge.
11   Describe a limit system with which you are familiar, and explain how the part drawings, the gauges, and the inspection procedure are linked up.

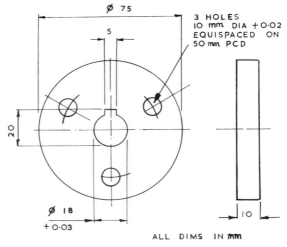

Fig 26.20

12 Discuss the advantages of fitting automatic 'sizing' devices to machine tools. Sketch and describe one such device.

13 Describe an inspection system with which you are familiar, and state what occurs (*a*) when a part is rejected by inspection, (*b*) when a part is outside the drawing limits, but be rectified, (*c*) when a part is wrong and cannot be made to coincide with the drawing, but is considered usable if slight modifications are made. If you consider that the system is faulty, suggest improvements.

Chapter 27
Machine-shop Process Planning

27.1

When the product-design department has cleared the production drawings to the production department, the sequence of operations to be followed during the manufacture and assembly of the components is planned. In the case of large-scale production, this may take place many months before the manufacture is due to start, so that the shape of forgings and castings can be determined and ordered, the machine-tool allocation made, the time taken for each operation determined, and the machine-shop loading studied. At the same time, the jig and tool design department can start designing the special equipment required during the manufacture of the product, and the costing department can determine the selling price of the product. During the manufacture of the product, the process details assist in the organisation of production, and in the maintainance of the desired quality.

27.2 Process sheets, and choice of planning method to suit production volume

The amount and the type of information given in the process depends upon the class of labour used in the manufacture, and the volume of production. For example, a prototype product, or a workholding fixture, will be produced in an experimental shop, or in the toolroom, and highly skilled machinists will be involved in its manufacture. It will neither be economical nor necessary to supply a detailed process and workholding devices such as fixtures and jigs. Some information must be given regarding the sequence of operations, so that the work can be allocated to the sections involved, and so that each machinist will know what other work is involved; a turner, for example, will need to know that his work is followed by hardening and grinding, so that he can leave a suitable grinding allowance. If, for example, the part is to be machined in large quantities, some features will be used for location purposes; these features must therefore be made to the accuracy specified by the planner, so that they will fit the location holes or posts used at following operations.

The process-planning information for the tool-room may therefore

PROCESS CHART			M 122/007
NAME OF PART - TRAILER PIN			MAT. - C.H.S.
PART DRG P. 127/071		ASSEMBLY - REAR FRAME	
STANDARD QUAN. 300		DATE	
NO.	OPERATION	SHOP	REMARKS
1	CUT OFF	BAR	1·5 M. LENGTHS
2	TURN AND SCREW	L.M.	WARD NO. 7 DRG L 028/411
3	DRILL PIN HOLE	L.M.	MACHINES 427 – 30
4	CASE HARDEN	H.T.	CYANIDE
5	PASS TO HEAVY VEHICLE STORES		

Fig 27.1 Operations list for tool-room

J. BLANK & Co. LTD					
COMPONENT		OP. 615/007		DETENT ASSEMBLY	
OPERATION 5 MILL SLOTS IN DISC					
MACHINE. HORIZONTAL MILLING M/C.					
JIGS	FIXTURES	TOOLS		GAUGES	
FIXT.	771/093	CUTTER	771/094	GAUGE	PR.017/802

DIMS IN mm		
M.H.A.K. 13.6.70	E.U.P 18.6.70	OP. 615/007
DRAWN	CHECKED	OP. NO. 5

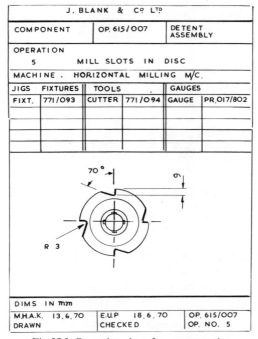

Fig 27.3 Operation sheet for one operation

be in the form of a written list of operations, giving just sufficient information (fig. 27.1); but, if the part is more involved, the information may be in the form of a 'strip cartoon', combining brief details with simple sketches, as required, to avoid any misunderstanding regarding datum faces, etc.

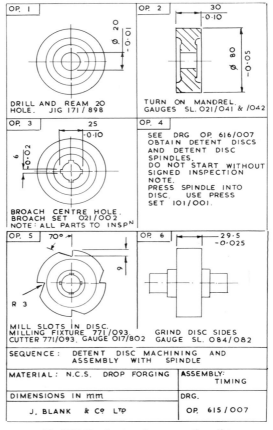

Fig 27.2 Production-shop operations list

The process-planning information for the production shop is usually much more detailed. It may be in the form of a more detailed 'strip cartoon', as shown in fig. 27.2; but, if there are many operations involved, each operation may be detailed on a separate sheet, a mounted copy of which would be issued, with the equipment for that operation, to the machinist concerned. Figure 27.3 (p. 417) illustrates a typical operation sheet of this type.

If the operation is to be done on a capstan or turret lathe, a drawing may also be prepared, to indicate the positions of the tools and holders on the turret faces and the tool posts, and the stroke required at each stage in the operation. Details of speeds and tool feed-rates may also be given, if necessary.

27.3 The work of the machine-shop process planner is therefore to determine the best sequence of machining operations, and to allocate the most suitable machines available. The main differences between planning for small-quantity production and for large-quantity production are the type of machine tools used, the use, or otherwise, of special equipment, and the amount of detailed information given on the process sheets.

27.4 Choice of datum points
A number of basic 'rules' are given later in this chapter, but at this point it can be stated that the main object must be to establish at the start of manufacture, a datum point or points from which measurements can be taken, or, in the case of large-scale production, from which the part can be located during the operations that follow. These datum or location points must, if possible, be used throughout the machining sequence, so that various features will be positioned correctly, relative to each other. Thought must be given to the problem of holding the part during the machining operations that follow; this may well influence the order in which two otherwise similar operations are carried out. Care must also be taken to ensure that the maximum work is done at each setting, because, each time the workpiece is positioned on a machine, there is a tendency for errors to be introduced.

27.5. The planner must know the type of machine tools associated with small-scale production, compared with large-scale production, and the capabilities of each machine tool. Planners working for a specific concern will know every machine tool available, and very often the characteristics of each individual machine.

27.6. Very often, the machining sequence for large-scale production will be very similar in principle to that for small-scale production, but differ mainly because semi-skilled workpeople are engaged in the work. A difference may also be that the large-scale production will justify the use of special equipment. The following chart shows some typical machining activities, and illustrates the difference between small-scale production and large-scale production.

Activity	Small-scale production	Large-scale production
Positioning of workpiece and cutter	Castings and forgings marked out	Marking out used only on trial material, to check for 'cleaning up'
	Work located by 'setting up' to marking out, or using a dial-indicator	Extensive use of 'tooling aids', such as jigs for drilling and similar operations, and fixtures for other operations. These tooling aids incorporate locators such as posts (for location from holes) and holes (for location from shafts and spigots)
Holding	Workpiece held in a vice, or clamped to the machine table if the seating faces are flat	Workpiece located in jigs or fixtures that incorporate clamping devices
	Cylindrical parts held in 4-jaw chuck, between centres, or clamped to a stump, turned by the machinist	Cylindrical parts held in a 3-jaw self-centring chuck with soft jaws, in a collet, or in a fixture attached to machine spindle
	Parts with a flat seating face held on a faceplate for turning or boring	
Machining of plane surfaces (roughing)	Shaping, planing, or universal milling machine	Vertical or horizontal milling machine. Special planing machine may be used for large workpieces
Machining of plane surfaces (finishing)	The same machines as for roughing, but surface grinding used if tolerances are fine, or after heat-treatment	Extensive use of grinding, because semi-skilled labour can be used to produce very accurate work

Activity	Small-scale production	Large-scale production
Machining of cylindrical surfaces (roughing)	Centre lathe usually used, but the skilled machinist may use a capstan or turret lathe, set up by himself, for the convenience of tool-holding	Extensive use of capstan lathes (small work) or turret lathes (for large work)
Machining of cylindrical surfaces (finishing)	Centre lathe; but a universal grinding machine is used for fine tolerances, or after heat-treatment	External or internal grinding for many applications, but special machines, such as centreless grinding machines, used for very large-scale production
Production of holes	Holes started using centre drills, from centre positions marked out on workpiece	Workpieces located and held in jigs with bushes that control the drills, etc. No centre drill operation required
The spacing of holes and slots, etc.	Spacing with the aid of a dividing head or circular table	Spacing using an indexing jig or indexing fixture (the production version of the dividing head or circular table)
Screw-threads (external)	Single-point tooling using centre lathe	Die box using a capstan or turret lathe
Profiles	Extensive use of a circular table	End mill used, and guided by use of profile plate
	Cylindrical parts with complicated shape turned using form tools	Cylindrical parts with complicated shape turned using form tools, as for small-scale production
Radii and awkward shapes	Radii may be produced by tool radius, but, when part of a profile, usually filed to shape	Hand work not done; all work is machined; if not, 'as cast' or 'as forged'

27.7. The choice of the location features is of special importance. A large plane surface on a workpiece is an ideal location surface, and should be machined at an early stage. A plane surface alone does not completely locate the workpiece on the location surface, and is used in conjunction with other features. For example, the profile can be located from pins or V-plates in the location surface (figs. 27.4 and 27.5).

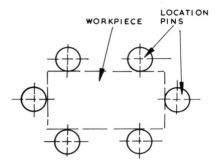

Fig 27.4 Profile-location by pins

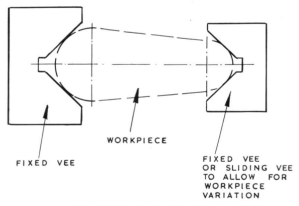

Fig 27.5 Profile-location by vees

A cylindrical feature is a good location feature, because it locates the workpiece almost completely. The only 'freedom' is that of rotation about the axis of the cylinder, and a second location point is necessary to obtain complete location (figs. 27.6 and 27.7).

Location features must be chosen with due regard to the ease with which the workpiece is located; for example, the operator must be able to see the locators when locating the workpiece.

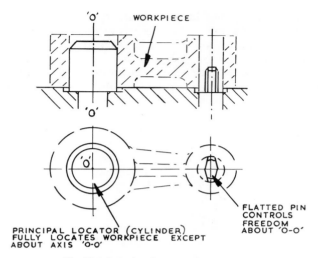

Fig 27.6 Location from two holes

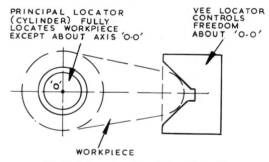

Fig 27.7 Location from hole and profile

27.8 Planning method

An operation lay-out must be planned in a methodical way, because its object is to produce method. If the following procedure is adopted, the work of process planning will be simplified, and be more effective. It is important that the work be approached with an open mind, that the process be developed gradually, and that the order of machining be modified until the best method has been produced.

1. The component drawing is first studied so that the function of the component is understood, and the relative importance of its features determined. This study will show the feature that is used when locating the component upon assembly with mating parts (such a feature is an ideal location point), and it will also show if tolerances on dimensions are applied to produce desired fits, or to ensure clearance between the

component and mating parts upon assembly. As a result of this study, the planner should also be familiar with the shape, size, and weight of the component, and know if it is likely to produce handling and balancing problems.

2. The dimensions of features that are to be machined are listed or ringed, to indicate if they need roughing followed by final machining. The features that are to be used for location are also indicated at this stage.

3. A rough draft process is then prepared. The following basic rules should be followed.

(a) Establish *at least* one datum at the first opportunity. For example, when turning, face the end, so that distances can be measured from it; and, when milling, face a large plane surface, so that it can serve as a location face. Very often, a second datum can be produced at the same time; for example, when turning, a bore can be produced square with the end face.

(b) Produce as much as possible from one setting. It must be realised that dimensions can vary, so, every time the workpiece is reset, the possibility of accuracy is reduced. Clamping can cause distortion, and so reclamping can also cause inaccuracies.

(c) The original datum features must be used as long as possible, to ensure a very accurate relationship between features. In large-scale production, a feature cannot be finish-machined and also be the location feature for that operation, so another location feature must then be used. The location feature must have been machined as a result of location from the original location feature; the inaccuracy caused by change of location feature will thus be minimised.

(d) Similar operations must, if possible be produced in a group; for example, turning operations, then drilling operations, then milling operations, etc. This grouping will reduce the time taken in moving the workpiece from section to section, and will also assist the progress department in their work of 'following' the workpieces through the machine shop.

(e) The final operations upon accurate features are performed at the end of the machining sequence, so that damage to the features is minimised. Note that a feature may be left oversized, for finish machining, and still be used for location, provided that it is machined accurately enough. In these cases, the rough size is stipulated, together with a suitable tolerance.

(f) Inspection operations are introduced at strategic stages in the sequence, to reduce the wasted effort and scrap that will be produced if incorrectly machined parts are allowed to proceed. The dimensions stipulated by the planning department are worked to at this stage by the inspection department.

(g) A burr-removal operation is introduced, if necessary, immediately before a feature is used for location; and again, if necessary at the end of the sequence.

(*h*) The location system is checked to ensure that all the features are position-controlled.

4. The draft process is then checked to ensure that all the machining has been covered, and then the process is finalised.

The reader should realise that the planner rarely produces a new process without some modifications, such as the splitting up of long operations, the grouping together of shorter operations, and the change in the order in which certain operations are performed.

27.9 Specimen operation lay-outs

The following two operation layouts will illustrate planning techniques. These examples do not include heat-treatment operations, but, when hardening is carried out, it is usually followed by grinding, to remove the distortion caused by quenching.

27.9.1 Operation lay-out for drill stop nut (fig. 27.8). This is a one-off tool-room job, and so tooling aids are not called for. A centre lathe

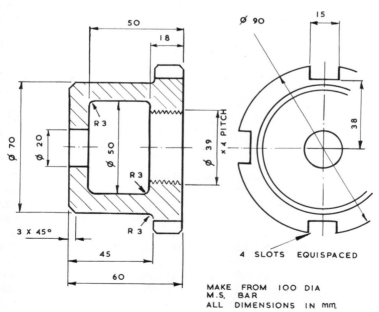

FIRST ANGLE PROJECTION

MAKE FROM 100 DIA
M.S. BAR
ALL DIMENSIONS IN mm

Fig 27.8(*a*) Drill stop nut

is used for the turning operations, and a single-point tool is used to
cut the thread. A milling cutter cuts the four slots, and the dividing
head is used for the spacing. The operator holds the workpiece in
a chuck attached to the dividing head, and protects the workpiece
from damage by putting soft packing between it and the chuck
jaws—there is no need to instruct a skilled man to do this, or to remove burrs.

Operation number	Description	Machine
1	Face end. Break down and turn 70 mm dia × 45 mm long, forming a radius. Turn 90 mm dia. Chamfer 3 mm × 45°. Drill 18 mm dia × 60 mm deep, ream 20 mm dia × 15 mm deep. Part off + 1 mm	Centre lathe
2	Reverse. Face end to length. Open out 50-mm recess dia. Bore thread minor diameter. Cut screw-thread	Centre lathe
3	View	View bench
4	In dividing-head chuck. Hold from 70-mm diameter. Mill four slots	Horizontal milling machine
5	View	View bench

Fig 27.8(*b*) Operation layout for drill stop nut

27.9.2 Operation lay-out for connection (fig. 27.9). This is a quantity-
production job; it is not machined all over, because gravity die-casting
gives a suitable finish for all but important features. A turret lathe is
used for turning operations, because it provides ample tool holding,
and means of controlling lengths. Specially shaped jaws are used at the
first operation, so that the casting is roughly located from the flange
profile. The bore is machined at the first operation, to provide a datum
feature. The flange profile is used as the feature from which rotational
location about the bore axis is controlled. Drilling jigs would
be used for the 'drill' operations, so that the component is located, and
the drills, etc. controlled.

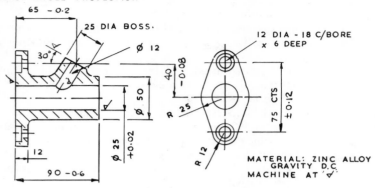

Fig 27.9(*a*) Connection

Operation number	Description	Machine
1	In special jaws. Hold from body. Face flange to thickness, and open out bore to size	Turret lathe
2	Reverse. Locate from flange face, and bore. Face end to length	Turret lathe
3	View	View bench
4	Locate from bore, flange face, and flange profile. Drill, ream, and counterbore two holes in flange	Drilling machine
5	Remove burrs	Burr bench
6	View	View bench
7	Locate from bore, flange face, and one 12-mm-dia hole in flange. Spot-face 25-mm-dia boss, and drill 12-mm-dia hole	Drilling machine
8	View	View bench

Fig 27.9(*b*) Operation layout for connection

Summary

1   The aim when process planning is to determine the best sequence
    of machining operations, and to allocate the most suitable machine
    tools available.
2   The method of presentation and the amount of detailed infor-
    mation given depends upon the quantity to be produced, and the
    type of labour to be used.
3   The main object is to establish, at the start of the sequence, a
    suitable datum point or points from which measurements can be
    taken, or from which the workpiece can be located. Thought must
    be given to the problems of seating and clamping, and operations
    should be grouped to minimise the movement of workpieces
    around the machine shop.
4   The choice of machines, the methods, and the equipment used will
    depend upon the quantity to be produced, and the accuracy
    required.
5   An operation sequence must be planned in a methodical way for
    best results.

Questions

Set A
1   Draw up a proces for large-scale production of the component
    shown in fig. 27.10.

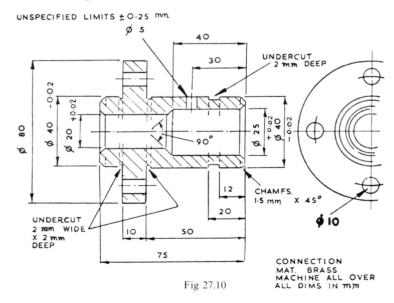

Fig 27.10

2 Draw up a process for large-scale production of the component shown in fig. 27.11. This part is to be produced from a small forging. Sketch the shape of a suitable forging.

3 Draw up a process for large-scale production of the part shown in fig. 27.12, to be produced from die-castings machined as shown.

Set B (questions requiring further study)

4 A large factory with a wide variety of machinery is setting up a machine-shop for maintenance purposes. Choose about ten machine tools to equip this shop, and explain the reasons for your choice.

5 Sketch suitable jigs/fixtures to be used in the production of the components shown in figs. 27.10, 27.11, and 27.12. (Refer to questions 1, 2, and 3.)

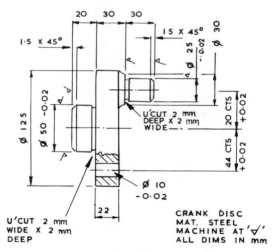

Fig 27.11

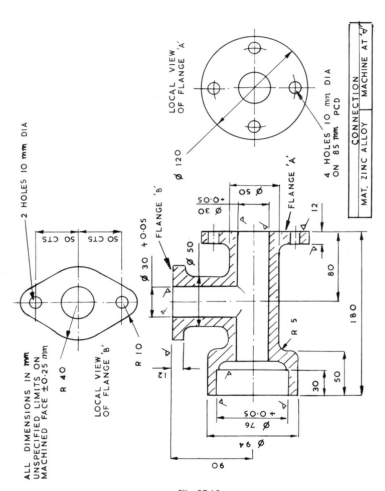

Fig 27.12

Chapter 28
Floor-to-floor Times

28.1 Introduction

A floor-to-floor time is usually associated with one component, and is given for each operation in turn. It can be defined as the time between picking up the component at the start of the operation and depositing it at the end of that operation; in the case of bar material, the operation is considered to have started when the material-advancing mechanism is operated. The floor-to-floor time may include preparation time, but the machine is usually set by a setter, and the time given separately.

The floor-to-floor times for a product can be evaluated only when the operation sequence is known, the actual machines have been allocated, and the details regarding jigs and fixtures, etc. are available.

The times are used for payment by incentive, to study machine 'loading', to form the basis of costing and delivery programming, and as a means of examining the production efficiency of the plant.

28.1.1. Floor-to-floor times comprise calculated times and observed times. The calculated times are those for elements involving automatic machine movements, and are obtained by simple arithmetic.

The observed times are those for operator movements, such as loading the machine, starting the machine, indexing the tool-posts, and changing gear. These times are determined by observing the operators at work on the machines, and recording the times taken for these 'elements'. When observing the operators, the time-study engineer appraises the operator's 'rating' each time an element is performed ('rating' is the index of the rate at which the operator works), and this rating is used to adjust the time taken, and so to produce a time for an 'average' operator. This process is called 'levelling', and prevents slow operators from producing high times, and fast operators from producing low times.

The times are only considered valid if they are reasonably consistent over about fifty observations; the time used is the average for the set.

When the floor-to-floor time is determined, the operation is analysed, so that the machine movement times can be calculated, and the operator times calculated from the observed data.

The actual times given as a means of payment are larger than those calculated, to allow for operator fatigue and other contingencies.

28.2 Calculation of times for lathe work

28.2.1. The spindle speed to suit the workpiece material, its shape, the type of operation, and the cutting-tool material is first determined.

If cutting speed $= S$ m/s,
   diameter of workpiece at start of the element $= d$ mm,
   spindle speed $= N$ rev/minute,

then cutting speed $=$ circumference of workpiece at start of element $\times$ spindle speed

i.e. $$S = \frac{\pi \times d \times N}{60\,000}\,\text{m/s}$$

from which, $$N = \frac{60\,000 \times S}{\pi \times d}\,\text{rev/min}$$

The value of N so calculated is only theoretical, and it is necessary to base the time calculation upon the speed (N_a) available on the machine to be used. The nearest spindle speed to the theoretical speed is usually used, but in the event of the theoretical speed being midway between two widely different spindle speeds, some discretion must be exercised. Usually, the lower spindle speed would be used, for safety; but the choice depends upon the initial cutting speed used in the calculation—this may have been particularly high or low. Again, the type of operation will influence the selection: if the operation is one of end-facing or parting-off, the higher spindle speed may be used, because the actual cutting speed is reduced as soon as the tool is fed towards the axis of the workpiece.

28.2.2. The travel for each element must also be determined. For example, the automatic feed will be engaged before the tool reaches the workpiece, and this additional feed must be allowed for.

28.2.3. Having determined the spindle speed to be used, and also the length of the tool travel, the times can be calculated for a given feed-rate.

If the feed-rate is f mm/rev of the workpiece, the length of the tool travel is L mm, and the actual spindle speed is N_a, the number of revs of the workpiece during the tool travel of L mm is given by

$$\text{number of revs} = \frac{L}{f}$$

and the time taken in min $= \dfrac{L}{f \times N_a}\,\text{min.}$

If the tool is to make a number of passes, the time so calculated is multiplied by the number of passes to be made, unless the reduction in diameter is great, in which case a new calculation to suit each significant change in workpiece diameter is made.

28.3 Calculation of times for drilling-machine work

28.3.1. The spindle speed for drilling and reaming is first determined in a similar manner to that when turning, except that the diameter of the drill or reamer is used. It must be remembered that the drilling diameter must be less than the final size of the reamed hole. As before, the spindle speed N_a is determined by relating the calculated value to the speeds available.

28.3.2. The length of travel must include an approach length to suit the drill point, as shown in fig. 28.1.

From the diagram, $x = \dfrac{D \tan \theta}{2}$

The total feed length L must, in addition to the length of the hole to be drilled, and the above allowance, include an allowance for 'early feed engagement', and, in the case of through holes, a breakthrough allowance, to ensure that the hole is cleaned up.

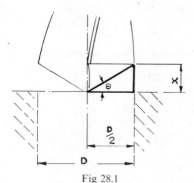

Fig 28.1

28.3.3. From the spindle speed, and the length of travel, the cutting time for a given feed-rate can be calculated.

If f is the feed per rev of the spindle, in mm, then the number of revs to advance a distance of L mm $= L/f$ revs.

The time to travel the distance L mm $= L/fN_a$ min.

It must be noted that this is for one hole. The time must be given for all the holes produced at the operation.

28.4 Calculation of times for milling-machine work

28.4.1. The spindle speed is first calculated as in drilling, the diameter of the milling cutter being used in the calculation. The theoretical spindle speed is adjusted to produce a speed N_a to suit the machine.

28.4.2. The table feed-rate is then determined from the feed per tooth (f mm) and the number of teeth in the cutter (n).

Thus,   the feed per rev of cutter = $f \times n$ mm

so   the feed-rate per min = $\dfrac{f \times n \times N_a}{1000}$ m/min

This theoretical value is used to select a suitable table feed F_a.

28.4.3. The length (L m) of the pass must include an approach length x. For example, when a peripheral-cutting cutter is used to cut a slot, the approach length x can be determined as shown in fig. 28.2.

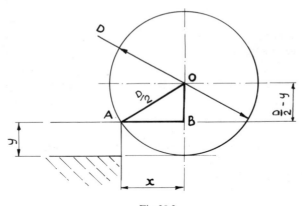

Fig 28.2

Considering triangle ABO,

$$\left(\frac{D}{2}\right)^2 = \left(\frac{D}{2} - y\right)^2 + x^2$$

If the cutter is to run out under power, the same allowance is made at the exit end.

In the case of an end-cutting cutter being used to produce a slot, the approach length $x = D/2$, as illustrated in fig. 28.3.

FIRST ANGLE PROJECTION

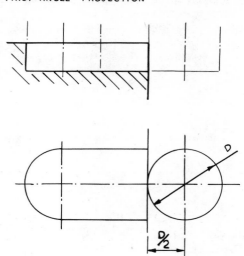

Fig 28.3

28.4.4. The time taken for each pass is the total length, i.e. the length to be cut, plus an allowance for approach and, if necessary, run-out, and a small allowance for early engagement of feed, divided by the table feed-rate.

$$\text{time taken in mins} = L/F_a.$$

28.5 Calculation of times for reciprocating-machine work

28.5.1. The cutting time per stroke is given by:

$$\frac{L}{60\,000 \times S}\text{min}$$

where L is the length of the stroke in mm (including approach and overrun), and S is the available tool or table speed in m/s.

28.5.2. The cutting time (T_c) is given by

$$T_c = \frac{n \times L}{60\,000 \times S}\text{min}$$

where n is the number of strokes per pass—this is the width of the surface to be cut, plus approach allowance, divided by the feed-rate.

28.5.3. The total machine occupation time per pass (T) must also include the return-stroke, as follows.

$$T = \frac{n \times L}{60\,000 \times S} + r\left(\frac{n \times L}{60\,000 \times S}\right)\text{min}$$

where

$$r = \frac{\text{average cutting speed}}{\text{average return speed}}$$

The time must be multiplied by the number of passes, which depends upon the depth of cut and the amount of metal to be removed.

28.6 Calculation of times for cylindrical grinding

28.6.1. Although the times for cylindrical grinding are calculated in a similar way to those for turning, it is less easy to produce reliable times, because the work speed, rate of traverse, and the feed per pass may be changed during an operation, as these factors influence the efficiency of grinding, the dimensional accuracy of the work, and the quality of the surface finish produced. The principles of calculation are as follows.

28.6.2. The work spindle speed (N rev/min) is given by

$S =$ circumference of the workpiece $\times$ workspindle speed in rev/min

$= \pi \times d \times N$

and so $N = \dfrac{60\,000 \times S}{\pi \times d}$ rev/min

where S = workpiece speed in m/s
d = workpiece diameter in mm.

An acceptable workspindle speed (N_a) is selected from this theoretical value.

28.6.3. The traverse rate is determined from the traverse per rev of work (t) and the workspindle speed in rev/min. The value of t is usually between $\frac{1}{3}$ and $\frac{2}{3}$ of the wheel width, for uniform rate of wheel wear.

traverse rate (F) $= t \times N_a$

From this value, a suitable traverse rate, F_a, is selected.

28.6.4. The time taken for one traverse is L/F_a, where L is the length of the traverse including approach and over-run.

28.6.5. The feed is applied at the end of each traverse, the amount of feed depending upon the material being cut, the machine, and the results required. The number of traverses (p) depends upon the amount of metal to be removed, and the feed per pass.

The total machining time $= \dfrac{pL}{F_a}$.

28.7 Calculation of times for surface grinding

28.7.1. The times for surface grinding using a reciprocating table are calculated in a similar manner to those for reciprocating machines (see section 28.5), except that cutting takes place in both directions, so a quick return is not used. As in cylindrical grinding, it is less easy to produce accurate times, since the cutting conditions may be changed during an operation, to suit the grinding wheel and the required results.

28.7.2. The number of traverses (n) for a workpiece width W is given by W/t, where t is the feed per traverse.

28.7.3. The time per traverse is given by L/S, where L is the traverse length (workpiece length plus approach and over-run allowances), and S is the table speed.

28.7.4. The time per pass is given by

$$\text{time per pass} = \frac{n \times L}{S}\,\text{min}$$

where $n =$ number of traverses required (see section 28.7.2).

Again, this must be multiplied by the number of passes required, which depends upon the amount of metal to be removed and the depth of cut per pass.

28.7.5. When a rotating table is used for surface grinding, the number of table revs is determined from the feed per rev and the 'radial' feed distance. The time taken is calculated from the number of table revs and the speed of table rotation.

438 *Workshop Technology for Technicians*

28.8 Examples of calculations

Some typical calculations are shown in the following pages. To save space, the expressions derived in the foregoing sections are used without further explanation. It will be seen that tabulation is used in the calculations, and it will be found that this speeds up the calculation work, and also enables a continuous check to be made, by comparison of figures.

TIME STUDY

Component: Screwed plug   Operation 1

Operation drawing:

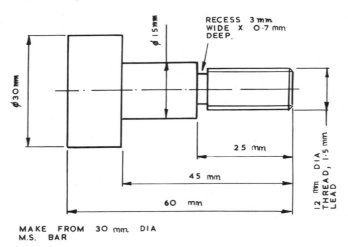

MAKE FROM 30 mm DIA
M.S. BAR

Fig 28.4

Machine: Capstan lathe   Spindle speeds (revs/min)
                                30, 49, 74, 118, 195, 310, 465, 750

Machining data: Face end at 0·5 m/s, 0·25 mm/rev feed

Rough turn 15-mm dia (leave 0·7 on dia for finishing) at 0·4 m/s, 0·35 mm/rev feed. Length of pass 45 mm

Finish turn 15-mm dia at 0·5 m/s, 0·25 mm/rev feed. Length of pass 45 mm

Recess 3 mm wide—estimated 0·5 min

Turn thread diameter at 0·5 m/s, with two passes

Part off by hand at 0·4 m/s, 0·07 mm/rev feed

Non-cutting time: 2 min per component

Element	Spindle speed $= \dfrac{60\,000 \times S}{\pi \times d}$ revs/min	Time $= \dfrac{L}{f \times N_a}$ min
Face end	$\dfrac{60\,000 \times 0\cdot5}{\pi \times 30} = 319$, say 310	$\dfrac{18}{0\cdot25 \times 310} = 0\cdot230$
Rough turn	$\dfrac{60\,000 \times 0\cdot4}{\pi \times 30} = 256$, say 195	$\dfrac{48}{0\cdot35 \times 195} = 0\cdot705$
Finish turn	$\dfrac{60\,000 \times 0\cdot5}{\pi \times 15\cdot35} = 625$, say 465	$\dfrac{48}{0\cdot25 \times 465} = 0\cdot414$
Turn recess		Estimate $= 0\cdot500$
Turn thread diameter	$\dfrac{60\,000 \times 0\cdot5}{\pi \times 15} = 638$, say 465	$\dfrac{25}{0\cdot25 \times 465} = 0\cdot216$
Screw	$\dfrac{60\,000 \times 0\cdot05}{\pi \times 12} = 79\cdot5$, say 74	$\dfrac{2 \times 25}{74 \times 1\cdot5} = 0\cdot451$
Part off	$\dfrac{60\,000 \times 0\cdot4}{\pi \times 30} = 255$, say 310	$\dfrac{18}{0\cdot07 \times 310} = 0\cdot830$

Non-cutting time $= 2\cdot000$

Total $= 5\cdot346$

Total time $= 5\cdot5$ minutes

TIME STUDY

Component: Flanged cover   Operation 4

Operation drawing:

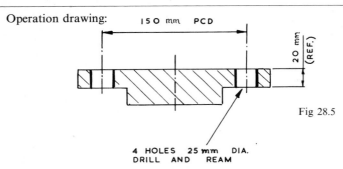

Fig 28.5

4 HOLES 25 mm DIA.
DRILL AND REAM

Machine: Radial-arm drilling machine with drilling jig	Spindle speeds (revs/min) 105, 200, 350, 1060
	Feeds (mm/rev) 0·080, 0·16, 0·25, 0·35, 0·50, 0·60, 0·75

Machining data: Drill at 0·4 m/s with 0·25 mm/rev feed
Ream at 0·15 m/s with 0·50 mm/rev feed
Non-cutting time: 4 min each component

To find approach x: $x = 12·3 \tan 31° = 7·4$ mm
Depth of hole = 20 mm
Length of pass = 20 + 7·4 mm, say 30 mm to allow for over-run

Element	Spindle speed $= \dfrac{60\,000 \times S}{\pi \times d} \text{revs/min}$	Time taken $= \dfrac{L}{f \times N_a} \text{min}$
Drill 4 holes	$\dfrac{60\,000 \times 0·4}{\pi \times 24·6} = 310$, say 350	$\dfrac{4 \times 30}{0·25 \times 350} = 1·376$
Ream 4 holes	$\dfrac{60\,000 \times 0·15}{\pi \times 25} = 115$, say 105	$\dfrac{4 \times 23}{0·5 \times 105} = 1·750$

Non-cutting time = 4·000

Total = 7·126

Total time, say 7·5 minutes

TIME STUDY

Component: Guide block   Operation 7

Operation drawing:

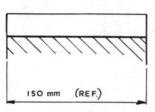

Fig 28.6

Machine data: Horizontal milling machine, with milling fixture

Spindle speeds (revs/min)
23, 31, 41, 54, 72, 95, 126, 167, 222, 293, 388, 514, 680, 903, 1200

Table feeds (m/min)
0·02, 0·03, 0·04, 0·05, 0·07, 0·08, 0·15, 0·20, 0·30, 0·40, 0·55, 0·75

Milling cutter: 150-mm dia, 25-mm wide. 16 teeth
Cutting speed: 0·4 m/s
Feed: 0·25 mm/tooth
Cut slot with one pass. Approach and run-out under power feed
Non-cutting time: 2 min each component

$$\text{Spindle speed} = \frac{60\,000 \times S}{\pi \times d} = \frac{60\,000 \times 0.4}{\pi \times 150} = 51 \text{ revs/min}$$

$$\text{say 54 revs/min}$$

$$\text{Feed} = \frac{f \times n \times N_a}{1000} = \frac{0.25 \times 16 \times 54}{1000} = 0.226 \text{ m/min}$$

$$\text{say 0·2 m/min}$$

To determine approach and over-run:

$$\left(\frac{d}{2}\right)^2 = \left(\frac{d}{2} - y\right)^2 + x^2$$
$$75^2 = (75 - 25)^2 + x^2$$
$$x^2 = 3125$$
$$x \simeq 60 \text{ mm}$$

Machining time $= \dfrac{L}{F} = \dfrac{(60 + 150 + 60)}{0 \cdot 2 \times 1000} = 1 \cdot 35$ min

Total time = 3·35 minutes

TIME STUDY

Component: Base member	Operation 1

Details of operation: Set up and machine base face
Casting size 600 mm × 300mm

Machine: Shaping machine
Cutting speed: 0·5 m/s
Ratio of cutting speed to return speed: 5 : 9
Feed per traverse: 3 mm
Number of passes: 2
Non-cutting time: 5 min

Length of stroke, allowing for cutter over-run = 530 mm
Width of stroke, allowing for approach = 630 mm

Number of strokes per pass $(n) = \dfrac{630}{3} = 210$

Time for cutting per pass $= \dfrac{n \times L}{60\,000 \times S} = \dfrac{210 \times 530}{60\,000 \times 0 \cdot 5} = 3 \cdot 72$ min

Machine occupation time per pass $= 3 \cdot 72 + \frac{5}{9}(3 \cdot 72)$ min
$$= 3 \cdot 72 + 2 \cdot 06 \text{ min}$$
$$= 5 \cdot 78 \text{ min}$$

Allowing for two passes, total machine time = 11·56 min
Total time, including non-cutting time = 16·56, say 17 min

Total = 17 minutes

TIME STUDY

Component: Shaft	Operation 10

Details of operation: Finish grind 50-mm dia

Machine: Plain hydraulic grinding machine	Work spindle speeds (revs/min): 66, 111, 175, 268 Range of table traverse rates (mm/min): 75–6100 Number of work spindle speeds: infinite

Data: Grinding allowance: 0·3 mm on diameter
     Work speed: 0·3 m/s
     Rate of feed: 0·012 mm per pass (applied at each end of traverse)
     Rate of traverse: 0·5 W, where W is wheel width
     Wheel width: 50 mm
     Length of traverse: 600 mm (includes over-run at each end)
     Non-cutting time: 2 min each component.

Work spindle speed: $N = \dfrac{60\,000 \times S}{\pi \times d} = \dfrac{60\,000 \times 0\cdot3}{\pi \times 50}$

$$= 115, \text{ say } 111 \text{ revs/min}$$

Traverse rate: $F = t \times N_a = 0\cdot5\,(50) \times 111 = 2790$ mm/min

$$\text{say } 2800 \text{ mm/min}$$

Time for one traverse $= \dfrac{L}{F_a} = \dfrac{600}{2800}$ min

Number of traverses $(p) = \dfrac{0\cdot3}{2} \times \dfrac{1}{0\cdot012} = 12\cdot5$, say 15

Total machining time $= p\left(\dfrac{L}{F_a}\right) = 15\left(\dfrac{600}{2800}\right) = 3\cdot12$ min

Including non-cutting time $= 3\cdot12 + 2 = 5\cdot12$, say 5·5 min

Total time = 5·5 minutes

446 *Workshop Technology for Technicians*

Summary

1   Floor-to-floor times comprise calculated times and observed times.
2   Floor-to-floor times are used as the basis of cost and delivery estimates, as a means of payment by incentive, and as a check upon production efficiency.
3   Floor-to-floor times can only be produced when the process sequence has been determined, and the machine allocated.
4   The calculation of times follows the same general pattern for all operations. First of all, the theoretical cutting speeds and feeds are selected, and the machine speeds and feeds calculated; these are then adjusted to suit the actual speeds and feeds available. The length of cutting passes are determined, taking into account the required approach and over-run distances. Finally, the cutting times are calculated from the cutting rate and the distances.
5   The operator times are synthesised from observed data, and added to the calculated times. Additions may be made to allow for contingencies, or local arrangements regarding payment schemes.

Questions

Set A

1   Estimate a machining time for making ten pins in the centre lathe, to the particulars given in fig. 28.7.

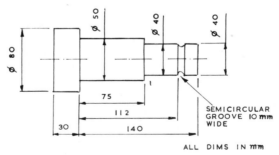

Fig 28.7

2   Four bushes, each 18 mm in diameter, 14-mm bore, and 50-mm wide, are to be made from the material (brass) shown in fig. 28.8 Calculate a suitable machining time. The finished bushes are to have a tolerance of 0·05 mm on all dimensions.
3   Give a suitable machining time for shaping the surfaces marked ▽, and drilling the two holes in the mild-steel component shown in fig. 28.9.

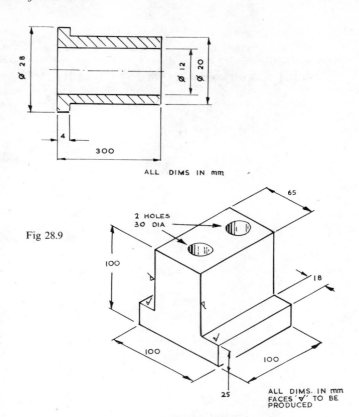

Fig 28.9

ALL DIMS IN mm

2 HOLES
30 DIA

ALL DIMS. IN mm
FACES '√' TO BE
PRODUCED

4 Estimate a total machining time, including drilling the hole, for sixteen bolts to the particulars given in fig. 28.10. The bolts are to be made from bright-drawn hexagon bar, in a centre lathe.

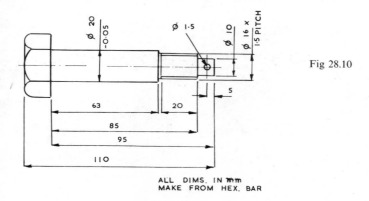

Fig 28.10

ALL DIMS. IN mm
MAKE FROM HEX. BAR

Set B (questions requiring further study)
5   Discuss the advantages and the disadvantages of using estimated times as a means of obtaining data for costing and production control, and also as a means of payment by incentive.
6   Outline how you would introduce synthesised times into a running concern, and discuss the problems you may have to overcome in doing so.

INDEX

INDEX

449